ARCTIC and ALPINE ENVIRONMENTS

Edited by W. H. OSBURN and H. E. WRIGHT, Jr.

For countless centuries high mountains and arctic regions have exerted a powerful influence on living processes by presenting effective barriers to invasion of all types, and permitting isolated pockets of interacting organisms (man included) to develop. The effectiveness of these barriers is demonstrated by how poorly these regions are known; less than 100 years ago speculation about their effects on life processes was steeped in the same broth as space research is today. Now with efficient transportation and rapid population increases man is encroaching on these last frontiers of terrestrial landscapes.

Arctic and alpine regions have long been regarded by many as being so similar that they could be considered as one unit, an arctic-alpine zone. But their differences far exceed their similarities—to the point that one wonders if other than being treeless a common denominator actually exists. Both are of interest to a number of scientific disciplines, as they are testing grounds for evolution—especially the high mountains. Many organisms border the tundra periphery, some of which become adapted to enter the arctic or alpine region. Afterwards, few re-enter lower regions. The process is somewhat analogous to a semi-permeable membrane or filtration system—new organisms can come in but few leave. This fixation enables arctic plants to be used as indicators of their environments.

H. E. WRIGHT, Professor of Geology and Geophysics at the University of Minnesota, is co-editor of THE QUATERNARY OF THE UNITED STATES.

Arctic and Alpine
Environments

Arctic and Alpine Environments

Volume 10

Proceedings

VII CONGRESS

(International Association
for
Quaternary Research)

Boulder-Denver, Colorado
August 14-September 19, 1965

Sponsored by

U.S. National Academy of Science-National Research Council

Edited by

H. E. Wright, Jr.
and
W. H. Osburn

Indiana University Press

Bloomington & London

1968

Copyright © 1967 by Indiana University Press
All rights reserved

No part of this book may be reproduced or utilized in any form or by any means, electronic or mechanical, including photocopying, recording, or by any information storage and retrieval system, without permission in writing from the Publisher

Library of Congress Catalog Card Number: 68-14609

Manufactured in the United States of America

Introduction

The Quaternary Period, constituting the last two or three million years, attracts the interest of natural scientists of diverse backgrounds who are challenged to apply their knowledge of current natural processes to interpreting a bit of recent geologic history. Much of the record of the Quaternary is safely buried in sediments, but even there it may be incomplete, whether it consists of fossils or soils or the sediments themselves. In any case, accuracy of Quaternary reconstruction depends on how well we understand the processes under which these buried objects were formed, or how clearly we recognize certain unburied features, such as landforms or plant distributions, as relics of the past.

Because a dominating fact of Quaternary history was the advance and retreat of glaciers in regions that are now temperate or in mountains throughout the world, many Quaternary scientists are attracted to presently cold landscapes of the world — the polar and subpolar regions and the alpine zones of high mountains. An understanding of these environments aids in the reconstruction of the glacial and periglacial scene of earlier times.

The convening of the Seventh Congress of the International Association for Quaternary Research (INQUA) in Boulder, Colorado, in 1965 provided the occasion for several symposia on special aspects of Quaternary studies, and one of these was on Arctic and Alpine Environments. The present volume includes many of the papers presented in this symposium, as well as a few from other sections of the congress. It is published to focus attention on these vast and fascinating regions about which so little is known. Another volume, growing out of an INQUA symposium on Arctic Environment and Processes held during the Alaska Field Conference, is being published as Volume 11 of the INQUA Proceedings by the McGill University Press for the Arctic Institute of North America, under the title *The Periglacial Environment*.

The arctic region (north of the tree line) and the alpine region (above the tree line) have long been regarded by many as being so similar that they are a unit, an arctic-alpine zone. A critical comparison between the two environments, however, shows perhaps as many differences as similarities. For example, differences in day length and atmospheric density between the two regions affect the regime of solar radiation at and near the ground. Alpine regions generally have a greater variety of bedrock and soils and a less extensive cover of surficial sediment. Their diverse topography and aspect provide distinctive microclimatic effects, such as strong katabatic winds, as well as a highly irregular distribution of snow and frozen ground. Steep slopes promote solifluction and rock creep, rapid runoff and erosion, and local development of glaciers and rock glaciers. Mountain uplift causes changes in local climate without regard to the broader regional controls on climate.

All these physical factors, and many others, mean a greater diversity of microhabitats for organisms in alpine than in arctic regions. With climatic change, relic populations can persist in mountains in favorable habitats. Even without climatic change, the local climatic and other physical barriers to migration give rise to isolated populations, which ultimately may develop into endemic species.

In contrast, arctic regions have certain other distinctive features, such as the great frozen floodplains and deltas of the streams that flow north to the Arctic Ocean, dotted with thawlakes, pingos, and well-drained stream banks. Vast expanses of uniform landscape allow free genetic interchange within large populations of organisms. Unlike the alpine regions, the arctic terrain of North America was largely covered by ice sheets during the last glaciation of the Pleistocene, so all organisms in the glaciated areas have immigrated within the last 7,000 to 15,000 years — none is the relic of a distribution before this glaciation.

Regardless of the dissimilarities in the details of the climatic and geomorphic environment, arctic and alpine regions are linked by low temperature, frost, and related factors that limit the composition of the flora and fauna. Where the extremes of the environment thus approach limits to life, one can study the relations between organisms and their environment more effectively than in temperate regions. Some of the more remarkable conditions reflect the adaptability of certain organisms to environmental extremes. For example, certain insects live on alpine glaciers, feeding on airborne organic detritus or on algae that obtain their mineral nutrients from dust. Or, in the high mountains of Mexico, "cold-loving" voles occupy the same region as "warmth-loving" lizards, the former being active during the cold of the night and the latter active during the heat of the day. In the same area, distinctive assemblages of plants precisely follow patterns of winter snow accumulation.

Because of the limitations and diversity of arctic and alpine environments, the landscape may be visualized as a gigantic environmental testing laboratory. Many organisms are common to both arctic and alpine regions, and the various combinations of the environmental factors mentioned above provide the opportunity for detailed autecological studies. The greater frequency of polyploidy in arctic and alpine plants implies a greater genetic plasticity than in temperate

INTRODUCTION

regions, so the changes in distribution of ecologically sensitive organisms may result from genetic conditioning as well as from climatic change. Once genetically conditioned to a tundra environment, however, reversal may not be possible; i.e., the organism may no longer tolerate temperate conditions. Thus disjuncts of tundra species in temperate regions are generally confined to tundra-like microhabitats, and they can generally be considered as relics.

For centuries the arctic and alpine regions have had an influence on man's activities. They have presented barriers to migration and invasion and have served as a home for distinctive groups of people. The isolation and inaccessibility of these regions account for the lack of knowledge concerning their natural history. The mysticism and even the fear that these regions engendered have inhibited their exploration. Less than a century ago the speculation about the "unknown environments" of the arctic was as active as speculation today about outer space. In fact, in those days the preparations to explore arctic and alpine regions seem as complex as those today for space travel.

Now with efficient transportation and with the great expansion of population, man is encroaching on these "last frontiers" of terrestrial landscapes. These regions have such limiting environments that forms of life, once destroyed, may return very slowly, if at all, and it is wise to learn the consequences of disturbance before such regions are utilized extensively. This requires careful and comprehensive studies of the total landscape, to establish base lines, in the manner accomplished for the Cape Thomson region in arctic Alaska in preparation for the nuclear explosions proposed for that region. The international program of scientific work in Antarctica is another model for research and conservation. Perhaps similar attention should be paid to relatively untouched segments of arctic and alpine regions before it is too late.

The book is divided into several sections. The first two chapters, by Clark and Peterson and by James, are concerned with the measurement and variation of microclimatic effects in mountain regions. One can appreciate, for example, that temperature inversions near the ground can have so much effect on local geomorphic processes and vegetation that a Quaternary scientist may find it difficult to reconstruct regional atmospheric temperature relations from landforms or plant fossils formed under these conditions.

The ecological and biogeographic aspects of arctic and alpine areas are considered in eight chapters. Swan describes ecological conditions in high mountains not only above the tree line but above the limit of autotrophic vascular plants — the aeolian region, in which nutrients are brought by the wind to nourish such lower plants as algae, fungi, and moss. Here airborne pollen or organic detritus in snowfields may supply the nutrient for bacteria and fungi; the prevalence of scavenging insects at these high altitudes implies a similar nutrient base, and these animals in turn serve as food for higher forms of life such as birds.

Alpine ecosystems of Australia and other parts of the south Pacific are treated by Costin in a comprehensive paper in which, among other items, the physiological controls of climate on plant growth at the tree line are discussed. Major and Bamberg consider particularly the floristic aspects of alpine ecosystems, with attention to studies by Russian scientists. Tatewaki describes the alpine flora of the Japanese mountains. Zimina is concerned principally with the alpine vertebrates of the Soviet Union.

A stronger historical treatment of arctic and alpine biotas is offered by Hoffmann and Taber, who face squarely the problem of the origin of tundra ecosystems and especially the faunas. They contrast arctic and alpine tundras in such climatic factors as day length and radiation characteristics related to atmospheric density, and in such edaphic factors as slope stability and soil cover, and they give evidence that the two vegetation types have had different histories. The arctic tundra developed in the early or middle Pleistocene, when worldwide cooling restricted the forest cover, but several phases of alternating cold and temperate climate passed before the Pliocene fauna was finally extinguished and the original steppe fauna of central Asia had evolved to forms tolerant of arctic conditions. The alpine tundra fauna, on the other hand, developed in the rising late Tertiary mountains of Central Asia, as is indicated by the richness in species there today, and this fauna spread via discontinuous mountain ranges westward to the Alps of Europe and eastward across Beringia to the cordillera of western America. In both of these migrational extremities, the faunas are much less rich. The migrations were favored during cold phases of the Pleistocene, and during warm phases some local extinctions or restrictions to refugia occurred. Even the post-Pleistocene interval of maximum warmth (the Hypsithermal) had an effect on animal distribution.

In a second paper, Major and Bamberg consider the origin of six disjunct plant species that occur on marble bedrock in the subalpine zone of the east slope of the Sierra Nevada in California. They postulate that during the Pleistocene these plants had spread to the region from the Rocky Mountains across the Great Basin, which is now a near desert but which then might have resembled the riverine bogs over permafrost that are found in the high, dry mountains of Central Asia. Such an hypothesis should be a challenge to Quaternary paleoecologists and others concerned with the Pleistocene history of the Great Basin, where the record for or against such a severe climatic change is not abundant from other evidence. Also, it points out how difficult it is to trace the distributional history of organisms that are probably never preserved as identifiable fossils.

A final chapter in the ecological group, by Viereck, summarizes the techniques and results of dating glacial advances and retreats in the western cordillera of North America by measurements of tree rings and lichen growth.

INTRODUCTION

In the geological group of papers, Clement and Vaudour describe variations in the pH of alpine snow and meltwater and discuss some possible effects of such variations on the weathering of rocks. Jane Soons describes some careful experiments in the New Zealand Alps in which the amount of erosion on unvegetated slopes, as measured by sediment traps, was proportional not to precipitation and runoff but rather to the amount of soil disturbance by needle ice during winter frost. In another paper concerned with frost action, Schenk emphasizes the electric attractions between water molecules, and he attributes frost-soil structures, including ice-wedge polygons, to growth of ice crystals by hydration of water molecules. Types of frozen-ground deposits in Siberia are described by Katasonov.

The geological group of papers also contains two on geomorphic processes in alpine regions — one by Linton describing the importance of sheet jointing in the wastage of divides between glaciated valleys, the other by Therese Pippan on the control on cirque form exerted by the structure and lithology of the bedrock and by the history of late Tertiary and Pleistocene uplift. Taillefer relates the size and distribution of Pleistocene glaciers in the Pyrenees to exposure, elevation, precipitation, drainage area, and lithology and reviews the glacial history of the range. Gerasimov and Zimina describe the high, cold, dry landscape of the Pamir, which lost its early Pleistocene glacier cover (by evaporation?) when the uplift of bordering mountains blocked off its source of moisture.

For arctic regions, Shilo describes the geomorphology of the vast lowlands bordering the Arctic Ocean in northeastern Siberia, most of which is underlain by Quaternary alluvial sediments with permafrost. The soils of arctic Alaska are discussed by Tedrow and Brown. Finally, the use of infrared and radar sensing instruments for delineating arctic geomorphic and vegetational regions is reviewed by Simonett and Morain.

Although many facets of arctic and alpine environments are untouched by the papers in this volume, there are enough to show how scientists of diverse disciplines can focus on the problems of a distinctive and fascinating type of region — in the same way that Quaternary scientists focus on a distinctive segment of geologic time. In fact, increased knowledge of modern arctic and alpine environments, as presented in this volume, will aid the Quaternary scientist in his efforts to reconstruct the glacial and periglacial environments that prevailed in now-temperate regions during the Pleistocene. The present is the key to the past, and historical studies are always enhanced by greater knowledge of the present.

H. E. Wright, Jr.
W. H. Osburn

Contents

CLIMATOLOGY AND GLACIOLOGY

Chapter 1   J. M. Clark and E. B. Peterson. Insolation in Relation to Cloud Characteristics in the Colorado Front Range   3

Chapter 2   J. W. James, Nocturnal Temperature Inversions in an Inland Valley in the California Coast Ranges   13

ECOLOGY

Chapter 3   L. W. Swan. Alpine and Aeolian Regions of the World   29

Chapter 4   A. B. Costin. Alpine Ecosystems of the Australasian Region   55

Chapter 5   J. Major and S. A. Bamberg. Comparison of Some North American and Eurasian Alpine Ecosystems   89

Chapter 6   M. Tatewaki. Distribution of Alpine Plants in Northern Japan   119

Chapter 7   R. P. Zimina. Main Features of the Fauna and Ecology of the Alpine Vertebrates of the USSR   137

Chapter 8   R. S. Hoffmann and R. D. Taber. Origin and History of Holarctic Tundra Ecosystems, with Special References to their Vertebrate Faunas   143

Chapter 9   J. Major and S. A. Bamberg. Some Cordilleran Plants Disjunct in the Sierra Nevada of California, and their Bearing on Pleistocene Ecological Conditions   171

Chapter 10   L. A. Viereck. Botanical Dating of Recent Glacial Activity in Western North America   189

Chapter 11   P. Clement and J. Vaudour. Observations on the pH of Melting Snow in the Southern French Alps   205

CONTENTS

GEOLOGY

Chapter 12	Jane M. Soons. Erosion by Needle Ice in the Southern Alps, New Zealand	217
Chapter 13	Erwin Schenk. Fundamental Processes of Freezing and Thawing in Relation to the Development of Permafrost	229
Chapter 14	E. M. Katasonov. Features of Deposits Formed under Permafrost Conditions	237
Chapter 15	D. L. Linton. Divide Elimination by Glacial Erosion	241
Chapter 16	Therese Pippan. Tectonic and Lithologic Control on Trough and Cirque Features in Caledonian, Hercynian, and Alpine Mountains of Europe	249
Chapter 17	François Taillefer. Extent of Pleistocene Glaciation in the Pyrenees	255
Chapter 18	I. P. Gerasimov and R. P. Zimina. Recent Natural Landscapes and Ancient Glaciation of the Pamir	267
Chapter 19	N. A. Shilo. Anthropogene Development of the Subarctic Lowlands of Northeast Asia	271
Chapter 20	J. C. F. Tedrow and J. Brown. Soils of Arctic Alaska	283
Chapter 21	D. S. Simonett and S. A. Morain. Remote Sensing from Spacecraft as a Tool for Investigating Arctic Environments	295

Index   307

Contributors

S. A. Bamberg, Department of Botany, University of California, Davis, California

Jerry Brown, U.S. Army CRREL, Box 282, Hanover, New Hampshire

John M. Clark, Institute for Arctic and Alpine Research, University of Colorado, Boulder, Colorado

Pierre Clement, Department of Geography, University of Sherbrooke, Sherbrooke, Quebec

A. B. Costin, CSIRO, P.O. Box 109, Canberra, Australia

I. P. Gerasimov, Institute of Geography, Academy of Sciences, Moscow, USSR

R. S. Hoffmann, Department of Zoology, University of Montana, Missoula, Montana

J. W. James, Department of Geography, University of California, Santa Barbara, California

E. M. Katasonov, Frozen Ground Institute, Siberian Section, Academy of Sciences, Moscow, USSR

S. A. Morain, Department of Geography and Meteorology, University of Kansas, Lawrence, Kansas

David L. Linton, Department of Geography, University of Birmingham, England

Jack Major, Department of Botany, University of California, Davis, California

E. B. Peterson, Institute for Arctic and Alpine Research, University of Colorado, Boulder, Colorado

Therese Pippan, Geographical Institute, University of Salzburg, Salzburg, Austria

Erwin Schenk, Professorenweg 6, 6300 Giessen, West Germany

N. A. Shilo, Academy of Sciences, Magaden, USSR

D. S. Simonett, Department of Geography and Meteorology, University of Kansas, Lawrence, Kansas

Jane M. Soons, Department of Geography, University of Canterbury, Christchurch, New Zealand

Lawrence W. Swan, Department of Biology, San Francisco State College, San Francisco, California

R. D. Taber, School of Forestry, Montana State University, Missoula, Montana

F. Taillefer, Institut de Géographie, Université de Toulouse, France

Misao Tatewaki, Botanical Institute, Hokkaido University, Hokkaido, Japan

J. C. F. Tedrow, Department of Soils and Crops, Rutgers University, New Brunswick, New Jersey

Jean Vaudour, Institut de Géographie, Faculte des Lettres, Université de Aix-en-Provence, France

Leslie A. Viereck, Northern Forest Experiment Station, U.S. Forest Service, Juneau, Alaska

R. P. Zimina, Institute of Geography, Academy of Sciences, Moscow, USSR

Climatology and Glaciology

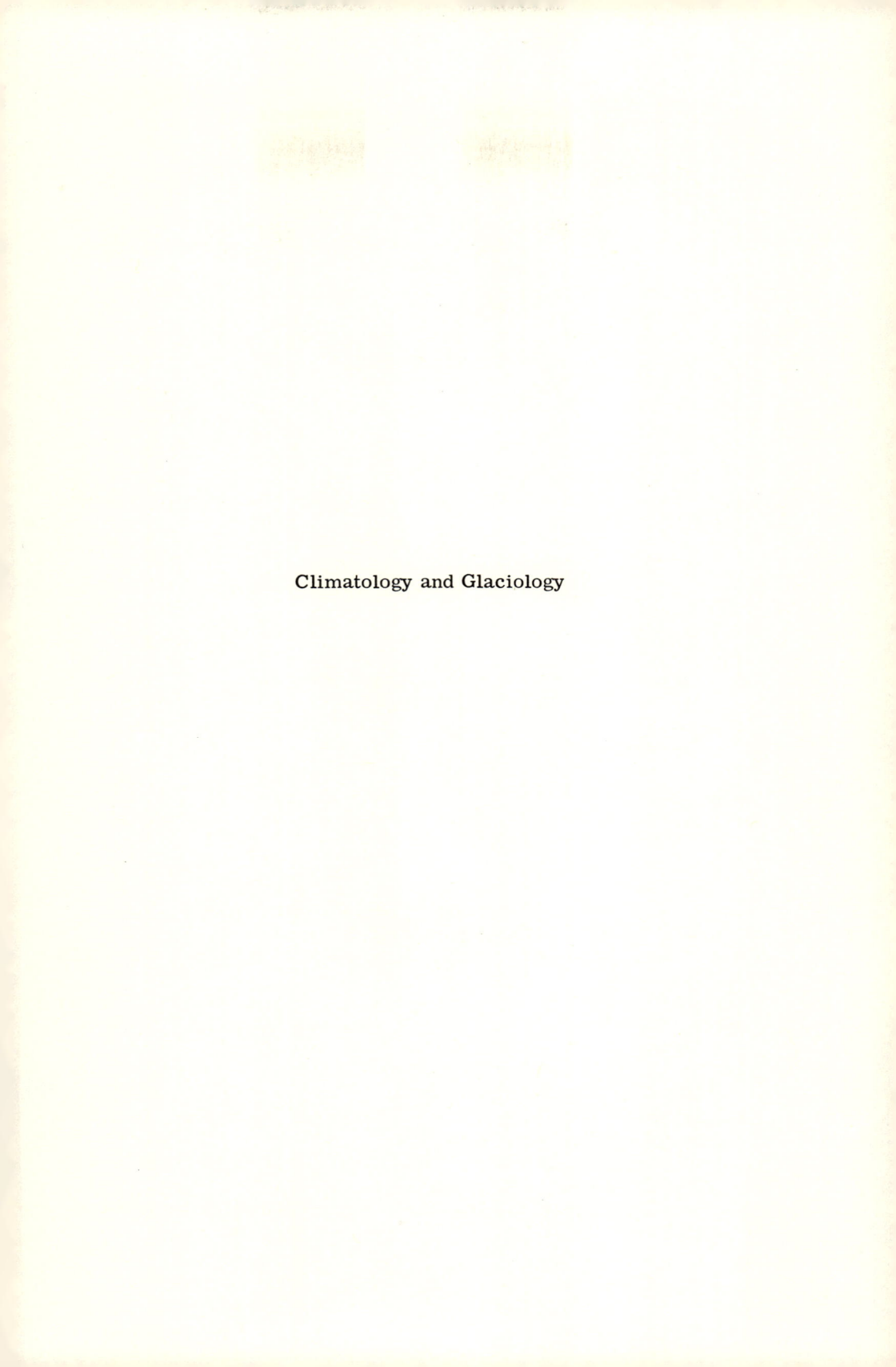

ARCTIC AND ALPINE ENVIRONMENTS (H. E. Wright, Jr., and W. H. Osburn, eds.), 3-11, © 1967 Indiana University Press

1
Insolation in Relation
to Cloud Characteristics
in the Colorado Front Range

J. M. CLARK and E. B. PETERSON
Institute of Arctic and Alpine Research
University of Colorado
Boulder, Colorado

Abstract

Measurements of incoming short-wave radiation were made at altitudes of 2590, 3050, and 3750 m on the east slope of the Colorado Front Range near Boulder. Approximate quantitative values of daily insolation were obtained from Robitzsch bimetallic actinographs at these altitudes, but data from these instruments may also be analyzed for cloud distribution and cloud duration. Differences in these cloud-cover characteristics are discussed for the upper montane, subalpine, and alpine regions. Insolation maxima that momentarily exceeded the solar constant were measured during early summer, when intense sunlight was reflected from cloud edges. Several ecological uses, other than the quantitative measurement of insolation, are suggested for the Robitzsch instrument.

As part of an environmental measurement program on the east slope of the Colorado Front Range, Belfort Company's Robitzasch bimetallic actinographs were installed at environmental measurement stations at altitudes of 2590, 3050, and 3750 m in October 1964. These sites are in the upper montane, subalpine, and alpine climax regions, respectively (Marr, 1961), and are designated as stations B, C, and D (see Table 1). This paper will discuss some of the altitudinal and seasonal differences in insolation* as measured with Belfort actinographs and will also focus on the uses and limitations of this instrument for ecological research.

---
*For brevity the term "insolation" is used to denote the intensity at a specified time, or the amount in a specified period, of total (direct and diffuse) short-wave radiation incident on a unit area of a horizontal surface.

TABLE 1

Location of Actinograph Stations Near Boulder, Colorado

Station	Inst. no.	Altitude, m	Latitude	Longitude	Exposure	Climax region
B	2	2590	40°01′15″	105°25′42″	S.E.-facing ridge	Lower Montane forest
C	4	3050	40°02′19″	105°32′48″	S.E.-facing ridge	Subalpine forest
D	3	3750	40°03′54″	105°36′58″	S.E.-facing ridge	Alpine tundra

METHODS AND RESULTS

The initial objective of the insolation-measurement program was to characterize daily, monthly, and annual insolation in three distinct vegetational zones of the Colorado Front Range. Actinograph data were available beginning October 1, 1964, at the subalpine and alpine stations, and November 1, 1964, at the upper montane station. Data are analyzed from these beginning dates until May 31, 1965, and provide gross characterizations of the insolation climates of these three climax regions during this interval.

Field Installation and Operation

Before installation, three actinographs were operated adjacently for several weeks. Comparisons of instantaneous values indicated that the instruments varied from one another by about 1 to 3% (Fig. 1). Because these actinographs were not calibrated with a standard pyrheliometer, the relationships shown in this paper are relative.

At the two lower, forested stations (B and C), actinographs were mounted approximately 10 m above ground so that tree shadows did not influence the readings. At the alpine station the instrument was mounted 3.5 m above ground on top of a laboratory building. The actinographs were serviced at 7-day intervals. A pan of silica gel kept in each actinograph case effectively reduced humidity so that moisture and frost accumulation inside the instrument domes was minimized. Snow accumulating outside an instrument dome could reduce the recorded insolation, and, as daily attention was not given to the actinographs, the days when this occurred were not always known. Data were rejected for days when condensation or snow was known to have accumulated on the domes.

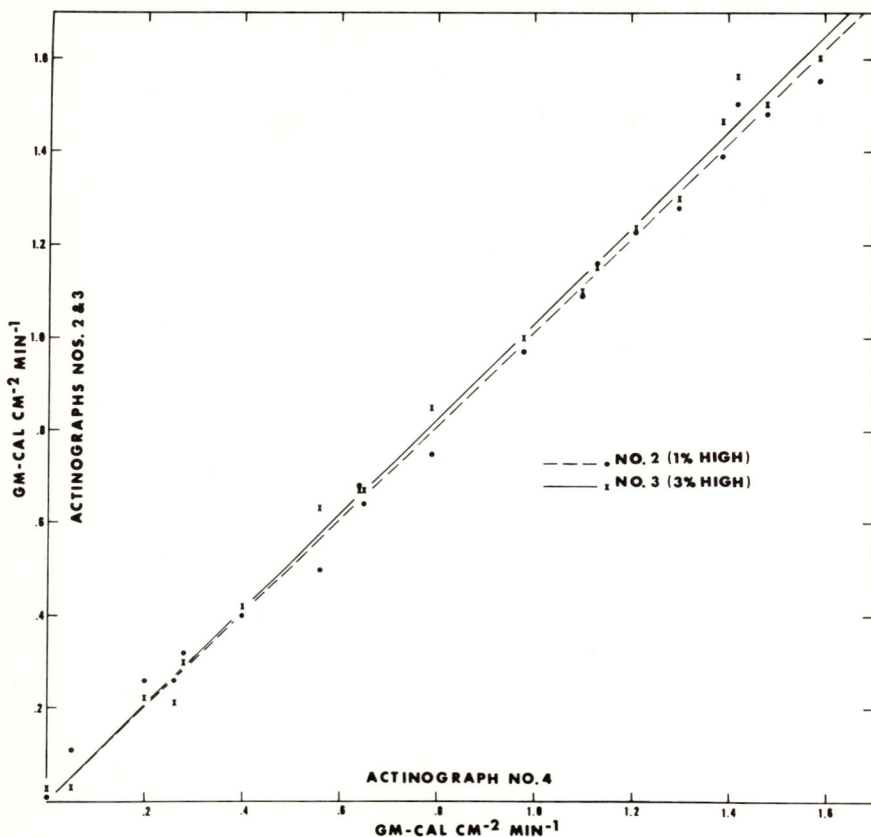

Fig. 1. Comparisons of simultaneous readings on three Robitzsch (Belfort) bimetallic actinographs, which were located side by side during September 1964.

Laboratory Analysis of Data

From weekly actinograph charts, daily values of maximum instantaneous insolation (g-cal cm^{-2} min^{-1}), total insolation (g-cal cm^{-2}), and cloud duration were determined. Daily totals were obtained by planimetry of the original actinograph charts. Cloud duration could be determined to an accuracy of ± 15 minutes on the weekly charts. Clouds were considered to be present whenever there were positive or negative deviations of at least 0.1 g-cal cm^{-2} min^{-1} around the hypothetical bell-shaped curve for a clear day. Because clear-day curves were not superimposed every day, there was some subjectivity in this method. Clouds that did not obscure the sun were not detected by this method.

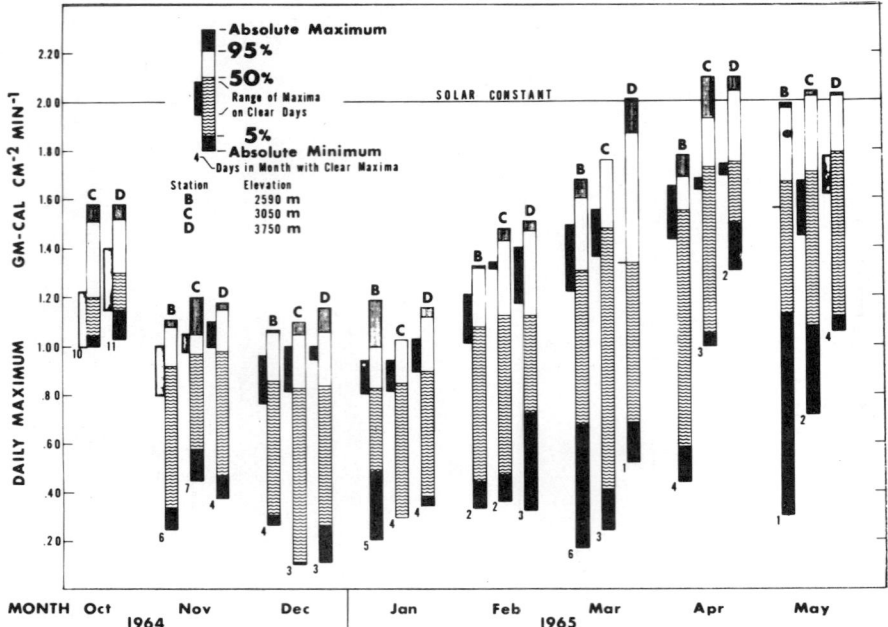

Fig. 2. Seasonal changes in daily insolation maxima at station B (upper montane), station C (subalpine), and station D (alpine). Number of days in each month with maxima uninfluenced by cloud is also shown, as is the range of maxima on clear days.

Station Comparisons

Stations were compared by month for daily insolation maxima (Fig. 2), daily insolation totals (Fig. 3), and percentage of daylight hours obscured by morning vs. afternoon clouds (Fig. 4). When readings were lost at any station on a given day, data were rejected from other stations for that same day. Thus station comparisons were only for days when all instruments were operating. The same days were used for calculation of total daylight hours and total extraterrestrial insolation (Fig. 4).

Daily Maxima. Despite the limited quantitative accuracy of the Robitzsch actinograph, most months between October and May showed the highest daily maxima at the highest station (Fig. 2). The range of daily maxima was least in October, a relatively cloudless month, and greatest during the spring months, when relatively dark days with upslope cloud and precipitation alternate with clear or partly cloudy days.

The daily maxima, as high as 2.10 g-cal cm^{-2} min^{-1} at the

INSOLATION IN RELATION TO CLOUD CHARACTERISTICS

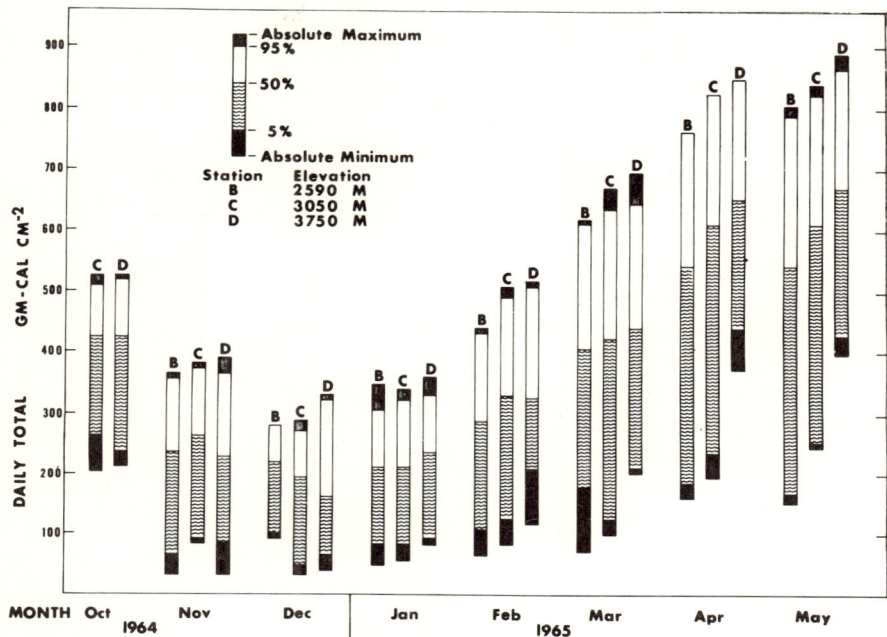

Fig. 3. Seasonal changes in daily insolation totals at station B (upper montane), station C (subalpine), and station D (alpine).

subalpine and alpine stations in April and May, are the result of multiple reflections from snow surfaces, cloud edges, and the instruments (Peterson and Clark, unpublished manuscript). With overcast skies, snow cover may be responsible for radiation increases at the surface as high as 29% (Bennett, 1964), and during such periods the solar constant is exceeded at mountain stations.

When the three stations were compared, there was no consistent difference in the number of days that were clear at the time of daily maximum insolation. One-third of the days in October had clear maxima, but during succeeding months usually less than 5 days in each month were clear at the time of daily maximum insolation (Fig. 2).

The relative importance of cloud effects, both for increasing and decreasing the daily maxima, is also shown in Fig. 2. Cloud reflections that cause increased daily maxima are relatively frequent in April, October, and May. In April and May at stations C and D, more than 50% of the daily maxima exceed those recorded on cloudless days. From November through March, the ranges of clear-day maxima are generally above the 50% level of the monthly range (Fig. 2). The reduced winter frequency of cumulus clouds, from which high reflections develop, and the increased frequency of stratiform clouds

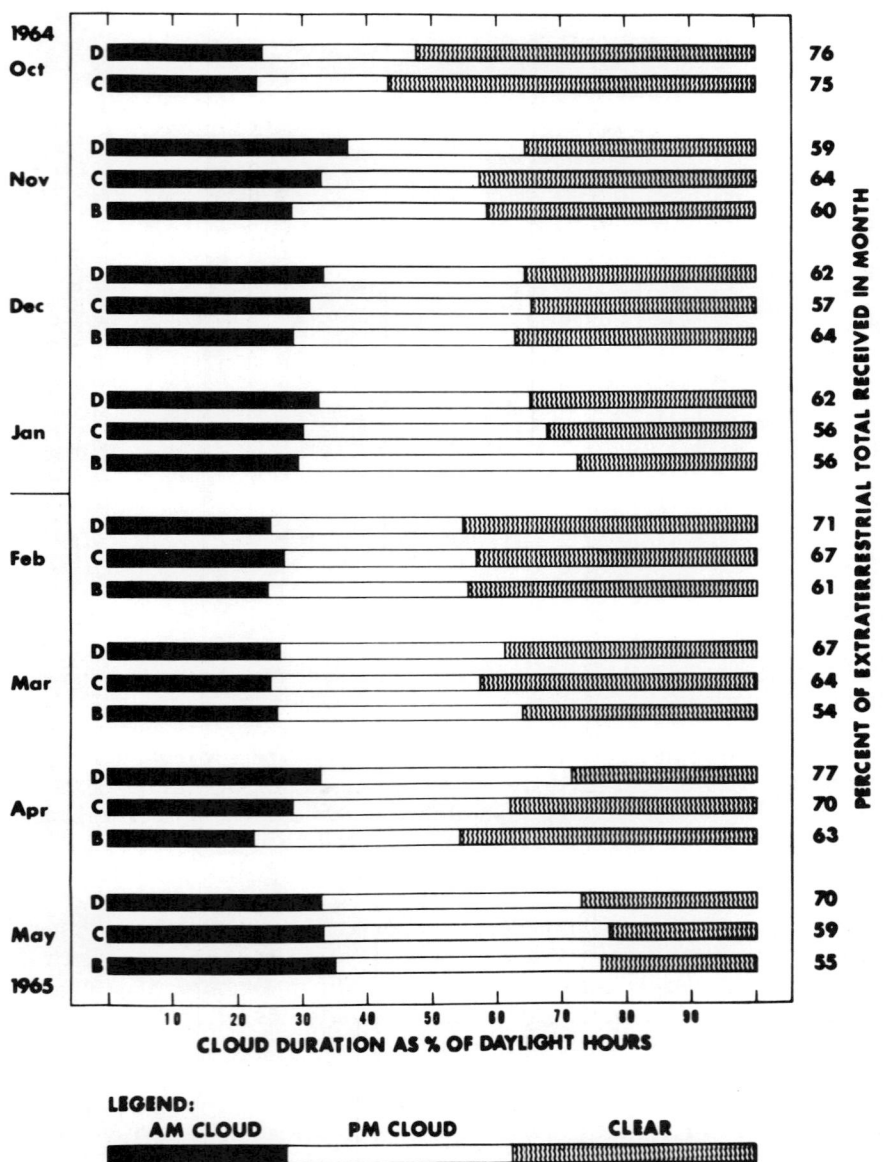

Fig. 4. Morning and afternoon cloud duration at each station, expressed as a percentage of total daylight hours. The monthly percentage of extraterrestrial insolation received by each station is shown by the column of figures at the right.

depress the monthly ranges of maxima relative to the ranges of daily maxima on clear days. With clear-day maxima there is an altitudinal gradient, with the highest values occurring at the tundra station.

Daily Totals. The ranges of daily insolation totals each month show expected relations between the three stations similar to those when daily maxima are compared. The largest differences between months occurred from October to November, when there was a change from clear autumn weather in October to more frequent frontal storms during November (Fig. 3).

The greatest monthly ranges in daily totals occurred in the upper montane and subalpine stations in April and May. The most likely reason for these high monthly ranges is the occurrence of relatively dark days at the two lower stations during frequent upslope storms in the spring. That clouds from some of these storms fail to reach the altitude of the alpine station is evident from the higher daily totals and daily maxima and smaller range at station D in April and May.

Cloud Duration. Comparison of actinograph charts from the three stations on specific days often revealed distinct differences in cloud duration. For example, the eastward movement of the leading and trailing edges of cloud systems could usually be detected. Shading by a standing lee-wave cloud extending north and south along the mountain front could also be determined for certain times of the day by careful comparison of the three actinograph charts. These examples suggested that cloud duration was another important factor that could be estimated with this instrument.

Total monthly duration of cloud, as compiled from actinograph charts, was expressed as a percentage of total daylight hours (Smithsonian Institution, 1963, Table 171). When these monthly values were compared, the upper montane, subalpine, and alpine regions were remarkably similar in total cloud duration (Fig. 4). During the period under discussion here, only in November and April were there greater monthly durations of cloud at the alpine station than at the upper montane station. In winter a crest cloud or foehn wall frequently obscures the alpine station and sometimes the subalpine station, but this cloud over the higher stations is apparently offset by a greater frequency and duration of upslope clouds at the upper montane station. In addition, standing lee-wave clouds during chinook conditions often shade the upper montane station but leave the higher-altitude stations in full sunlight.

A more noticeable difference between stations is that in most months there is a greater proportion of morning cloud in the alpine region than at lower stations. Also, the sun shines on the lower stations from under the cloud edge for a longer time. In winter months this fact is probably a result of the frequent occurrence of a morning foehn wall over the alpine station. These differences may be caused

TABLE 2

Number of Days in Each Month with Usable Actinograph Data

Month	No. of days used	Dates missed
Oct.	29	14, 15
Nov.	28	14, 23
Dec.	27	5, 14, 29, 31
Jan.	27	6, 7, 15, 19
Feb.	27	24
March	27	6, 14, 24, 25
April	29	28
May	29	18, 19

by the geometry of the path of the sun's rays relative to the station and the cloud edge. In months such as October and April, the formation of cumulus clouds near the Continental Divide causes shading of the alpine station earlier in the day than at stations located farther east on the Front Range. The bases of these clouds may actually be on the ground at 3700 m.

Figure 4 also shows the distinct difference between October and the succeeding months; less than 50% of the daylight hours were clouded in October, but over 70% were clouded in May.

The column of figures at the right of Fig. 4 shows the approximate percentage of monthly extraterrestrial insolation that was received in each vegetation region. The extraterrestrial totals, based on a solar constant of 1.94 g-cal cm^{-2} min^{-1}, were calculated for the days in each month that had complete actinograph data from each ground station (Table 2). Differences between stations are directly proportional to the differences in total insolation shown in Fig. 3.

A comparison of the monthly cloud duration with the percentage of extraterrestrial insolation received indicates seasonal differences in the effectiveness of cloud in reducing insolation. In October, when the azimuth of the sun is low, scattered cumulus clouds appear to provide more effective shade than in April or May, when the sun is more directly overhead. For example, at alpine station D in October, only about 48% of the daylight hours were clouded, and this cloudiness contributed a 24% depletion of the extraterrestrial insolation; at the same station in April, when total monthly cloud duration exceeded 70% of the daylight hours, approximately the same percentage of extraterrestrial insolation was received as in October. Although these values are approximate and are also influenced by atmospheric factors other than cloudiness, this example does demonstrate an additional use of actinometric data in environmental measurement programs.

SUMMARY AND CONCLUSIONS

Although the three Robitzsch bimetallic actinographs used in this study varied from one another by no more than ±3% before installation in the field, similar instruments have deviated by as much as ±10% while in operation. Despite the possible errors, regional differences at the upper montane, subalpine, and alpine stations were dedetectible. However, the magnitude of these differences (Figs. 2 and and 3) was usually less than the possible error of the instruments. Thus the regional differences indicated for the Front Range by these preliminary measurements should also be studied further to access their biologic and climatologic significance.

Because this instrument is inadequate for studies requiring a quantitative error of less than ± 10%, we suggest that the best ecological use of the Robitzsch actinograph is as an indicator of cloud duration and, to a lesser extent, of cloud type. The economy and the simplicity of operation justify its continued use by ecologists for nonquantitative purposes.

Acknowledgments

This work was supported by a grant from the United States Army Research Office through Contract DA-49-092-ARO-46. We thank John W. Marr, Director, Institute of Arctic and Alpine Research, University of Colorado, for assistance with this project.

REFERENCES

Bennett, I., 1964, A method of preparing maps of daily global radiation: Arch. Meteorol. Geophys. Bioklimatol. Ser., v. 13, pp. 216-248.

Marr, J. W., 1961, Ecosystems of the east slope of the Front Range in Colorado: Univ. Colo. Studies, Ser. Biol., No. 8, 134 pp.

Peterson, E. B., and J. M. Clark, Pyrheliometric traces associated with blowing snow and certain cloud types in the Colorado Front Range: unpublished manuscript.

Smithsonian Institution, 1963, Smithsonian meteorological tables, 6th rev. ed.: Smithsonian Inst. Misc. Collections Publ. 4014, 527 pp.

2

Nocturnal Temperature Inversions in an Inland Valley in the California Coast Ranges

JOHN W. JAMES
Department of Geography
University of California
Santa Barbara, California

Abstract

An analysis of temperature data from five sites in an inland valley in California's central coastal region in 1962-1964 indicated that a low-level nocturnal temperature inversion causes differences in minimum temperatures of a large magnitude (up to 30 to 35°F) between the valley floor and adjacent low hills. Minimum temperatures at the hilltop site (elevation 1615 ft) averaged approximately 5° higher than those at the upper hillslope site (1350 ft), 9° higher than at the lower hillslope site (1140 ft), 19° higher than those at the valley-terrace site (1040 ft), and 21° higher than those at the valley-bottom site (1015 ft).

Certain synoptic meteorological factors together with local relief and the particular situation and orientation of the area with respect to its larger geographic surroundings are responsible for the local nocturnal inversions that make these large temperature differences possible in an area only 14 air miles from the Pacific Ocean.

During a recent climatological investigation of the Hunter Liggett Military Reservation in the central California coastal region it was noted that very large differences in minimum temperatures were prevalent over a small area in a hilly setting in the San Antonio Valley west of King City (Fig. 1). To measure the magnitude of these differences, five weather stations were maintained in a small area (2 1/2 sq miles with a relative relief of only 600 ft) for a total of 6 months. As anticipated, the great variations in daily minimum temperatures in this area were shown to be primarily dependent on local

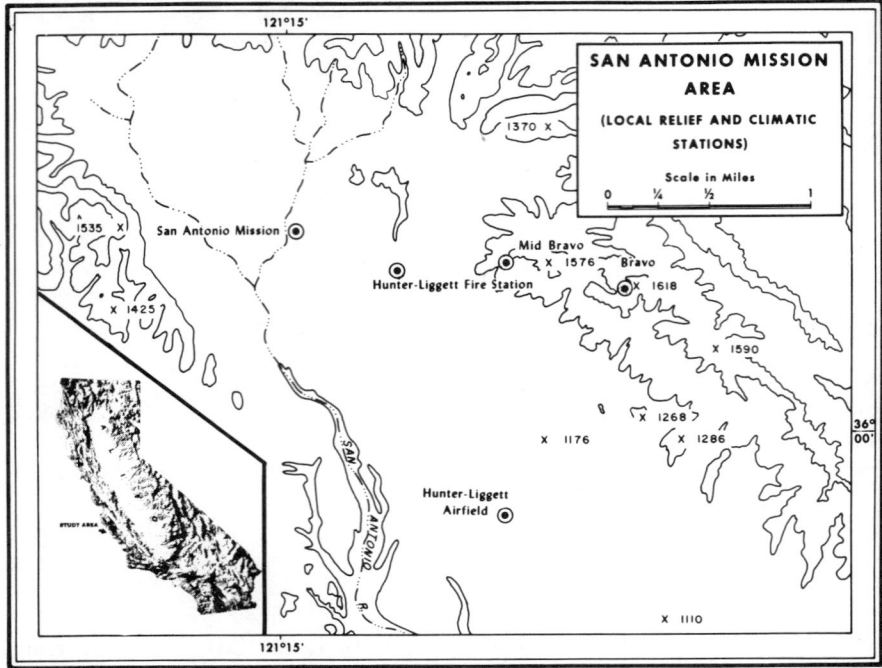

Fig. 1. Index map of the San Antonio Mission study area showing local relief and climatic stations. Contour interval is 200 ft. The inset map locates the area with respect to its surroundings.

physical features and on the synoptic weather situation, wherein a low-level nocturnal ground-temperature inversion is often present.

During the study period (November 1962 through November 1964) three recording and two nonrecording temperature stations were in operation in the San Antonio Mission area. One nonrecording station, San Antonio Mission, is a United States Weather Bureau cooperative climatic station. The results of this field investigation, together with an analysis of the physical bases for the large temperature differences that exist in the area, are the subject of this paper. Two sample periods serve to illustrate the point.

OTHER STUDIES

Among the more interesting studies concerning temperature inversions are those of Young (1921), Cox (1923), Dyke (1929), Schmidt (1934), Blackadar (1957), Tanner (1963), and a United States Weather Bureau report for the Atomic Energy Commission (1953). Coming quite early, Young's study was particularly enlightening for the western United States. Geiger (1965, Chaps. 2, 6, and 7) and Austin (1957) are excellent sources of bibliographic information concerning temperature inversions, in addition to including a fairly complete discussion of the subject. Also, Dickson's field study in Utah (1958) has added much to our understanding of temperature inversions in the eastern portion of the Great Basin.

IDEAL CONDITIONS FOR, AND CHARACTERISTICS OF, TEMPERATURE INVERSIONS

Some ideal conditions for nocturnal ground-temperature inversions are (1) long nights, when outgoing earth radiation exceeds incoming solar radiation for a relatively long period; (2) a clear sky or only high clouds, so that loss of heat by terrestrial radiation is rapid and unretarded; (3) relatively dry air that absorbs little earth radiation; (4) slight air movement, so that little mixing will take place and the surface layer will therefore have time, by conduction and radiation, to become excessively cold; and (5) an anticyclonic circulation (related to items 2, 3, and 4). In regions of uneven surface configuration (such as the Hunter Liggett area), this surface cooling is accentuated as the dense layer of colder air seeks the lower elevations.

In the San Antonio Valley study area all but the first of the above items (long nights) are prevalent during much of the year. Skies are clear nearly 80% of the time, the air is dry, calm or light wind conditions prevail most of the time on the valley floors because of the shielding afforded by the orientation of the area with respect to its larger physical surroundings, anticyclonic circulation is dominant most of the year, and local relief is such that cold air drainage into the lowlands is prevalent.

A few of the characteristics of a ground-temperature inversion are (1) a large diurnal temperature variation; (2) generally light or calm wind conditions, especially on valley floors; (3) large temperature contrasts with little change in elevation; and (4) poor visibilities because of haze (not particularly true for the San Antonio Valley).

GENERAL DESCRIPTION OF THE STUDY AREA

Hunter Liggett Military Reservation is located in the central California Coast Range approximately 220 air miles northwest of Los Angeles, 140 miles southeast of San Francisco, and 100 miles westsouthwest of the San Joaquin Valley city of Fresno (Fig. 1). It is 60 air miles from Monterey on the north and an equal distance from San Luis Obispo on the south.

The central California Coast Ranges extend for about 225 miles between the Transverse Ranges on the south and San Francisco Bay on the north (Fig. 1). These mountains are characterized by several parallel ridges oriented northwest-southeast parallel to the coast, at elevations of 2000 to 4000 ft, and occasionally of nearly 6000 ft. Between the ridges are generally narrow valleys ranging from near sea level (Lower Salinas Valley) to slightly over 1000 ft (Upper San Antonio Valley). The San Antonio Mission area, in the upper portion of the valley of the same name, is only 14 miles from the Pacific Ocean, with the Santa Lucia Mountain range (elevation 3000 to 5000 ft) located between.

The relief of the local area varies from the gently sloping San Antonio Valley (elevation 980 to 1060 ft) to the adjacent rugged hills (elevation generally from 1300 to 1500 ft, but up to slightly over 1600 ft at the Bravo climatic site) (Fig. 1).

There are no permanent water bodies in the area. Because of the seasonal nature of precipitation, the San Antonio River, the intermittent stream that drains the area, normally contains running water only from October or November through May or June, depending on the duration of the rainy season. Water flow is greatest during the winter months (December to February), when heavy rains are possible. The insignificant snowfall in the surrounding mountains is not a factor in runoff.

Vegetation in the area consists of grass and scattered oak trees on the valley floor, with cottonwood, willow, and other water-loving trees near the stream beds and chaparral and scattered oak and pine trees in the hills, and some fairly dense stands of oak at low elevations of the foothills.

The San Antonio Valley, lying east of the main Santa Lucia mountain block, has a climate markedly different from that on the coast west of the mountain crestline, where the influence of westerly winds and a cool ocean current produces a distinct maritime climate. Winters are mild, with frost normally only once in 3 or 4 years; summers are cool and foggy; high relative humidity exists year-round; and very small diurnal and seasonal temperature ranges are prevalent. The San Antonio Valley, east of the crest of the Santa Lucia Mountains, has little or no maritime influence, and the climate, with the exception of the precipitation regime, is more continental, with warm summers, colder winters (nights, not days), much lower relative humidity, and great diurnal and seasonal temperature ranges. However, the entire area, with the exception of the Upper Salinas Valley, has a Mediterranean-type climate (James, 1966).

Prolonged cloudiness is infrequent in the San Antonio Valley, even during the winter rainy season, with nearly 80% of the possible sunshine normally recorded each year (nearly 50% in January, and over 90% from April through September, the dry season). Relative humidity is very low from May through October and high only during late night and early morning, during winter rainy spells, or during periods of radiation fog in winter and early spring. This fog is prevalent on less than one-quarter of the days from December through early March in the early forenoon, except during dry years, when little fog is noted. Calm winds prevail, with moderate westerly and southerly winds possible during wet-season frontal passages. Because of the orientation of the surrounding mountains, winds on the valley floors are much lower than on adjacent hillsides, especially on west-facing hillsides.

INSTRUMENTATION, METHODS, AND SITE EXPOSURES

Of the five climatic stations in simultaneous operation during the study period, three had Belfort hygrothermographs (Hunter Liggett Military Reservation Airfield, Mid-Bravo, and Bravo), and the Mission station and the Hunter Liggett Military Reservation Fire Station site were equipped with liquid-in-glass maximum-minimum thermometers, read once daily. In all cases, standard shelters housed the equipment. Weekly charts were kept on the hygrothermographs, and to ensure accurate readings three-day-a-week psychrometric checks were made on the instruments in the field. Unfortunately, equipment failure was still a plague and prevented a complete analysis of the 6-month period involved.

Exposures at the various sites were as follows:

Hunter Liggett Military Reservation Airfield. Elevation 1015 ft, in a valley-bottom site, although not in the extreme bottom, about 35 ft lower and 3/4 mile southwest of the station (Fig. 1). The local terrain slopes gently to the southwest and south. No water stands anywhere nearby, even in the winter wet season. Vegetation consists of grass, with no trees nearby.

San Antonio Mission. Elevation 1040 ft, on a terrace bordering Mission Creek, an intermittent stream tributary to the San Antonio River. The creek bed is approximately 25 ft lower than the nearby climatic site. The terrain slopes gently to the west and then more abruptly to the stream bed, which is only 300 ft west. Surface water is prevalent in the creek only during winter rains and then for a shorter period than in the San Antonio River (approximately December to April, depending on the normality of precipitation). Other local intermittent streams have water only during heavy winter rains. Local vegetation consists of grass with a nearby oak tree. A few willows are prominent along the stream bed.

Hunter Liggett Military Reservation Fire Station. Elevation 1140 ft, on a south-facing hillslope approximately 90 ft above the local valley floor. The terrain slopes west, south, and east from this point into the main valley below. The only vegetation in this area is a grass ground cover, with chaparral beginning farther up the hillside.

Mid-Bravo. Elevation 1350 ft, on top of a northeast-southwest spur of the main northwest-southeast ridge mass. The terrain slopes away sharply in all directions, except to the northeast, where a steep upslope begins. The predominant vegetation cover is chaparral.

Bravo. Elevation 1615 ft, on the high point of a northwest trending highly dissected ridge 2 1/2 miles long. The terrain slopes away sharply in all directions, especially to the southwest. Grass forms the vegetation cover, with chaparral, scattered oak, and pine trees 100 to 200 ft away in all directions.

In all cases no buildings or other manmade features were nearer the climatic sites than 100 ft.

DISTRIBUTION OF MINIMUM TEMPERATURES, WITH PARTICULAR EMPHASIS ON TWO SAMPLE PERIODS

During the 6-month study period, November 1962 through February 1963, and October and November 1964 (minus 24 days of equipment failure), mean daily minimum temperatures were as follows at the five climatic sites in the study area:

Bravo: 51.5°F
Mid-Bravo: 46.5°F, or 5° lower than Bravo (many missing days)
Fire Station: 42.9°F, or 8.6° lower than Bravo
San Antonio Mission: 32.3°F, or 19.2° lower than Bravo
Airfield: 31.1°F, or 20.4° lower than Bravo

Included in the 156-day period are (1) 26 rainy days during which a low-level ground inversion was not prevalent and temperatures were somewhat uniform over the study area, and (2) 22 other days on which cloud cover between 9 P.M. and 9 A.M. either prevented the formation of a significant local inversion or greatly reduced the differences that existed. Thus only 108 of the 156 days measured during the study period experienced clear or partly cloudy skies. Although the measurement of sky cover was strictly qualitative and not continuous, visual observations were made at 9 P.M., 12 midnight, 6 A.M., and 9 A.M. These observations determined that, on 26 of the 108 clear or partly cloudy days, partly cloudy conditions were prevalent between 9 P.M. and 9 A.M., possibly also restricting the maximum effect of the nocturnal ground inversion. Thus the differences mentioned previously (for example, 20.4° colder at the Airfield site than at Bravo) involve many days (48 percent of the observations) during which cloudy skies and/or rain prevented the occurrence of significant differences in minimum temperatures over the area, and partly cloudy skies possibly subdued the differences. This fact emphasizes the magnitude of minimum temperature contrast in the local area during clear weather. Not included in the tabulation were the number of days

NOCTURNAL TEMPERATURE INVERSIONS

during which wind movement in the valley played a role in the mixing of air and resultant restriction of an intense ground inversion. Sporadic wind observations at the Bravo and Airfield sites showed that during clear weather at least a light wind occurred almost nightly at the hilltop site, but seldom at the valley-bottom site, except occasionally as a downslope wind early in the evening.

Sample Period 1 (November 6 to 12, 1962)

This was a week of typical autumn weather with clear skies, warm days, and cool nights on the valley floor and mild days and nights in the hilly areas. No precipitation fell in the local area during the 7-day period. Figure 2 shows the minimum temperatures at four of the five sites in the study area. Data from the upper hillslope site (Mid-Bravo) are not shown, because equipment failure caused much data loss from this site. However, available data from that location will be periodically mentioned in the text.

Minima at the Bravo hilltop site averaged 8° higher than those at the upper hillslope site, 11.3° higher than those at the lower hillslope Fire Station site, 19.6° higher than at the Mission station on the valley terrace, and 22.2° higher than at the Airfield valley-bottom site. Greatest departures at the Bravo site were 27° higher than the Airfield

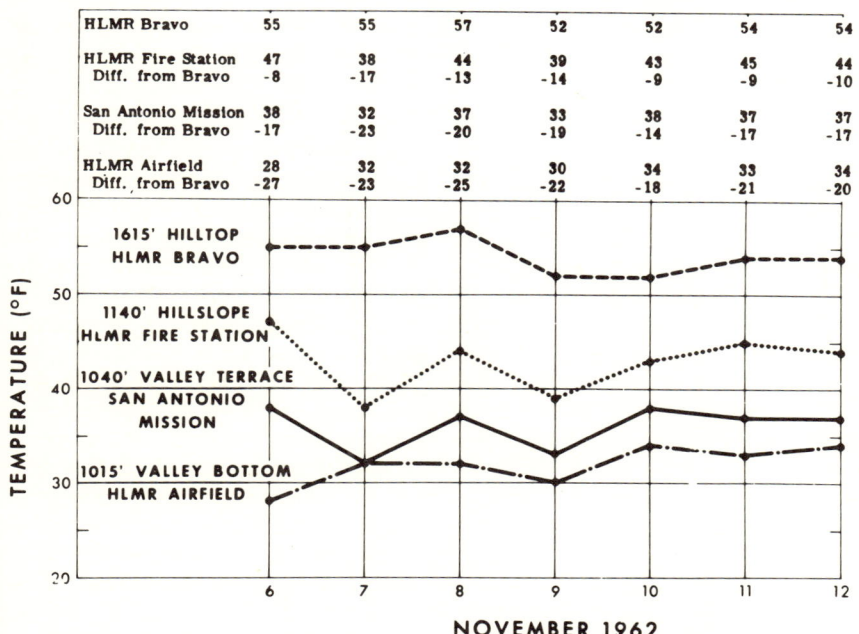

Fig. 2. Daily minimum temperatures at four sites in the San Antonio Valley area, November 1962.

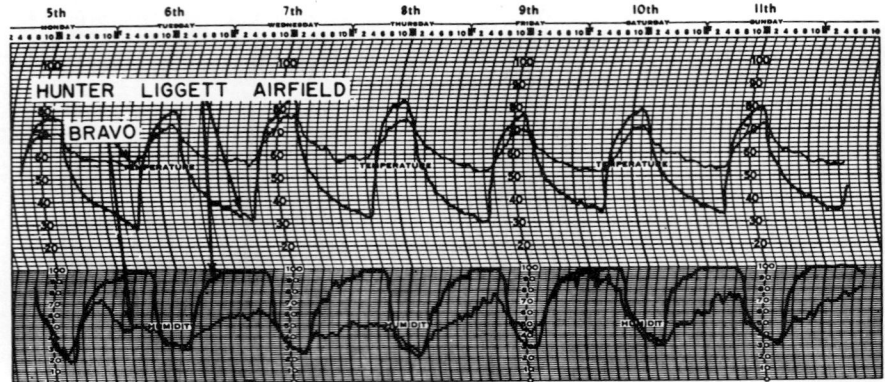

Fig. 3. Temperature and humidity regimes at two sites in the San Antonio Valley area during a week of typical autumn weather, November 1962.

on the 6th, 23° warmer than the Mission on the 7th, and 17° higher than the Fire Station on the 7th also. The smallest differences recorded were only 18° warmer than the Airfield, 14° higher than the Mission, and 9° warmer than the Fire Station—all on the 10th. The lower half of Fig. 2 indicates that the layer of colder air near the ground in the valley was fairly shallow and did not seem to fluctuate in depth appreciably during the week, with freezing temperatures being confined to the valley-bottom site on four of the nights and observed at the terrace site on only one night.

Figure 3 shows an almost monotonous temperature trace during the week at two of the sites, with diurnal ranges of near 50° at the valley-bottom site but only near 20° at the hilltop location. The humidity trace is included in this instance to show that the humidity regime also reflects a large diurnal range on the valley floor and a much smaller range on the hilltop, the differences (similar to that of the temperature regime) being not in the afternoon readings but in those at night.

Minimum temperatures on the 8th at the hilltop site were somewhat modified by a moderate easterly wind, which set in shortly after midnight and caused the temperature to rise. However, at the bottom of the valley wind conditions remained calm, and the temperature fell to the freezing point at 6 A.M. A similar light to moderate easterly wind also was present at the Bravo site on the nights of the 6th/7th and 8th/9th and the morning of the 10th, again causing temperatures to moderate at that location. Cooling at the Airfield site was somewhat impaired by a very light easterly wind on the morning of the 7th and especially the 10th. It might be recalled here that the smallest temperature difference between the two sites (18°) was on the 10th, when there was wind at both sites, and the second largest (25°) was on

NOCTURNAL TEMPERATURE INVERSIONS

the 8th (no wind at the valley-bottom site) (Fig. 2). Thus in this case wind movement as a mixing agent, and not cloud cover, acted as the modifying factor.

Synoptically, at the surface a large high-pressure area was centered over southern Idaho early in the week and shifted slightly southeast to center over northern Utah during the middle of the week (Fig. 4). Toward the weekend this high divided, with one center over northern California and another over northern Utah, and with some ridging in between. Pressure gradients were slight over central California throughout the week, and local surface winds were generally light and easterly. The Sonoran Low was weak, with only a slight trough up the southern California coast. A very weak cold front passed the local area late on the 9th, becoming stationary over southern California until the 12th. The Aleutian Low was prominent in the Gulf of Alaska all week but had no influence over central California.

At the 500-mbar height, winds were generally light and from the west and northwest (Fig. 5) but light to moderate and southwesterly toward the end of the week. Early in the week a slight ridging existed over the southwestern United States, and later a slight troughing.

The greatest temperature inversion (that is, the largest difference between the hilltop and valley-bottom sites) in the local area occurred early in the week, when the surface high was centered over

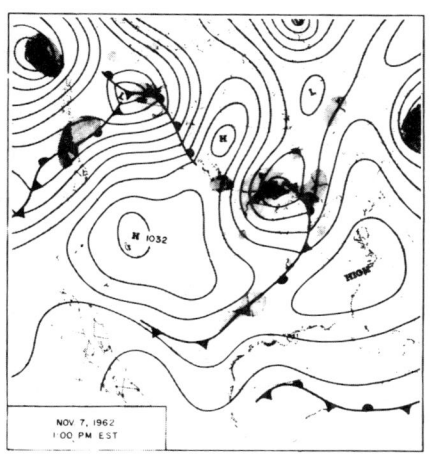
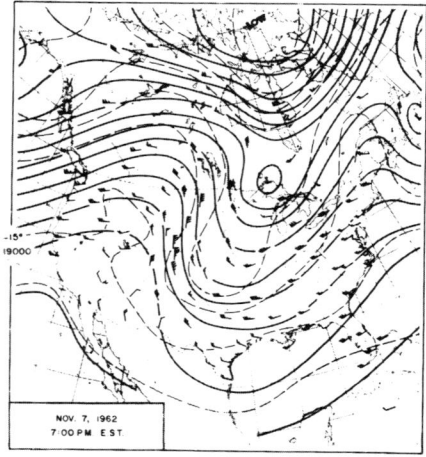

Fig. 4. Surface weather map at 1:00 P.M. E.S.T., November 7, 1962. (Isobaric, frontal, and precipitation patterns are indicated in conventional symbolic form.)

Fig. 5. The 500-mbar height contours at 7:00 P.M. E.S.T., November 7, 1962. (Solid lines indicate height contours in feet above sea level. Dashed lines are isotherms in degrees centigrade. Arrows show wind direction and speed at the 500-mbar level.)

northern Utah and southern Idaho, with the study area in the southwestern sector of the high (Fig. 4), and with a high-pressure ridge at the 500-mbar height over California with very light upper-level winds (Fig. 5). In essence, surface and upper-air conditions over the study area were quiescent, with a light easterly flow at the surface and a slight northwesterly flow aloft.

Sample Period 2 (January 14 to 28, 1963)

During this two-week period, clear skies, normally warm days, unusually cold nights (only on the valley floors), and light surface winds were dominant. No precipitation fell in the local area, but by the last 3 days of the period this unusually dry, clear, and cold midwinter spell was deteriorating. With January 29 began 3 days of some of the heaviest rains ever recorded in the local area—nearly 10 inches at the Mission station, or one-half the normal *annual* total.

Figure 6 shows the minimum temperatures in the study area during this period. Minima at the Bravo hilltop site averaged 7.2° higher than at the lower hillslope Fire Station site, 22.2° higher than at the Mission station on the valley terrace, and 23.6° higher than at the Airfield valley-bottom site. Greatest departures at the Bravo site were 31° higher than at the Airfield on the 14th, 28° warmer than

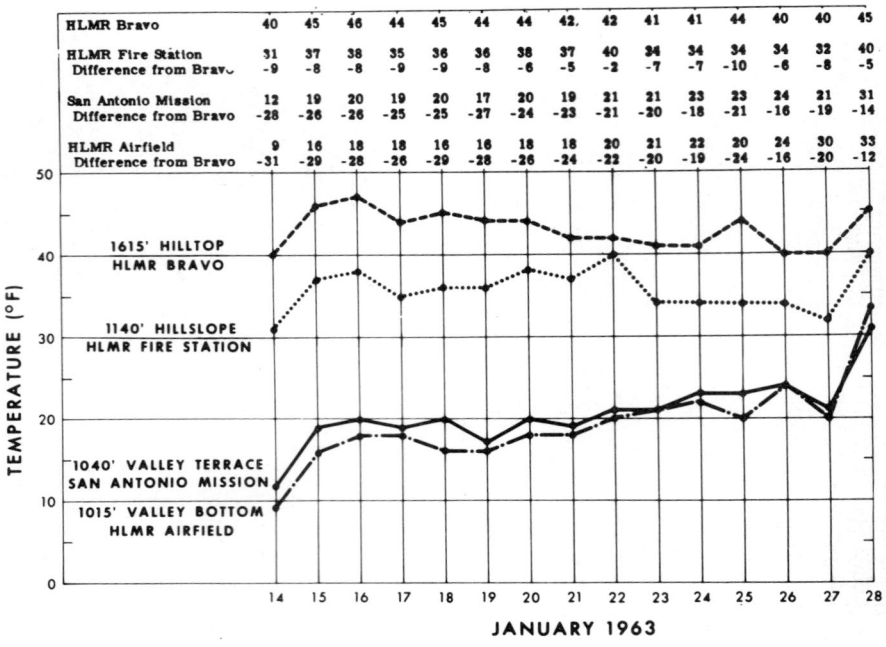

Fig. 6. Daily minimum temperatures at four sites in the San Antonio Valley area, January 1963.

at the Mission also on the 14th, and only 10° higher than at the Fire Station on the 25th. The 31° difference noted was not the greatest observed during the study period—a 35° difference existed on March 1, 1963, the last day of observations for that year. The smallest differences recorded were 12° warmer than at the Airfield and 14° warmer than at the Mission site, both on the 28th, and only 2° warmer than at the Fire Station on the 22nd. The lower half of Fig. 6 indicates that the layer of cold air near the ground in the valley was extremely shallow but very intense, especially during the first half of the period —in fact, so shallow that minimum temperatures at the hillslope site only 100 ft higher than the valley terrace averaged 15° higher than those at the terrace site. This difference was much more pronounced during the first half of the period than at the end. It is also interesting to note that the temperature never fell below 40° at the hilltop site or below 34° at the upper hillslope site (although a few days of records are missing from that location), but it was at 20° or below on 11 of the 15 nights at the valley-bottom site. An almost complete cloud cover tended to neutralize minimum temperatures on the 28th.

Figure 7 again shows an almost monotonous temperature trace during the 2-week period, with diurnal ranges of near 50° at the valley-bottom site, but of less than 20° at the hilltop location. During the last 2 days of the period clouds modified the temperature regime at both sites. An increasing cloud cover during the night of January 27

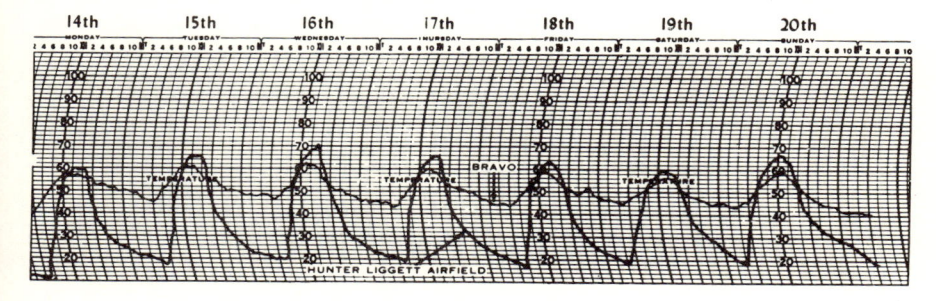

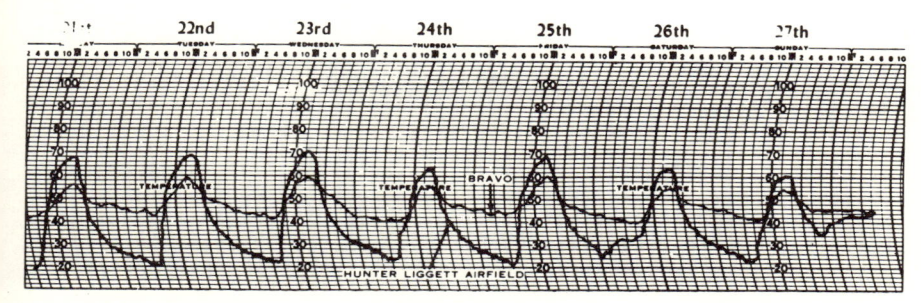

Fig. 7. Temperature regimes at two sites in the San Antonio Valley area during a portion of January 1963.

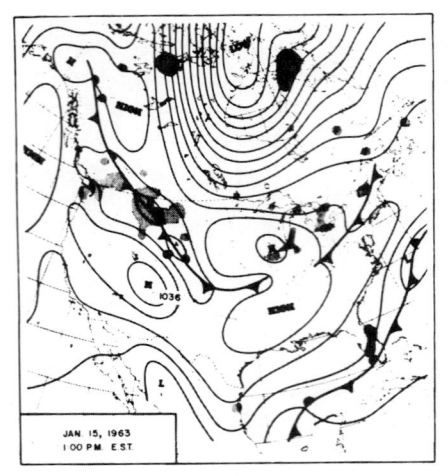

Fig. 8. Surface weather map at 1:00 P.M. E.S.T., January 15, 1963. (Isobaric, frontal, and precipitation patterns are indicated in conventional symbolic form.)

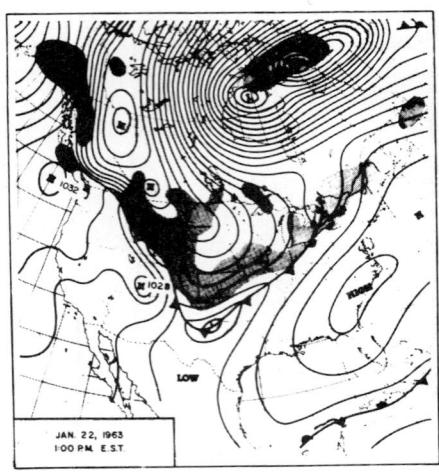

Fig. 9. Surface weather map at 1:00 P.M. E.S.T., January 22, 1963. (Isobaric, frontal, and precipitation patterns are indicated in conventional symbolic form.)

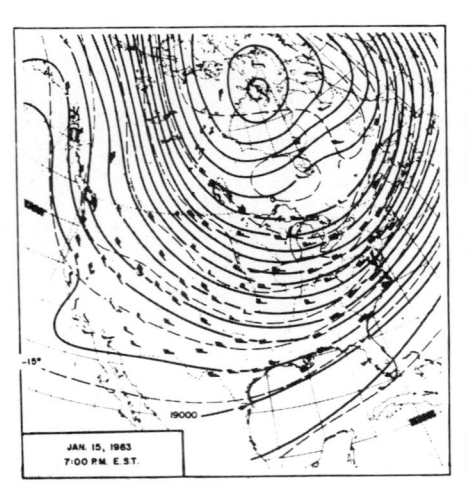

Fig. 10. The 500-mbar height contours at 7:00 P.M. E.S.T., January 15, 1063. (Continuous lines indicate height contours in feet above sea level. Solid lines are isotherms in degrees centigrade. Arrows show wind direction and speed at the 500-mbar level.)

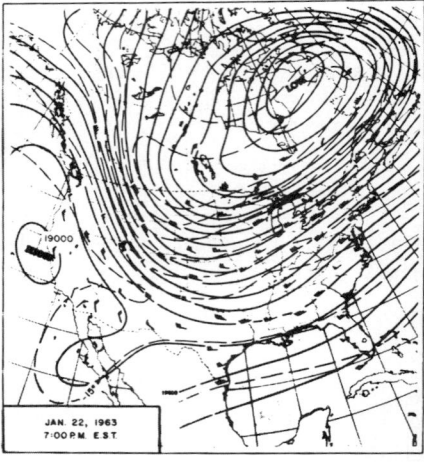

Fig. 11. The 500-mbar height contours at 7:00 P.M. E.S.T., January 22, 1963. (Continuous lines indicate height contours in feet above sea level. Solid lines are isotherms in degrees centigrade. Arrows show wind direction and speed at the 500-mbar level.)

brought an end to the intense nocturnal ground inversion that had prevailed almost without interruption since mid-December, and by 6 A.M. January 28 the temperatures at both stations were nearly the same.

Synoptically, at the surface a large high-pressure area was centered over the Utah/Idaho area (not the same high all 15 days) during most of the 2-week period, with a secondary high off the Vancouver Coast and ridging in between (Figs. 8 and 9). Toward the end of the period the high-pressure area began to break down, and low pressure from the northwest assumed more importance. Pressure gradients over central California were slight during the entire period, and local surface winds were generally very light and easterly. The Sonoran Low was fairly weak, with only a slight troughing up the southern California coast early in the period.

At the 500-mbar height, winds were generally light and from the northwest (Figs. 10 and 11) but became moderate northwesterly at the end of the period. A weak upper-level high-pressure area was located off the coast of northern California the first 13 days of the period. In essence, the synoptic situation over central California during the period, both at the surface and aloft, was quiescent and stagnant, much the same as Sample Period 1 in November 1962. At the same time, east of the Rocky Mountains the opposite was true: much weather activity, with large highs, intense lows, strong winds, heavy snow, and quick changes in the weather, etc. (Fig. 9).

The greatest inversion in the local area (that is, the largest difference between the hilltop and valley-bottom sites) occurred during the first week when the main surface high was centered over Utah; in the study area, in the southwestern sector of the high, there were very light easterly winds (Fig. 8), and off the California coast, a high-pressure area at the 500-mbar height and light northwesterly winds aloft (Fig. 10). The split of the surface high to twin centers over Utah and off the Vancouver coast (Fig. 9) served only to decrease slightly the intensity of the nocturnal inversion, not to destroy it.

SUMMARY

A nocturnal ground-temperature inversion in the San Antonio Valley during most of a 6-month period in fall and winter created great differences in minimum temperatures (up to 30 to 35°) between adjacent low hills and the valley floor. This inversion was a direct result of the synoptic weather situation and local physical features. With clear skies, dry air, slight wind movement, and cold-air drainage into the valley lowlands frequently prevalent as a result of anticyclonic circulation, conditions are excellent for an intense local inversion. It was found that inversions were most pronounced when (1) a surface high-pressure area was centered over Utah so that the study area was located in the southwestern sector of the anticyclone, with a light easterly surface flow over central California; (2) an upper-level (500-mbar) high was centered just off the California coast with light northwesterly winds aloft; (3) pressure gradients were slight over the study area; and (4) the synoptic situation was stagnant and quiescent, both at the surface and aloft.

Acknowledgments

Acknowledgment of financial support for the conduct of this study is given to the Earth Sciences Division, U.S. Army Natick Labs, Natick, Mass. Meteorological observations were performed by the U.S. Army Signal Corps Meteorological Team, Hunter Liggett Military Reservation.

REFERENCES

Austin, J. M., 1957, Low level inversions: Cambridge, Mass., Massachusetts Institute of Technology, Contract DA-19-129-QM-377, 153pp.

Blackadar, A. K., 1957, Boundary layer wind maxima and their significance for the growth of nocturnal inversions: Bull. Am. Meteorol. Soc., v. 38, pp. 283-290.

Cox, H. J., 1923, Thermal belts and fruit growing in North Carolina: Monthly Weather Rev. Suppl., No. 19, 98 pp.

Dickson, C. R., 1958, Ground-layer temperature inversions in an interior valley and canyon: Salt Lake City, Univ. Utah, Contract DA-19-129-AM-399, 136 pp.

Dyke, R. A., 1929, Nocturnal temperature inversions near the Gulf Coast: Monthly Weather Rev., v. 57, pp. 500-502.

Geiger, R., 1965, The Climate near the ground: Cambridge, Mass., Harvard Univ. Press (especially Chaps. 2, 6, and 7), 611 pp.

James, J. W., 1966, A modified Köppen classification of California's climates according to recent data: Calif. Geographer, v. 7, pp. 1-12.

Schmidt, W., 1934, Observations on local climatology in Austrian mountains: Quart. J. Roy. Meteoral. Soc., v. 60, pp. 345-351.

Tanner, J. T., 1963, Mountain temperatures in the southeastern and southwestern U.S. during late spring and early summer: J. Appl. Meteorol., v. 4, pp. 473-483.

U.S. Weather Bureau, 1953, A meteorological survey of the Oakridge Area: U.S. Atomic Energy Commission, ORO-99.

Young, F. D., 1921, Nocturnal temperature inversions in Oregon and California: Monthly Weather Rev., v. 49, pp. 138-148.

Ecology

ARCTIC AND ALPINE ENVIRONMENTS (H. E. Wright, Jr., and W. H. Osburn, eds.), 29-54, ©1967 Indiana University Press

3
Alpine and Aeolian Regions of the World

LAWRENCE W. SWAN
Department of Biology
San Francisco State College
San Francisco, California

Abstract

Timberlines extending from 72°N lat. to 56°S lat. delimit the alpine regions of the world with a maximum altitudinal extension to approximately 14,000 ft. A mean temperature of approximately 50°F (10°C) for the warmest part of the year appears to be a prominent limiting factor for forest growth in most mountain regions of the world. The upper border of the alpine region can best be distinguished by the upper limit of vascular plants, and the characteristics of this boundary indicate three basic types of alpine regions, namely, the high-latitude alpine region, the low-latitude alpine region, and a depressed equatorial alpine region. The low-latitude alpine environment permits the growth of vascular plants at altitudes in excess of 20,000 ft (6100 m) and is characterized by a long growing season. The aeolian region, which is devoid of autotrophic vascular plants, is supplied with air-borne nutrients. Three phases of the aeolian region can be distinguished, namely, the terrestrial phase, the nival phase, and the aquatic phase. Autotrophic algae, lichens, and moss, as well as a wide variety of heterotrophic animals and plants, occupy this region, which is broadly characteristic of most high mountain ranges and extends into the polar regions. The upper limit of the aeolian region extends to the summit area of Mount Everest, where bacteria, fungi, and yeasts occur.

The primary ideas of high-mountain ecology have emanated from studies devoted to the typical alpine regions of Europe and North America. The preponderance of work in these localities is set in contrast with the amount of similar research accomplished elsewhere in the world. As a result of this imbalance, there is some need for the development of unifying concepts that appropriately link the ecological characteristics of the treeless zones of widely scattered mountain ranges. It is toward this end that a summary of ecological attributes of the high-mountain regions of the world is attempted here.

When the whole world is compared with Europe and North America, the connotation of the term "alpine" is sometimes molded to fit diverse ecosystems. In the massive portions of the Himalaya and the Andes, where the upper limits of vascular plants are greatly exceeded by the highest peaks, the upper fringe of the alpine region merges into a zone of life that even an elastic definition of "alpine" cannot embrace. In the eastern Himalaya, in particular, the life above the level of the highest plants forms a distinct category. This aeolian region, which is supplied by nutrients carried in the atmosphere, is nevertheless linked with the alpine region and, when broadly defined, is a recognizable feature of high mountains throughout the world. It is significant that among the unifying principles that bind together the diverse alpine regions of the world, there is, at the upper level, the general proximity of the aeolian zone and the upward transition from autotrophic to heterotrophic nutrition. At the lower level, the alpine regions are united by their common boundary — the timberline.

TIMBERLINE AND THE LOWER LIMITS OF THE ALPINE REGION

The alpine regions occur above forests. When the forest line is an abrupt feature of the vegetation, the lower limit of the alpine region is obvious. However, in many mountain areas, trees exist far above the forest line, and an upper limit of trees can also be distinguished. If the trees are scattered and isolated they may be considered as vagrants within the alpine region that attest to the vigor of the individual trees or to restricted favorable climatic or edaphic conditions. In other areas the forest line is confused by the occurrence of dwarf or shrublike trees, and on still other mountain slopes the diminution of the forest near its limit is so gradual that a definable forest line is not apparent. The term timberline, with a long history of various meanings, is intruded into this confusion, and it is not clear how the timberline differs from the forest line and whether the term has any meaning when the forest line is itself ill-defined. For the purpose of comparing the altitude at which trees grow successfully in different areas of the world, the timberline is here assumed to be the highest elevation where forests or groups of trees are found. At the highest level, local effects of wind, slope, and snowfall tend to be minimal. The timberline, by this definition, usually coincides with the highest forest line and is not the same as the upper limit of trees (the treeline). For the most part it defines the elevation at which the alpine vegetation becomes continuous.

Daubenmire (1954) and Troll (1948) have attempted to determine the timberlines of the world, but because of differing interpretations of the limits of trees and forests, large discrepancies exist between their estimates. In Fig. 1 timberline altitudes are based upon more recent literature and upon personal observations in various parts of the world. The ascending timberline from 72°N lat. to the vicinity of 36°N lat. coincides closely with Daubenmire's mean altitude for timberline along the North American Cordillera. The slope has less altitude than that given by Troll. Near 30°N lat., the Himalayan forest line and timberline is placed at 13,500 ft (ca. 4100 m), higher than Daubenmire's estimate and far less than Troll's spectacular figure of 4800 m (15,750 ft) for Tibet. Forest lines in Mexico at 19°N lat. are very close to 13,500 ft (Beaman, 1962; Swan, 1952), a figure that exceeds the estimates of both Daubenmire and Troll. Isolated trees (*Pinus hartwegii* Lindl.) may exceed 14,000 ft (4250 m) on the Mexican volcanoes. At 12°N lat., the timberline reaches its highest level in the dry highlands of Ethiopia. Various complications arise in defining African timberlines, and widely differing altitudes of tree growth have been cited. Nevertheless, fairly extensive growths of tall *Erica arborea* trees, rather than shrubs, exist at 14,000 ft (4250 m) on Ras Dashan in Ethiopia (Osgood, 1928; Chamber of Commerce, Addis Ababa, 1954), and there appears to be no forest of equivalent altitude elsewhere in the world. On the Ruwenzori peaks of the Uganda-Congo border, the transition from forest to alpine region is much lower, at 3800 m (12,467 ft), but groups of *Phillippia longifolia* trees continue growing to nearly 4000 m (ca. 13,000 ft) (Balle, 1953). The paramo of the Ecuadorian Andes is nearly devoid of trees, but scattered high forests establish a sporadic timberline at approximately 13,000 ft (ca. 4000 m) (Penland, 1941). This is also the altitude attained by forests composed largely of tree ferns on the equatorial Mount Carstenz in New Guinea (Colijn, 1937).

South of the equator, forests reach to 13,000 ft in the Peruvian and Bolivian Andes. Isolated *Polylepis* trees of the puna ascend up to 14,000 ft (4250 m) (Pearson, 1951), and the altitude of 4900 m (ca. 16,000 ft) cited by Troll (1959) appears to refer to the maximum altitude of *Polylepis* shrubs. Both Daubenmire and Troll fail to record the 10,000 ft (ca. 3050 m) *Podocarpus* forests near the summit of the Drakensberg Range in South Africa at 32°S lat. (Bews, 1917). South of 35°S lat., *Nothofagus* forests establish well-defined forest lines in New Zealand and Chile, the southern limit of trees being at 56°S lat. on the islands southwest of Tierra Del Fuego.

Timberlines at equivalent latitudes in different parts of the world vary greatly in response to the differing climates that prevail along any latitude. Hence the alpine region may exist at much lower altitudes than that which is shown by the primary timberline in Fig. 1, and, as indicated for such regions as the northeastern U.S., Japan, Taiwan, and Hawaii, there is a minimum, as well as a maximum, altitude for timberline at any given latitude.

In a number of studies that have attempted to distinguish the major

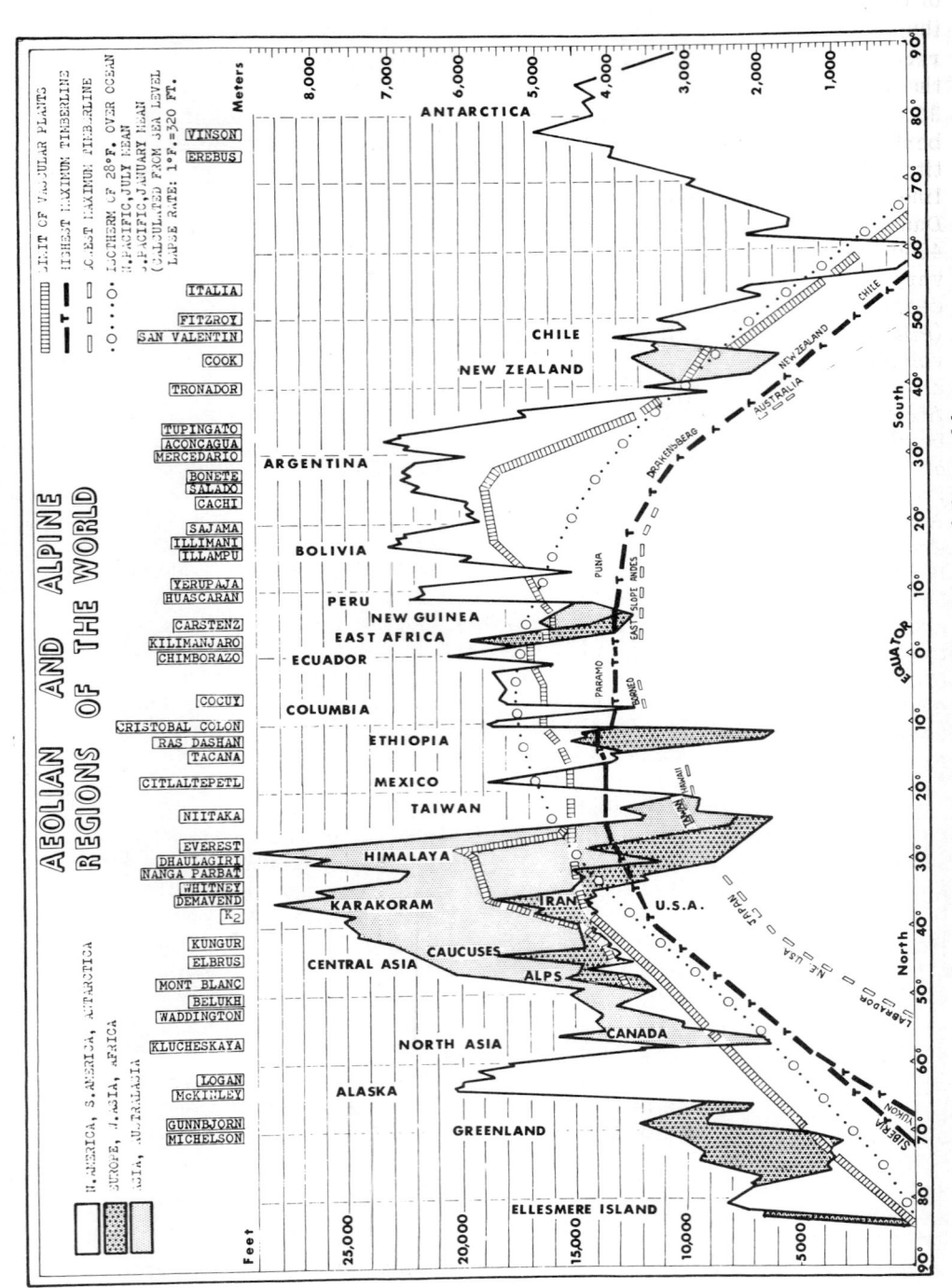

Fig. 1. Alpine and aeolian regions of the world.

environmental factors determining the limit for the successful growth of trees, it has become apparent that a prominent limiting factor is the temperature of the warmest part of the year. Timberlines in the Northern Hemisphere closely parallel the isotherm for the mean monthly temperature of 50°F (10°C) for July (Griggs, 1946; Pearson, 1931; Marr, 1961). It appears that the ability to survive cold winters does not materially determine the altitude limit of a tree, although winter cold may select the species of tree that can exist at timberline.

The southern extension of trees at 56°S lat. in South America, when compared with the northern extension of trees at 67°N lat. in North America, superficially suggests that the southern beech (*Nothofagus* spp.) is less hardy than the spruces and poplars of the far north. Although winter temperatures at the northern timberline are far colder, the mean temperatures during the season of growth at the northern timberline and the southern timberline are closely comparable and coincide with the isotherm of 50°F. Similarly, the position of the 50°F mean isotherm for the warmest month approximates the mountain timberlines in New Zealand and Australia.

This broad correlation exists for most natural timberlines throughout the world — even in the tropics, where seasonal differences are greatly reduced. It is curious to note that in various parts of the world, such diverse trees as *Nothofagus, Podocarpus, Philippia, Erica, Polylepis, Picea, Pinus, Populus, Betula, Abies, Rhododendron, Eucalyptus*, and tree ferns have independently adapted to cold growing conditions and have universally approached limiting factors for growth that are most obviously expressed by the mean temperature of approximately 50°F for the warmest month.

The effect of common limiting factors on various types of tree is illustrated in the eastern Himalaya, where the Asian timberline reaches a maximum. Three types of tree, each with differing altitudinal limits in other parts of Asia, coincide at a common timberline at 13,500 ft (ca. 4100 m). *Abies spectabilis* (Don), an evergreen conifer with a much lower maximum altitude in the drier and colder western Himalaya, coincides with *Betula utilis* (Don), a broad-leafed deciduous tree that exceeds the fir in altitude in the western Himalaya. These two trees combine with evergreen broad-leafed *Rhododendron* trees (*R. hodgsonii* Hook., *R. campylocarpum* Hook.) in an abrupt timberline where the mean monthly temperature for July is very close to 50°F. In other areas where these trees diverge at timberline, at least one species, in most instances the birch, assumes a timberline approximating the July isotherm of 50°F.

The consistency of this example weakens when the Tibetan plateau is included. Trees of the high, dry valleys of Tibet and Ladakh at elevations in excess of 13,000 ft are usually cultivated or cared for. The mean temperatures for July at Gyantse (13,100 ft, 4000 m) and Leh (11,530 ft, 3515 m) are 58°F (14.5°C) and 63°F (17°C), respectively. With a normal lapse rate of 3°F for 1000 ft of elevation, a mean temperature of 50°F would occur at over 15,500 ft. Records of forests at this altitude are unknown to me, although Troll (1948) indicates a maximum tree line of 15,750 ft (4800 m) for Tibet. Whether forests exist at this altitude or not, it is apparent that timberlines are not always where the mean temperatures suggest they should be. In other words, temperature is not the sole factor in determining timberline.

In some restricted mountain regions of the world it appears that no local tree species have evolved adaptations for growing in a cold environment, and the local timberline is depressed. In the Organ Mountains of Southern Brazil, at 22°S lat., the timberline is only 6000 ft (ca. 1800 m), and no cold-growing trees are in evidence (Clausen, 1963). In such a situation, the accompanying alpine region may represent an exceptional category that in turn emphasizes the broad ecological unity of the major alpine regions of the world. In spite of all the varying alpine biota and the broad range of seasonal phenomena, an underlying similarity — a basic climatic relationship — nevertheless permits comparison among the alpine regions of the world in terms of environmental stress.

THE ALPINE REGION AND ITS UPPER LIMITS

Mani (1962) has summarized various interpretations of the divisions of the alpine region, and, from his analysis, it is apparent that work in different mountain ranges has yielded various conclusions. He has himself utilized the broad category "nival zone" which embraces the region between the "highest peaks down to the timberline." Mixed opinion is further compounded when definitions are applied specifically to the upper limits of the alpine region. This boundary is frequently ignored or considered variously to extend to the summit of neighboring peaks or to the limit of alpine animals, or defined by the position of permanent snow. It seems most appropriate to consider the upper limits of the alpine region to coincide with the upper limit of vascular plants. This limit approximates the line of permanent snow, but in many parts of the world the snow line and the plant line diverge, and each may exceed the other. The altitude of permanent snow is often difficult to establish, and there are a multitude of interpretations of the phenomenon itself. The altitudinal limits of flowering plants may be obtained with greater accuracy, but this border requires closer inspection, and altitudinal records of flowering plants are not reported from all parts of the world. Webster (1961) has assembled much of the information concerning the maximum altitudes at which plants have been collected in diverse mountain ranges, and the basic data present in Fig. 1 are from his summary. Some corrections and additions to Webster's information permit a fairly accurate portrayal of the world plant line from 83°N lat. at the northern end of Greenland to 64°S lat. on the Antarctic Peninsula.

The prominent altitudinal bulges of the world line for vascular plants in the Himalaya and the Bolivian Andes stress the fact that the highest plants and the highest snow line are found some distance north and south of the equator. These high points delimit a depression of the plant line in the equatorial regions. The ecologic and geographic factors that influence this anomalous distribution have been summarized elsewhere (Swan, 1963b). In Fig. 1 an attempt is made to indicate the degree to which the elevation or depression of the plant line departs from a theoretical normal altitude. The basis for assuming a hypothetical isopleth rests upon the convenience that the extreme northern and southern limits of flowering plants approximate the summer isotherm for 32°F. Open-sea isotherms of the Pacific and Arctic Oceans are somewhat colder than 32°F at the latitude of 83°N lat. and 64°S lat.; hence a basic isotherm of 28°F (-1.1°C) has been employed because it corresponds with the open-sea monthly mean of July in the Northern Hemisphere at 83°N lat. and January in the Southern Hemisphere at 64°S lat. It should be noted, however, that the northern and southern limits of plants are actually more closely associated with the isotherm of 32°F. The value in assuming the 28°F isotherm stems entirely from the manner in which the open-sea isotherm corresponds with the latitude reached by arctic and antarctic flowering plants on land.

In comparing the representative isotherm for 28°F (based on a lapse rate of 1°F = 320 ft) with the altitude of the upper limit of plants, the effect of climatic factors associated with continental mass becomes apparent. In the Northern Hemisphere the plant line exceeds the isotherm, whereas in Chile the isotherm and plant line are closely parallel. The greatest departures from the isotherm occur in the Himalaya and Bolivia in the highest mountain ranges, and the depression of the plant line in the tropics is more clearly indicated. Essentially three basic types of alpine regions are delineated. They are: (1) high-latitude alpine regions, (2) low-latitude alpine regions, and (3) equatorial alpine regions.

High-latitude alpine regions are continuous with the arctic and antarctic regions and possess many of the climatic attributes of the polar zones. They are characterized by strong seasonal differences between winter and summer, and the winter season is generally enhanced by large accumulations of snow. Growth periods are brief but usually uninterrupted. High-latitude alpine regions of the Southern Hemisphere show less seasonal contrast, being milder in winter and cooler in summer. Much of what is known concerning alpine ecology has been derived from studies in Europe, North America, Australia, and New Zealand, all of which contain high-latitude alpine regions.

Equatorial alpine regions exhibit minor temperature distinctions between winter and summer, and seasonal dissimilarities are often relegated to drier and wetter periods. The majority of equatorial peaks that harbor alpine regions are relatively isolated and characterized by cloudiness. It is perhaps the latter feature of equatorial peaks that most effectively depresses mean temperatures and lowers the level of permanent snow. Inasmuch as seasonal differences are reduced, it is possible for temporary or extended colder conditions to occur more than once a year. Citlaltepetl in Mexico at 19°N lat., as an example, exhibits cold conditions during the winter months that are nearly equaled during the summer months. In a wet, cloudy summer season, the snow descends, and insolation is greatly reduced. During the spring and autumn the snow ascends and drought conditions prevail on the snowless slopes. Under these circumstances the alpine biota is subject to two cold and two dry seasons each year. The warmer, drier periods are each relatively brief and apparently do not permit successful plant development at the higher levels. The highest plants on the south slope remain about 2000 ft below the line of permanent snow. The absence of extended warmer periods and the repetition of cold periods is typical of other equatorial peaks.

Low-latitude alpine regions are primarily the product of high mountains, where the interior ranges are protected. Relatively arid conditions with reduced snowfall combine with abbreviated winters to produce a long growing season. Under these conditions flowering plants exceed 19,000 ft (5800 m) in the Bolivian Andes and 20,000 ft (6100 m) in the Himalaya. The effect of aridity, elevated snow line, and long growing season is carried north, where, in the Karakoram Range at a latitude comparable to that of Mount Whitney in the Sierra Nevada, plants grow at an altitude of 5850 m (ca. 19,200 ft) (Webster, 1961).

The effect of protection is exemplified in the eastern Himalaya, where the snow line and the plant line coincide at approximately 15,000 ft (4600 m) on the outer, southern ranges exposed to the monsoon. In winter, snow falls in sufficient amounts to produce snow fields at 15,000 ft, which are replenished during the monsoon months. Behind the exposed front of the Himalaya, climatic conditions change rapidly, and in less than 15 miles the snow line rises from 15,000 ft to about 20,000 ft (Fig. 2). The ecological and climatic characteristics of this inner zone have been discussed in previous reports (Swan, 1961, 1963b), and hence the primary phenomenon associated with the Himalayan low-latitude alpine region, the extended growing period, is discussed here.

In Fig. 3 the presence or absence of flowers furnishes a guide to the length of the growing season. Flowers that demarcate the beginning and the end of the flowering season are included, together with plants having an unusually long flowering season. In addition, some genera, *Rhododendron, Primula,* and *Gentiana,* well known for conspicuous flowers, have been selected for inclusion in the diagram.

The abrupt onset of flowers in the spring, when less than 2 weeks separate the onset of flowers at 8000 ft (2440 m) and 15,500 ft (4724 m), is most distinctive. This ascent, however, represents a crossing of the exposed, snow-covered outer ranges of the Himalaya into the inner

ALPINE AND AEOLIAN REGIONS

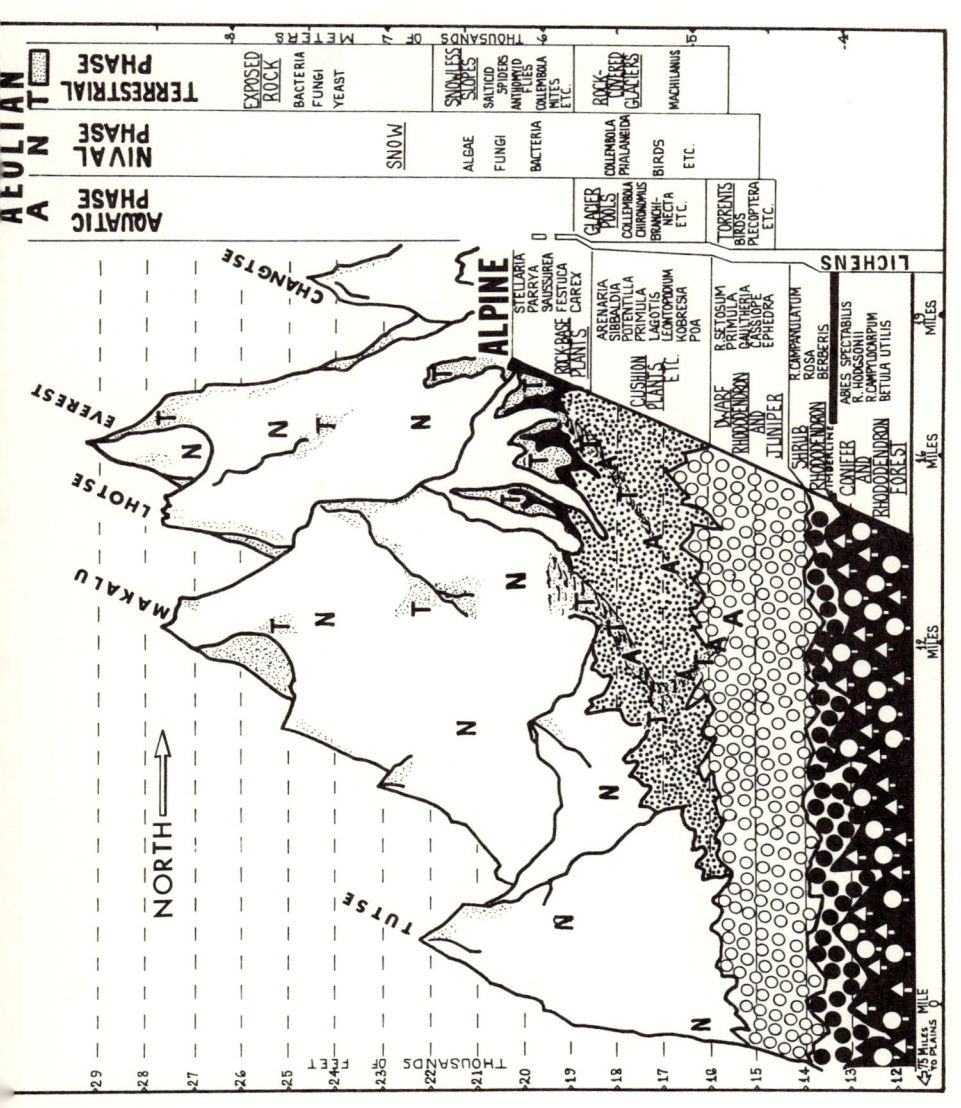

Fig. 2. Alpine-aeolian zonation in the eastern Himalaya.

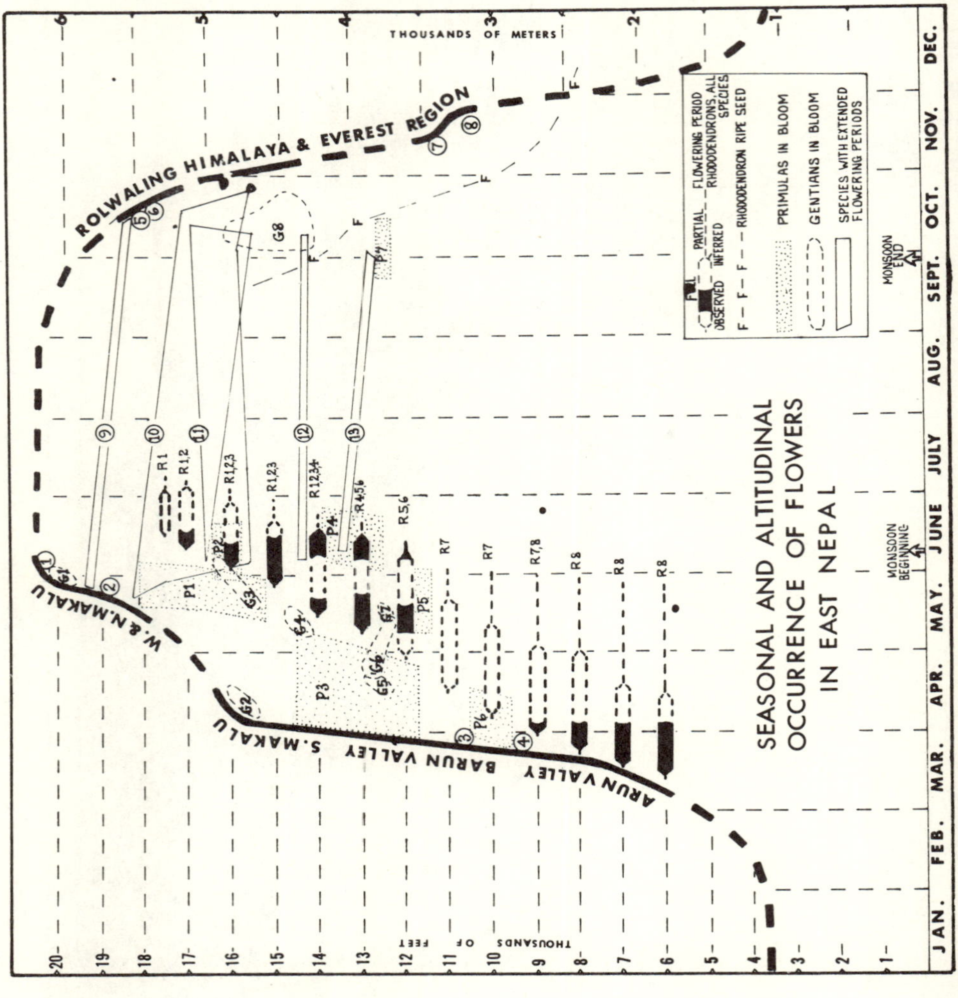

... occurrence of flowers in East Nepal.

Key to Fig. 3 —Seasonal and altitudinal occurrence of flowers in East Nepal.

Early- and late-flowering plants

1. *Parrya lanuginosa* Hook & Thoms.
2. *Saxifraga englerana* H. Smith
3. *Daphne retusa* Hemsl.
4. *Magnolia campbelli* Hook. & Thoms.
5. *Delphinium brunonianum* Royle
6. *Selinum cortiodes* Norman
7. *Anaphalis cinnamomea* C. B. Clarke
8. *Anaphalis contorta* D.C.

Species with extended flowering plants

9. *Saussurea gossypiphora* D. Don
10. *Allardia glabra* Decne.
11. ? *Swertia multicaulis*
12. *Anaphalis nubigena* D.C.
13. *Anaphalis tenella* D.C.

Primula spp.

P1 *P. caveana* W. W. Smith
P2 *P. concinna* Watt
P3 *P. denticulata* Sm.
P4 *P. uniflora* Klatt
P5 *P. stromosa* Balf. & Coop.
P6 *P. petiolaris* Wall
P7 *P. glomerata* Pax

Gentiana spp.

G1 *G. urnula* H. Smith
G2 *G.* sp.
G3 *G.* sp. nova
G4 *G. strobilacea* H. Smith
G5 *G. pedicellata* Wall
G6 *G.* cf. *pedicellata*
G7 *G. capitata* Ham.
G8 *G. ornata* Wall

Rhododendron spp.

R1 *R. anthopogon* D. Don
R2 *R. selosum* D. Don
R3 *R. nivale* Hook.
R4 *R. campanulatum* D. Don
R5 *R. hodgsonii* Hook.
R6 *R. campylocarpum* Hook.
R7 *R. barbatum* Wall
R8 *R. arboreum* Smith

Himalaya. Whereas the first appearance of flowers of all types suggests an abrupt onset, with some primulas and gentians following this trend, the onset of flowering among all species of rhododendrons is proportionately delayed by altitude in a manner more characteristic of flowering in northern mountains. Relatively few species bloom continuously during the premonsoon, monsoon, and postmonsoon periods, and the five species indicated in Fig. 3 are the only verified species collected in flower from approximately 200 species of plants collected above 12,000 ft. Two of these species, *Saussurea gossypiphora* and *Allardia glabra,* were among the first to appear and among the last to cease flowering. Between 18,000 ft (5500 m) and 19,900 ft (5800 m), *S. gossypiphora* blooms over a period of 140 days, and between 16,000 ft (4870 m) and 18,000 ft, *A. glabra* blooms for 157 days.

The highest plant collected on the northern slope of Makalu was *Stelleria decumbens* var. *pulvinata* Edgew. & Hook., which was not in bloom at 20,130 ft (6136 m) on May 28. However, *Parrya lanuginosa, Pegaeophyton scapiflorum* (Hook. & Thoms.) Marqu. & Shaw (both Cruciferae), and *Gentiana urnula* H. Sm. were beginning to flower at 20,000 ft on this date. The truncated appearance of the phenological curve suggests that flowering plants may ascend considerably higher than this spectacular altitude. Wollaston (1922) collected *Arenaria musciformis* at 20,100 ft in the Kharta valley east of Mount Everest and may have obtained plants at 20,400 ft (6220 m). Zimmermann (1953) has collected plants in the Western Cwm of Mount Everest at 20,850 ft (6355 m), and unauthenticated reports from mountaineers suggest that flowering plants may be found at even higher altitudes. The occurrence of rock-base plants, however, is strongly influenced by the presence of water in snowless areas, and the primary limitation for successful growth at these maximum altitudes may be associated more with aridity than with low temperatures and seasonal brevity (Fig. 4). Nevertheless, the singular expansion of the season of growth even at altitudes above 20,000 ft strikingly emphasizes the climatic distinction of the low-latitude alpine region.

AEOLIAN REGION AND ITS LIMITS

The primary characteristics of the aeolian zone and the basic differences that distinguish the aeolian and alpine regions have been summarized elsewhere (Swan, 1963a). The distinction between the two regions is founded upon contrasting sources of nutrition: The alpine biota are dependent upon local autotrophic flowering plants, whereas aeolian organisms are basically supplied by air-transported nutrients that are not usually of local origin. Hutchinson (1965), in a discussion concerning the limits of life on earth, considers the aeolian region to be essentially equivalent to the hyperallobiosphere or that portion of the eubiosphere at high altitudes where heterotrophic organisms are

Fig. 4. *Saxifraga englerana*. H. Smith. A rock-base plant growing in isolation at 18,800 ft (5730 m) beside the Barun Glacier in East Nepal. Flowers in late May.

dominant. Although the distinction between alpine and aeolian regions has a nutritional basis, the separation of the regions is also geographical. Hence the aeolian region includes some portions of the high alpine zone and the nival zone of European investigators as reviewed by Mani (1962).

The aeolian region is most readily recognized where established or semipermanent organisms exist in the absence of flowering plants. Vascular plants may be absent in localities at lower altitudes, and, in winter, when the ground is covered with snow containing wind-blown nutrients and dependent snow organisms, the limits of the aeolian region may appear diffuse and confusing. In the interest of simplicity, the aeolian region is considered here as being confined to areas above or near the upper limits of flowering plants. In Fig. 2 it is apparent that in the eastern Himalaya there is a wide overlap in altitude between alpine and aeolian regions; however, the primary lower extensions of the aeolian life are the products of long tongues of glaciers that extend below the level of the general snowline of the inner Himalaya to altitudes near 15,000 ft (Fig. 5).

The nutrition of the aeolian zone is still largely hypothetical. Where pollen on snow supports fungi and bacteria, the inference of aeolian nutrition is clear. When animals are found at altitudes far above the level of the highest vascular plants, it seems apparent that wind-blown nutrition is involved. Similarly, insects and crustaceans in temporary glacial pools suggest the presence of organic food that

Fig. 5. Aeolian zone. At 17,500 ft (5330 m) on the Barun Glacier. The rocks in the foreground harbor machilid thysanurans (*Machilanus* sp.), and at the base of the ice a temporary glacial pool contains a crustacean (*Branchinecta* sp.). On the left in the distance the Everest massif indicates the upper limit of the aeolian region.

was initially of atmospheric origin on old snow fields and ultimately released from melting ice. Large populations of insects in the torrents near the mouths of glaciers must also obtain food from melting ice. Arthropods and birds feeding on wind-blown insects are clearly aeolian, but some of these scavengers may be too transient in their behavior to qualify as significant representatives of the aeolian region. Unfortunately, in many if not most instances the type and quantity of nutrients involved in supporting aeolian life and the degree to which animals and plants are dependent upon atmospheric nutrition are not known.

The variety of particles of organic matter carried by the atmosphere has been investigated on numerous occasions, particularly in reference to pollen, bacteria, fungal spores, and insects (Gregory, 1961). The particulate load of the atmosphere appears to be enormous, and the variety of contaminants is nearly endless, but specific information concerning air-borne materials in mountainous areas is very scarce. However, large quantities of pollen, insects, miscellaneous organic debris, and dust are commonly found on snow fields, and it would appear that the aeolian region, especially the nival phase, is not deficient in nutrients.

NIVAL PHASE OF THE AEOLIAN REGION

Descending air over snow fields may concentrate atmospheric particles, and snow fields may also give an exaggerated impression of the distribution of debris, inasmuch as wind-blown particles may blow on and off other surfaces but remain captured in the snow. In the course of studies on the fate of radioactive fallout contamination of snow, Osburn (1963) recorded the phenomenon of concentration of particles in a snow patch as it melted. Presumably as the result of adsorption to surfaces within the snow, radioactive debris was held to a large extent within a shrinking snow patch and was released in reduced quantities in the melt water.

The autotrophic green algae of snow are considered to be aeolian organisms, because their nitrogen and other nutrient elements ordinarily must be derived from the air. Bettler (1964) suggests that the decomposition products of the bacterial decay of pollen enhance the growth of the snow alga *Chlamydomonas nivalis* Bauer. She also implicates fungi in the pollen-bacteria-algae sequence. Bettler has also verified the presence of pollen in the intestine of the snow worm *Mesenchytraeus solifugus* Emory that was discovered on a glacier on the north face of Mount Beelzebub in British Columbia (Fig. 6). These unusual aeolian annelids are apparently confined to the mountains of northwestern United States, western Canada, and Alaska.

The role of air-transported proteinoid materials, detected in uncontaminated snow in New Zealand (Wilson, 1959a, 1959b), is open to conjecture. Recent work on the manner in which dissolved organic materials of the ocean are precipitated by bubbles, thus furnishing nutrients to marine organisms, suggests that the organic precipitate is also donated to the atmosphere (Wangersky, 1965). Wilson's work with ocean spray and mountain snow anticipated this possibility, and the unusual nutrient link between high mountains and distant ocean seems worthy of much further study.

Large accumulations of dead and dying insects on snow fields at high altitudes have been reported on numerous occasions (Mani, 1962), but very little is known concerning the actual quantity of this wind-blown material. I have recently found large numbers of insects in snow between the altitudes of 15,000 ft (4600 m) and 18,000 ft (5500 m) on Citlaltepetl in Mexico. Counts ranged from zero to a maximum of 23 in an area of 1.1 sq ft of snow surface at an altitude of 16,500 ft (5030 m).

The role of scavengers feeding on dead insects in the snow has also been reported by many observers (Mani, 1962). On Citlaltepetl the yellow-eyed or Mexican juncos, *Junco phaeonotus* Wagler, were

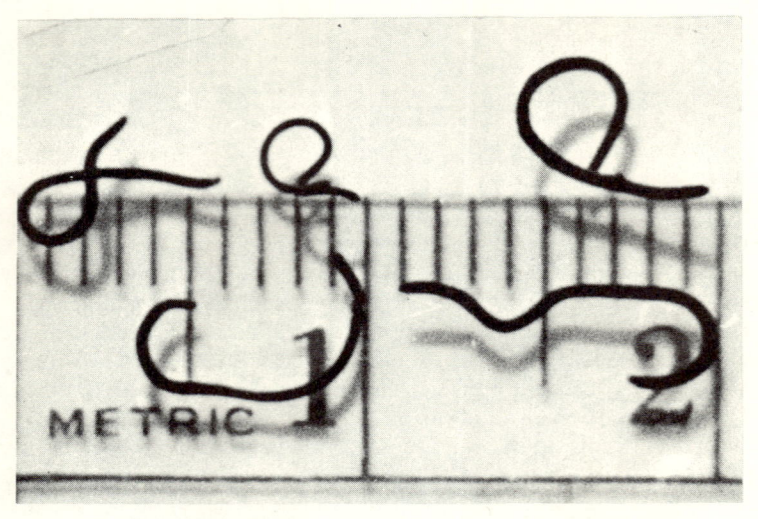

Fig. 6. Snow worms. *Mesenchytraeus solifugus* Emory from a glacier in British Columbia. (Photo courtesy of Mrs. Philip Bettler.)

commonly seen feeding on snow insects up to an altitude of 16,500 ft. A single adult female lycosid spider was also found actively feeding on insects trapped in the snow at 16,500 ft. Perhaps the most admirable adaptation to life on the snow surface on the part of arthropod scavengers is exemplified by an eastern Himalayan phalangid. At 18,000 ft (5500 m), it may be found as much as 300 ft from the nearest snowless areas. Dead insects in high-altitude snow sink into small holes because they absorb more heat than the adjacent snow. The phalangid, with its long, stiltlike legs, is able to feed on the insect cache by lowering its body into such a depression without touching the snow. The temperature of the snow surface in the sun is often near 32°F, whereas a thermometer painted black to approximate the color of a small animal may register 90°F (32°C) less than an inch above the snow. The utilization of this sharp temperature gradient by phalangids may account for the widespread success of these arachnids in high mountain areas and their occurrence, even in midwinter, on high-mountain snow.

A consideration that applies to both aeolian and alpine regions involves the contribution of nival organic and inorganic debris with its nutrient potentials to the soil after the disappearance of the snow. These considerable quantities must materially affect the soil environment or the underlying plants. As an indication of this fact, Osburn (1963) has demonstrated that the radioactivity of a standard snow sample amounted to 3380 micromicrocuries per gram of snow-field debris, whereas debris released to small litter-filled depressions after the melting of the snow amounted to 70,000 micromicrocuries per gram. The concentrating ability of the snow and the relatively sudden release of debris as the snow disappears are mirrored in these figures.

AQUATIC PHASE OF THE AEOLIAN REGION

Organic materials of the nival phase are ultimately contributed to the glacial pools and torrents of the aquatic phase of the aeolian region. The nature and quantity of the organic materials that furnish food in these localities are unknown, and the various organisms that live in the aquatic phase are considered aeolian because much of their food supply is inferred to have been transported originally by the atmosphere. A review of torrential fauna reveals many instances of turbellarians, crustaceans, hydracarinids, and various insects that exist primarily or solely near the source of torrents or, where their nutrition is closely linked, with the organic material released by snow and ice. Temporary glacial pools up to 19,000 ft altitude in the eastern Himalaya contain large populations of a fairy shrimp, *Branchinecta* sp. The intestinal contents of these small crustaceans reveal a major quantity of fine granular glacial dust mixed with traces of an unidentifiable organic material. No algae are found. The presence of algae in more permanent ponds suggests food sources from autotrophic plants. If, however, the primary algae are green algae, there is a strong inference that the nitrogenous material supporting these plants in more permanent bodies of water was derived from the organic debris of snow. If the algae are blue-green cyanophytes, the aeolian status of such aquatic environments becomes even more problematical. Some reference to this indefinite state of knowledge is given in later paragraphs of this report. It would appear, however, that many so-called alpine lakes derived directly from meltwater are, in reality, aeolian lakes.

TERRESTRIAL PHASE OF THE AEOLIAN REGION

Organic materials transported by the atmosphere and readily seen on snow are also deposited on snowless areas; they are effectively trapped in crevices, cracks, and apertures of all sorts, where air turbulence is reduced and the particulate contents of the air can fall out. These accumulations of the terrestrial phase are often obvious and largely account for the accumulations of dust under rocks on the mountainside. Newly fallen rocks are distinguished by the lack of dust accumulations beneath them and the absence of debris in cracks. Snowless rock slopes harbor more scattered and thicker accumulations of debris than snow-covered slopes, and in these areas of concentration aeolian organisms find the organic materials that sustain them.

Terrestrial aeolian animals extend to lower altitudes on rock-covered glaciers. This fauna is exemplified in the Himalaya by machilid thysanurans, *Machilanus* spp., which are apparently represented by different species on different glacier systems. On the snowless slopes on the sides of the glacier, various mites, collembolans, and flies exist in the absence of plants, and their nutrition is clearly associated with wind-blown organic debris. Salticid spiders (*Euophrys* sp.), which have been collected as high as 22,000 ft (6700 m), are found in association with collembola and presumably feed on these insects, as well as on the anthomyid flies. As in the case of spiders found at high altitudes in other mountain ranges, they may also feed on wind-blown insects.

On the northern slope of the isolated peak of Citlaltepetl (Pico de Orizaba) in Mexico, the wind in July is often from the east, and clouds indicate a sweeping uplift of air onto the peak from the tropical valleys of Vera Cruz. As indicated earlier, in connection with the nival phase, a great many insects are carried onto the mountain because of this current. On rocky slopes above timberline, the lizard *Sceloporus microlepidotus* Wiegmann is relatively abundant and very active during brief periods of sunshine in the morning hours (Swan, 1952). As higher altitudes are approached, the populations do not appear to diminish, and at 15,200 ft (4633 m) lizards were apparent every 3 or 4 ft in pursuit of wind-blown insects. The numbers of lizards diminished somewhat at higher altitudes but were still abundant at 15,800 ft (4816 m), at an altitude approximately 700 ft (214 m) above the highest flowering plants on the north slope of the mountain (Fig. 7).

The aeolian region thus includes exothermic reptiles and stresses the role of available food as a limiting factor rather than harsh environment. The lizard colonies were visited by the raven *Corvus corax sinuatus* Wagler and the sparrow hawk *Falco sparverius sparverius* Linn., the latter being observed to capture the reptiles. The salamander *Pseudoeurycea gadovii* (Dunn) was collected at 15,000 ft, the highest altitude achieved by a caudate amphibian, and a rattlesnake *Crotalus triseriatus* Waller was obtained at 14,850 ft (4528 m) in an area where few plants were in evidence (Fig. 8). The dominant role of wind-blown insects in the nutrition of lizards at these altitudes, and the poor representation of insects associated with plants, suggest strongly that salamanders are also aeolian feeders. The scarcity of mice at these altitudes further implies that the snakes are attracted by lizards and invade the aeolian region in the upper reaches of their distribution. In equatorial high altitudes, where severe and prolonged winters are absent, animals with relatively poor cold tolerance are able to survive near the permanent snowline. Lizards at extreme altitudes are also found in southern Peru (Pearson, 1954) and the

Fig. 7. Citlaltepetl (5700 m, 18,701 ft) from the northwest. The arrow on the left indicates where lizards were collected at 15,800 ft (4816 m). The forest line at approximately 13,500 ft can be seen at lower right. The Orizaba Valley in the State of Vera Cruz, Mexico, is in the distance at left. (Photo courtesy of Compania Mexicana Aerophoto, Inc.)

Himalaya (Swan and Leviton, 1962). *Liolaemus multiformis,* found as high as 16,000 ft (ca. 4900 m) in Peru, and *Leiolopisma ladacensis* (Gunther), from 18,000 ft (5500 m) in Nepal, both representatives of low-latitude alpine regions, may also have aeolian associations.

The upper limit of the terrestrial phase of the aeolian region is open to some conjecture. As indicated in Fig. 9, the temperatures near the ground at 15,500 ft show a great diurnal range, as well as spectacular differences amounting to 78°F (43°C) between shade and sun. If it is assumed that temperatures of this range can be achieved at 15,500 ft, it appears plausible that, with minimum wind velocity, similar differences may occur at higher altitudes, including the snowless areas near the summit of Mount Everest. With a lapse rate of approximately 3°F for a 1000-ft increase of altitude, minimum shade temperatures near the summit of Everest would approximate -9°F (-23°C), and maximum shade temperatures would approach 20°F (-7°C). On the basis of information from free-air temperatures and comparative temperatures between snowless valleys and snow-covered slopes, it would appear that actual shade temperatures near the summit of

Fig. 8. The rattlesnake *Crotalus triseriatus* in the barren area at 14,850 ft (4528 m) on Citlaltepetl.

Everest are somewhat colder. Nevertheless, even when shade temperatures near the summit of Everest are about -30°F (-33°C), it is conceivable that on calm days surface sun temperatures near 50°F (10°C) may be reached. The presence of icicles where snow overlies dark vertical rocks at extreme altitudes bears witness to temperatures above freezing.

On the American Mount Everest Expedition of 1963, William Siri and Barry Corbet collected soil and snow samples in sterile vials. All samples between 25,000 ft (7600 m) and 27,500 ft (8400 m), the altitude above which granular soil was not readily available, have yielded microorganisms in large numbers. However, because of the period of several months between collecting date and culturing date, during which the samples were not exposed to cold temperatures, there is some question concerning the amount of alteration of the microflora in the vials, both in quantity and variety. Through the cooperation of Richard Young, Director of the Division of Exobiology, National Aeronautics and Space Administration, Moffett Field, California, and Donald Fletcher and Edward Ishiguro, San Francisco State College, many of the microorganisms have been isolated and identified. Mr. Ishiguro has supplied me with the following preliminary list of bacteria, fungi, and yeast obtained from between 26,000 and 27,500 ft on the south ridge of Mount Everest and between 25,000 and 27,500 ft on the west ridge of Mount Everest, the higher samples being from granular soil derived from the "yellow band" rocks near the summit.

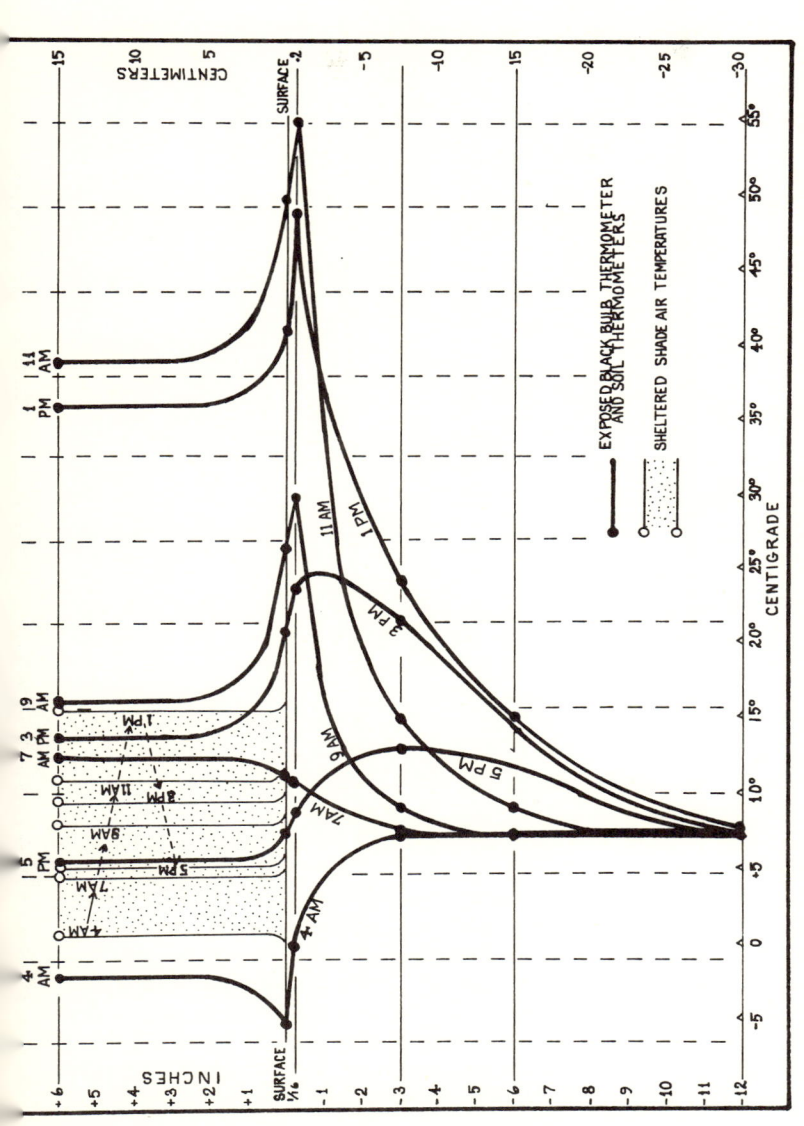

Fig. 9. Temperature profile of the soil and lower air: May 23, 1954, 15,500 ft (4724 m), Barun Valley, East Nepal. Temperatures were obtained on a level surface near prostrate plants (*Potentilla* sp., *Sibbaldia* sp., etc.). The soil was sandy but brown with humus. May 23 represented a relatively warm day. The effect of the sun was apparent at 9 A.M. Clouds intervened prior to 3 P.M., and full shade occurred before 5 P.M. Wind velocity was estimated at less than 10 mph. Temperatures at 1/16 inch below the surface were obtained by placing the thermometer on its side just under the surface so that a minimum thickness of soil intervened between the thermometer and direct sunlight. The black-bulb thermometer was an ordinary thermometer with the bulb painted with India ink.

Bacteria

    Nocardia — numerous strains
    Streptomyces — several strains
    Bacillus megaterium
    Bacillus cereus
    Bacillus alvei
    Bacillus sp. — several species, including bacteria from snow
    Flavobacterium — several pigmented strains, primarily pink or red, a few yellow
    Micrococcus roseus — several pigmented strains
    Arthrobacter pascens
    Arthrobacter simplex
    Arthrobacter tumescens
    Arthrobacter sp. — several yellow strains that could not be assigned to species
    ? *Mycococcus* sp. — highly unusual organisms; genus uncertain
    Corynebacterium sp. — one yellow strain, infrequent
    Pseudomonas aeruginosa — infrequent

Fungi

    Penicillium sp.
    Monocillium sp.

Yeasts

    Candida — several species
    Rhodotorula sp. — infrequent, pigmented

Chemolithotrophs and nitrogen-fixing bacteria were not detected. The poor representation of fungi in the samples — none having been isolated from west-ridge collections — appears anomalous, inasmuch as the remaining flora resembles an attenuated sampling of normal soil. The question of whether these organisms metabolize and actively survive near the summit of the highest mountain is still largely unanswered. The suggestion of periodic equable temperatures and water, the nearly universal supply of organic debris, the abundance of the microflora, the frequency of pigmented forms, and the fact that the Mount Everest microorganisms represent soil microflora rather than a miscellany of air-borne organisms tend to support the thesis that living things exist and grow at the summit of the earth. The aeolian zone thus extends into an environment with attributes of cold temperatures, diurnal contrast, extreme desiccation, atmospheric attenuation, and environmental harshness. In these respects it relates earthly ecology to hypotheses of exobiology and life on Mars.

The aeolian status of lichens, as with many high-altitude organisms, is open to question. These plants are widespread in alpine situations and often extend to a higher altitude than the local vascular plants. In very arid situations or in areas recently uncovered by permanent snow, they may be scarce or absent, and in the Barun Valley area of eastern Nepal the vascular plants that can obtain water from the soil grow at higher altitudes than noticeable lichens on rock surfaces. It may be considered that the retreat of the snowline in many parts of the world has revealed surfaces that require time for repopulation by living organisms. In such situations the aeolian life may be transitory and aid in establishing the ultimate alpine flora and fauna. In the high Himalayas the rocky areas recently exposed by retreating snow are usually free of lichens, although they may harbor a few flowering plants or aeolian animals. There is a strong suggestion that in these arid areas the invasion of lichens is extremely slow.

Lichens have been known to grow on glass and smooth rock surfaces without leaving any evidence of etching, so these forms must rely entirely upon nutrients supplied by rainwater and the atmosphere. Where such materials are not contributed by neighboring vegetation, there is a broad implication that lichens are aeolian. The ability of lichens to remove minute quantities of air-borne contaminants is aptly illustrated by their sensitivity to smog and their remarkable ability to remove and concentrate radioactive fallout. Experimental evidence from several sources also indicates that lichens are able to absorb intact a variety of organic materials. When the lichen association is represented by a green alga, the requirement of nitrate from the atmosphere is implied. A similar hypothesis may be applied to some mosses, which often grow on soil in cracks and crevices supplied by the wind and which absorb a wide variety of nutrients from the atmosphere.

On this basis, lichens and some mosses are the chief representatives of the aeolian polar counterpart of high mountains. Lichens, collembola, and mites found within a few hundred miles of the South Pole may survive more easily with the additional nutrients contributed by wind-blown guano (Llano, 1962).

Throughout the world where vascular plants are absent or minimal, the nutritional sources for living things become largely a matter of conjecture. In the literature of research on barren areas, particularly the Antarctic, very little consideration is given to air-transported sources of nutrition. Chemolithotrophs, nitrogen-fixing bacteria, and blue-green algae are often given credit for the enigma of the presence of organic material in nearly sterile soils when the principle of parsimony suggests atmospheric nutrients. Undoubtedly, in certain areas the presence of blue-green algae answers the problem of organic nutrition, and the only significant aeolian contribution would be inorganic. However, it appears artificial to exclude from the aeolian zone a mountain cliff that is covered with blue-green algae supplied by water and minerals from a higher snow field. At least some of the minerals are air-transported. Similarly, ponds filled with blue-green algae that are maintained by meltwater and its contained minerals are on the fringe of the aeolian zone and are closer to this ecological category than any other. The snow holes containing blue-green algae and associated animals in Greenland and the isolated lakes of Antarctica fit a quasi-aeolian status and come within a broadened interpretation of the aeolian region. Aside from the significant food chains developing from bird guano and similarly transported organic materials derived from marine food in the Antarctic, an association akin to the communities in caves, there is a broad aeolian link among the high mountains of the world, the barrens of the high Arctic, and the remote interior of the Antarctic continent.

Acknowledgments

Support for expeditions referred to in this paper was as follows: American Himalayan Expedition to Makalu, 1954, supported in part by the National Science Foundation and the Sierra Club; Himalayan Scientific and Mountaineering Expedition, 1960-1961, supported by the World Book Encyclopedia; and expeditions to Citlaltepetl, Mexico, 1964 and 1965, supported in part by the Society of Sigma Xi, the Research Corporation, and National Science Foundation Institutional Grants to San Francisco State College. Himalayan plants have been identified by the staff of the British Museum (Natural History) and by Harry Smith of Uppsala, Sweden.

REFERENCES

Balle, S., 1953, La végétation du Ruwenzori: Les Naturalistes Belges, Soc. Diffusion et Documentation Scientifiques, v. 34, pp. 75-83.

Beaman, J. H., 1962, The timberlines of Iztaccihuatl and Popocateptel, Mexico: Ecology, v. 43, pp. 377-385.

Bettler, G. T., 1964, Observations on selected plants and animals of the aeolian zone: Reno, Univ. Nev. Dept. Biol., Rept., 25 pp. (unpublished).

Bews, J. W., 1917, The plant ecology of the Drakensberg Range: Natal Museum Ann., v. 3, pp. 511-565.

Chamber of Commerce, Addis Ababa, 1954, Guide Book of Ethiopia, 445 pp.

Clausen, J., 1963, Tree lines and germ plasma: A study in evolutionary limitation: Science, v. 140, p. 380 (abstract).

Colijn, A. H., 1937, Naar de eeuwige sneeuw van tropisch Nederland: Amsterdam, Scheltens and Giltay, 286 pp.

Daubenmire, R. F., 1954, Alpine timberlines in the Americas and their interpretation: Indianapolis, Ind., Butler Univ. Botan. Studies, v. 11, pp. 119-136.

Gregory, P. H., 1961, The microbiology of the atmosphere: New York, Wiley (Interscience), 251 pp.

Griggs, R. F., 1946, Timberlines of northern America and their interpretation: Ecology, v. 27, pp. 275-289.

Hutchinson, G. E., 1965, The ecological theater and the evolutionary play: New Haven, Yale Univ. Press, 139 pp.

Llano, G. A., 1962, The terrestrial life of the Antarctic: Sci. Am., v. 207, pp. 212-230.

Mani, M. S., 1962, Introduction to high altitude entomology: London, Methuen, 302 pp.

Marr, J. W., 1961, Ecosystems of the east slope of the front range in Colorado: Univ. Colo. Studies Ser. Biol., v. 8, 134 pp.

Osburn, W. S., 1963, The dynamics of fallout distribution in a Colorado alpine tundra snow accumulation ecosystem: *in* Radioecology, V. Schultz and A. W. Klement (eds.): New York, Reinhold, pp. 51-71, and Am. Inst. Biol. Sci. Publ.

Osgood, W. H., 1928, Nature and man in Ethiopia: Natl. Geograph. Magazine, v. 54, pp. 121-176.

Pearson, G. A., 1931, Forest types in the southwest as determined by climate and soil: U.S. Dept. Agr. Tech. Bull., v. 247, 143 pp.

Pearson, O. P., 1951, Mammals of the highlands of southern Peru: Harvard Univ. Museum Comp. Zool. Bull., 106, pp. 117-174.

_____ 1954, Habits of the lizard *Liolaemus multiformis multiformis* at high altitudes in southern Peru: Copeia, 2, pp. 111-116.

Penland, W. T., 1941, The alpine vegetation of the southern Rockies and the Ecuadorian Andes: Colorado Springs, Colo. Coll. Publ. Ser. 32, pp. 5-29.

Swan, L. W., 1952, Some environmental conditions influencing life at high altitudes: Ecology, v. 33, pp. 109-111.

_____ 1961, The ecology of the high Himalayas: Sci. Am., v. 205, pp. 68-78.

_____ 1963a, Aeolian zone: Science, v. 140, pp. 77-78.

_____ 1963b, Ecology of the heights: Nat. Hist., v. 57, pp. 22-29.

_____, and Leviton, A. E., 1962, The herpetology of Nepal: A history, check list and zoogeographical analysis of the herpetofauna: Calif. Acad. Sci. Proc., v. 32, pp. 103-147.

Troll, C., 1948, Der asymmetrische Aufgau der Vegetationszonen und Vegetationsstufen auf der Nord- und Sudhalbkugel: Ber. Geobot. Forschungsinst. Rubel, 1947, pp. 46-83.

_____ 1959, Die tropischen Gebirge. Ihre dreidimensionale klimatische und pflanzengeographische Zonierung: Bonner Geograph. Abhandl., v. 25, 93 pp.

Wangersky, P. J., 1965, The organic chemistry of sea water: Am. Scientist, v. 53, pp. 358-374.

Webster, G. L., 1961, The altitudinal limits of vascular plants: Ecology, v. 42, pp. 587-590.
Wilson, A. T., 1959a, Organic nitrogen in New Zealand snows: Nature, v. 183, pp. 318-319.
_____ 1959b, Surface of the ocean as a source of airborne nitrogenous material and other plant nutrients: Nature, v. 184, pp. 99-101.
Wollaston, A. F. R., 1922, Natural history, *in* Mount Everest, the Reconnaissance, C. K. Howard-Bury (ed.), 1921: London, Edward Arnold, 356 pp.
Zimmermann, A., 1953, The highest plants in the world, *in* The Mountain World: New York, Harper, pp. 130-136.

ARCTIC AND ALPINE ENVIRONMENTS (H. E. Wright, Jr., and
W. H. Osburn, eds.), 55-87, ©1967 Indiana University Press

4
Alpine Ecosystems
of the Australasian Region

A. B. COSTIN
Division of Plant Industry
CSIRO, Canberra, Australia

Abstract

The alpine ecosystems of the Australasian Region occupy roughly 12,300 square miles in North Borneo, New Guinea, Australia, New Zealand, and the Subantarctic Islands.

The characteristics of each main ecosystem are reviewed with reference to physical conditions, soils, flora, fauna, vegetation, adjacent treeline communities, and the influence of primitive and European man.

Each ecosystem has its distinguishing characteristics, but there are certain features in common. These include a mean temperature (at treeline) of about 50°F for the warmest month, considerable freeze-thaw activity and superficial solifluction, floras of generally similar biogeographical and life-form composition, predominantly grassland or herbfield vegetation (except in Tasmania), and faunas that are virtually lacking in larger mammals. The ecosystems are not well adapted to human interference and have mostly undergone deterioration through recent activities of European man. They have low primary productivities which, with management difficulties, make them unsuitable for efficient grazing use. Their main importance is as nature and recreation reserves and water-catchment areas.

For more than a century the Australasian Region has been a rich field of enquiry for workers in the natural sciences. Most of the main environments have now been sampled, if not understood, and in some cases generalizations have been made, for example, tropical rain forest (Richards, 1952). Individual alpine environments have also been investigated and limited generalizations attempted (e.g., Costin, 1954a). The purpose of this study is to provide an over-all review of the alpine areas.

A particular alpine ecosystem can be more or less adequately delimited in terms of the properties of any one of several component parts—for example, the life forms or biogeographical affinities of the flora, the altitude, or some related element of climate such as temperature or snow cover. Important processes, such as solifluction, may also be used. When applied on a general basis, however, most of these criteria fail. In this general context, an *alpine ecosystem* is probably best defined as *the ecosystem between the climatic limit of tree vegetation and the nival zone* (cf. van Steenis, 1935). The main exceptions appear to be in very dry mountains such as the Pamirs, where subalpine tree vegetation may be absent, and in the tropical mountains of East Africa, where trees may extend into the alpine tract (Hedberg, 1951).

Other objections to this definition are that it may include various nonalpine environments where treelessness results from anthropogenic (e.g., burning; Lane-Poole, 1925), topographic (e.g., wind funneling; Costin, 1954a), edaphic, or historical factors (e.g., montane and subalpine grasslands in New Zealand; Molloy et al., 1963; and some "balds"; Webb, 1964); and that it does not differentiate between the

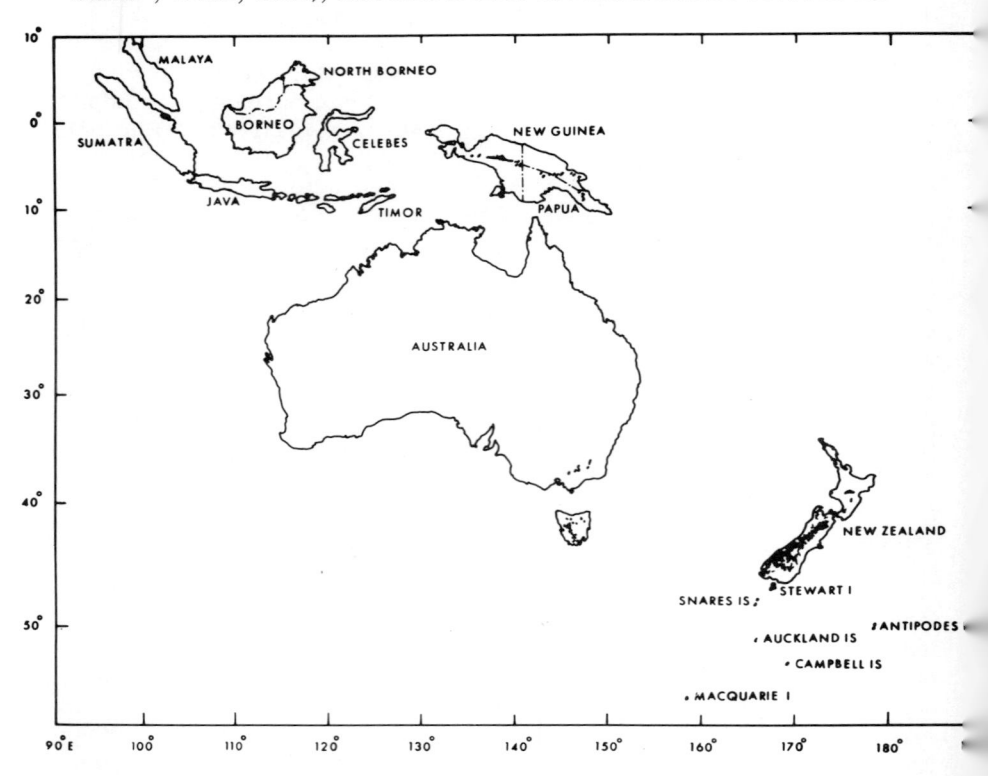

Fig. 1. Distribution of alpine ecosystems in the Australasian region.

TABLE 1

Main Occurrences of Alpine Ecosystems
in the Australasian Region and
Their Approximate Areas

Occurrence	Approx. area, sq miles	Source of information
North Borneo	2	Corner et al., 1962-1963; Gibbs, 1914
New Guinea		
west	2000	van Steenis, 1958; R. G. Robbins, Australian National University, and R. Schodde, CSIRO, pers. comm.
east	300	Perry et al., 1965; R. G. Robbins, Australian National University, and J. R. McAlpine, CSIRO, pers. comm.
Australia		
mainland	120	Costin, CSIRO, unpubl.
Tasmania	250	Directorate Ind. Devel., 1954
New Zealand		
North Is.	250	P. Wardle, D.S.I.R., pers. comm.
South Is.	9200	Based on McLintock, 1959
Stewart Is.	40	
Subantarctic Islands		
Antipodes, Auckland, Campbell, Snares	100	Chilton, 1909
Macquarie	40	Taylor, 1955

obviously different tropical-, temperate-, and antarctic-alpine conditions. The first group of nonclimatic effects are therefore excluded here, and reference is made to latitudinal position as required.

The distribution of the alpine ecosystems of the Australasian Region (*sens. lat.* cf. Good, 1963) according to the above definition is as shown in Fig. 1. Table 1 lists these occurrences and gives rough estimates of areas. Individual descriptions now follow. The treatment from place to place is regrettably uneven and incomplete, especially for the fauna and lower plants.

BORNEO

As far as can be ascertained from the literature (e.g., van Steenis, 1934, 1935), true alpine environments, as distinct from occurrences of "alpine" species, appear to be virtually lacking in the Indonesian group of islands. Most of the elevated treeless areas (10,000 to 12,000 ft) that have been described seem to be associated with recent disturbance by volcanic activity or by burning (e.g., Jacobs, 1958; Senn, 1925). The main exception is the summit section of Mt. Kinabalu (13,455 ft) in North Borneo, where there are about 2 sq miles of naturally treeless country above 12,000 feet (Corner et al., 1962-1963) (Fig. 2). The small size and rocky character of the Kinabalu summit do not favor a rich flora and fauna. About 30 species of dwarf shrubs and herbs have been recorded, growing as scattered plants and clumps in cracks of the otherwise fairly smooth granite dome of the mountain (Gibbs, 1914) (Fig. 3). The shrubs include species of *Coprosma, Eurya, Ilex, Kelleria, Leptospermum, Rhododendron, Rubus, Styphelia,* and *Symplocos;* and the herbs, species of *Agrostis, Aletris, Carex, Centrolepis, Deschampsia, Didiscus, Euphrasia, Haloragis, Lagenophora, Pilea, Potentilla,* and *Schoenus.* Few climatic data are available; general conditions probably resemble those of the New Guinea mountains described below.

Fig. 2. Summit area of Mt. Kinabalu, North Borneo, rising above dense subalpine forest and scrub. (Photo by Dr. M. E. D. Poore.)

ALPINE ECOSYSTEMS 59

Fig. 3. Part of summit area of Mt. Kinabalu, showing smooth rock surfaces, and sparse vegetation largely confined to cracks. (Photo by Dr. M. E. D. Poore.)

NEW GUINEA

The New Guinea alpine ecosystem, with a total extent of roughly 2300 sq miles above 12,000 to 12,500 ft, and a diversity of rock types and slopes, is the only well-developed tropical-alpine ecosystem in the Australasian Region. The highest and most extensive areas (ca. 2000 sq miles) occur in the western half of the island (maximum elevation Carstensz Peaks 16,500 ft), where there are small glaciers (Reiner, 1960). The snowline here stands at 15,000 to 15,500 ft but is thought to be receding. The alpine mountains in eastern New Guinea (ca. 300 sq miles), of which Mt. Wilhelm (ca. 15,000 ft) is the highest, do not carry permanent snow, but, like those in the west, they have been glaciated in the past, possibly down to 8500 to 9500 ft (Reiner, 1960). In places there was also strong Pleistocene vulcanism (Brass, 1964). The proximity of the New Guinea mountains to the surrounding ocean implies heavy precipitation from both the northwest and southeast monsoons. Although there are probably seasonal differences depending on location, and the alpine areas themselves may be above the zone of maximum precipitation, rainfalls are generally high (>100 inches per year), with a large number of rain days (>70 percent), and exceed free-water evaporation for most of the year (Brass, 1964; Perry et al., 1965). Snow is uncommon and does not persist, except at the highest levels in West New Guinea. Winds are not severe. There are no distinct seasons except of a daily nature, characterized by wide temperature fluctuations, from about 60 to 70°F to near freezing in clear weather. Long-term temperature records are not available. All that can be done at present is to extrapolate from the highest adjacent stations (Mendi 6000 ft, Wabag 6800 ft). Rutherford (1964) uses a lapse rate of 3°F/1000 ft, which is approximately correct below 7000 ft in New Guinea, but above 7000 ft it may be nearer 2°F under the mild moist air conditions which prevail (cf. Manley, 1953). A lapse rate of 25°F gives annual and monthly values of about 48°F at 12,500 ft (Appendix 1).

The above climatic conditions favor acid peat formation; mor peats and peat podzols occur on moderate slopes, and bog peats in flatter ground-water situations. Steeper slopes are characterized by lithosols, with a tendency to the formation of alpine humus soils. There are frequently signs of superficial solifluction in the form of poorly developed patterned ground (cf. Troll, 1958). Other data are sparse; tropical alpine soils are still incompletely understood (cf. Haantjens et al., 1958).

The large alpine flora (>200 spp. of vascular plants) has mainly Cosmopolitan and Tropical affinities, with a sprinkling of Australian, New Zealand, Antarctic, South American, and South African groups (Appendix 2). Hemicryptophytes, with chamaephytes and nanophanerophytes, are the main life forms (Appendix 3). The fauna appears to be relatively poor in species (e.g., Brass, 1964; H. M. Van Deusen, personal communication).

The vegetation is more uniform than at middle latitudes, possibly because of the absence of seasonal snow cover and strong winds. Grassland occurs in most situations (Fig. 4). Important physiognomic dominants include the tussock grasses *Danthonia archboldii* Hitchc. (apparently related to the *Chionochloa* group of Zotov, 1963), *Deschampsia klossii* Ridl. and species of *Poa* and *Hierochloe;* there are also many smaller herbs (e.g., *Monostachya oreoboloides* (F. Muell.) Hitchc.; species of *Epilobium, Euphrasia, Gentiana, Potentilla, Anaphalis, Gnaphalium, Tetramalopium, Ranunculus*); and scattered shrubs (see below) (Fig. 5). On steep, rocky sites the grasslands grade into grass heaths and heaths characterized by species of *Styphelia, Hypericum, Drimys, Hebe, Coprosma, Vaccinium, Rhododendron, Symplocos, Detzneria, Eurya,* etc., and in ground-water situations into bogs of mosses (including *Sphagnum* spp.) and minor herbs (e.g., *Juncus, Astelia, Trachymene, Drosera, Haloragis, Plantago, Ranunculus*). With increasing elevation the grasslands become simpler in floristic composition (except for cryptogams) and more open in structure, apparently grading into fellfield near the nival zone (cf. Archbold et al., 1942; Robbins, 1961). Well-developed cushion-plant

ALPINE ECOSYSTEMS 61

Fig. 4. Eastern peak of Mt. Giluwe, eastern New Guinea, showing extensive alpine grasslands. (CSIRO photo.)

Fig. 5. Alpine grassland, near former treeline, Mt. Wilhelm, eastern New Guinea. Note scattered shrubs on steeper, rockier sites. (CSIRO photo.)

Fig. 6. Western slope of Mt. Giluwe, eastern New Guinea, showing depression of subalpine forest and scrub caused by native fires. (CSIRO photo.)

communities seem to be lacking, although there are a few species of cushion plants in the flora (e.g., *Oreomyrrhis azorellacea* Buw., *Rhododendron saxifragoides* J.J.S.). Further details of the vegetation are available from Brass (1941, 1964), Haantjens et al. (1958), Hoogland (1958), Perry et al. (1965), Robbins (1961), and others.

The lower limit of alpine grassland is defined by low mossy forests or related subalpine scrubs characterized by species of *Podocarpus, Papuacedrus, Phyllocladus, Schefflera, Drimys, Eurya, Coprosma, Vaccinium, Rhododendron, Olearia*, etc. The natural limit is about 12,000 to 12,500 ft, but this is often depressed to as low as 9000 ft by cold-air drainage and particularly by native fires (Fig. 6). The pyric grasslands often contain remnant patches of rainforest or scrub and scattered tree ferns (*Cyathea* spp.) that are relatively favored by burning. Melanesian man is thought to have reached New Guinea at least 10,000 years ago (Bulmer, 1964; Bulmer and Bulmer, 1964), and although only the frost-free areas up to about 8000 ft are permanently occupied and used for native gardens, many of the alpine areas are nevertheless burnt during visiting and hunting expeditions. As yet, there has been no European interference.

ALPINE ECOSYSTEMS

AUSTRALIA

A distance of more than 2000 miles separates the New Guinea alpine ecosystem from that of southeastern mainland Australia, although there are a few small occurrences of alpine species in between. The total area (above approximately 6000 ft) is about 120 sq miles, mostly in the Kosciusko area of the Snowy Mountains, where several peaks exceed 7000 ft (7318 ft on Mt. Kosciusko). At the highest levels snow may persist locally from one year to the next, but there are no permanent snow fields. Glaciers were active 20,000 years ago, and probably more recently.

Most of the alpine ecosystem of mainland Australia is situated on relatively undissected plateaus (Costin, 1957) (Fig. 7). This terrain, and the absence of severe glaciation, have favored the development of a deep soil mantle. Alpine humus soils are widespread on the better-drained sites, with bog and fen peats and a variety of gleyed soils in wetter areas and lithosols in exposed places (Costin, 1954a, 1962a).

Precipitation is high (ca. 70 to 120 inches per year), well distributed but with a winter-spring peak, and includes heavy snowfalls that persist for several months. Mean annual temperatures at 6000 ft are about 40°F; the monthly means range from about 50°F in January to 27°F in July. Although the winter temperatures are not low by alpine standards (screen minimum recorded near treeline -8°F), there is a high frequency of frosts, with up to 200 freeze-thaw cycles

Fig. 7. Mt. Kosciusko, Australia, showing gentle terrain with widespread alpine herbfield vegetation. The darker patches are heath, on rocky sites.

per annum; superficial solifluction is therefore widespread on unvegetated surfaces. Strong winds are common (Appendix 1).

The alpine vascular flora of about 200 species has predominantly Cosmopolitan and Australian affinities, but other southern groups are also well represented (Appendix 2). Hemicryptophytes and chamaephytes predominate (Appendix 3). There is a rich insect fauna, but large vertebrates are few and uncommon (Costin, 1954a).

Herbaceous communities in the form of herbfields and grasslands are the main cover types (Fig. 7). The most important components are grasses of the *Poa caespitosa* group *(sens. lat.)*, *Danthonia frigida* J. Vickery (*Chionochloa* of Zotov, 1963), and the forb *Celmisia longifolia* Cass., with numerous other composites, umbellifers, and species of *Euphrasia, Ranunculus, Gentiana (Gentianella)*, etc. (Fig. 8). The lower limit of these communities is set by the treeline of *Eucalyptus niphophila* Maiden and Blakely at about 6000 ft, and under conditions of cold-air drainage they also extend down into the subalpine zone. The above communities grade into short alpine herbfields characterized by species of *Claytonia, Plantago, Caltha*, etc., in lower snow-patch situations; heaths of *Podocarpus, Phebalium, Orites, Grevillea, Leucopogon, Prostanthera, Kunzea*, and other shrubs in rocky sites; and acid *Carex* fens and *Sphagnum* bogs with marginal wet heaths (mainly epacridaceous shrubs) in wet places. In the most exposed sites the vegetation becomes open, as fellfield. There are two distinct communities, one in the most wind-exposed sites with the dwarf shrub *Epacris petrophila* Hook.f. and the other in upper snow-patch situations with the mat plants *Coprosma pumila* Hook.f. and *Colobanthus benthamianus* Fenzl.

Aboriginal man, probably present in Australia for about 20,000 years (Mulvaney, 1963, 1964) is reported to have made summer visits to the alpine areas to feast on the Bogong moth (Common, 1954). There was some local lighting of fires, but these appear to have had little effect on the alpine communities or on the adjacent treeline eucalypt vegetation, which is adapted to periodic fire. By contrast, European exploitation during the last 100 years, involving summer grazing and burning, has caused general deterioration of soils and vegetation (Australian Academy of Science, 1957) (Fig. 9). Locally the effects of engineering and tourist development have also been severe (Costin, 1959). Most alpine areas on the mainland are now protected from fires and grazing, and active rehabilitation measures have been commenced.

Although situated only 400 miles south of the alpine areas of the Australian mainland and separated by little more than 100 miles of ocean, the alpine ecosystem of Tasmania is distinct enough to be considered separately. Its lower limit is irregularly defined by one of several treeline species (*Eucalyptus coccifera* Hook.f., *E. gunnii* Hook.f., and the deciduous *Nothofagus gunnii* Seem.) at about 4000 ft; the highest peaks just exceed 5000 ft. The area of alpine country

Fig. 8. *Celmisia longifolia - Poa caespitosa* herbfield association at Kosciusko with associated major forbs *Craspedia uniflora* and *Euphrasia glacialis* in flower.

Fig. 9. Accelerated erosion of alpine herbfield area, Kosciusko, Australia, initiated by sheep grazing.

Fig. 10. Mt. Wellington, showing rocky character of Tasmanian alpine areas and widespread heath vegetation (dark areas between rocks). (CSIRO photo.)

between these levels is roughly 250 sq miles. Most of it is in the form of uplifted plateaus of resistant dolerite, formerly glaciated (David, 1950), but now all below the permanent snow line. In general the soils are either rocky (lithosols) or hydromorphic (peats, podzols, gleys); the alpine humus soils of the mainland are scarcely developed (Fig. 10).

Precipitation is fairly high (>50 inches per year) and well distributed, with moderate winter snow. Temperatures (as recorded on Mt. Wellington, 4166 ft) range from about 48°F in January to 32°F in July, with an annual mean of about 40°F. Owing to the surrounding ocean, there is much cloud and sustained (but not severe) winds; frosts are frequent but less so than in the mainland ecosystem, which is more continental (Appendix 1).

The flora of more than 100 vascular species has strong Australian and Cosmopolitan affinities (Appendix 2). Chamaephytes, with hemicryptophytes, are most strongly developed (Appendix 3). The fauna is poor and virtually lacking in larger vertebrates.

Heath is the predominant vegetation. There are two main communities. The most widespread, on the better-drained, rocky sites, is characterized by many of the small shrubs found in the mainland alpine heaths but in addition contains a number of endemic conifers,

Fig. 11. *Abrotanella forsterioides* cushion heath community on wet ground, Mt. Wellington, Tasmania. (Photo by Dr. D. Martin.)

including *Pherosphaera hookeriana* Arch., *Microcachrys tetragona* Hook.f., and *Diselma archeri* Hook.f. (Fig. 10). The other community, on wet ground, is largely composed of cushion plants (e.g., *Abrotanella forsterioides* Benth., *Donatia novaezelandiae* J.R. & G. Forst., *Phyllachne colensoi* Bergr., and *Pterygopappus lawrencei* Hook.f., with *Astelia, Oreobolus,* etc.), which also include endemic species (Fig. 11). This "cushion heath" community is probably the most distinctive feature of the Tasmanian alpine vegetation. It provides a strong link with the cushion bogs of southern New Zealand and the Subantarctic Islands (see later), but apparently does not accumulate peat like the latter communities. The alpine herbfield communities of the mainland are localized to the occasional pockets of well-drained relatively stone-free organomineral soil, and in seepage areas there is sometimes a small development of *Sphagnum* bogs, and fens.

Anthropogenic modification, mostly by fires, is relatively slight, as the largely shrubby character of the vegetation has discouraged grazing.

NEW ZEALAND

The alpine ecosystem of New Zealand is the most extensive in the Australasian Region. It extends in a broken fashion from Hikurangi,

Fig. 12. Alpine tract of Mt. Earnslaw, New Zealand, clearly defined by treeline of beech.

the Tongariro National Park, and Mt. Egmont in the North Island through the Southern Alps to Stewart Island at the tip of the South Island, a distance of more than 600 miles. Apart from some relatively flat-topped plateaus in Otago (cf. Billings and Mark, 1961), the areas concerned are mostly steep to precipitous in consequence of strong folding and uplift with faulting, followed by severe glacial and fluviatile dissection (Fig. 12); in the North Island, volcanic activity has been superimposed. The lower alpine limit ranges from about 3000 ft to 5000 ft, depending on latitude and local conditions (e.g., Mark and Bayliss, 1963; Elder, 1959; Wardle, 1962; Wraight, 1963). Nival conditions commence at 6000 to 8000 ft, the highest point being Mt. Cook (12,349 ft). The total alpine area is roughly 9500 sq miles (McLintock, 1959; P. Wardle, personal communication).

The rain-shadow effects that occur to the east of the main divide of the Southern Alps, although relatively unimportant in the alpine zone itself, complicate the lower delimitation of "alpine" in these areas. The interaction of these drier conditions and an ecologically poor tree flora (Costin, 1954b) results in the virtual failure of tree regeneration after fire and in the extension and mixing of herbaceous elements of alpine and lowland environments (e.g., Mark, 1965) (Fig. 13). In parts of the Tongariro area recent volcanic destruction of soils and vegetation and current secondary successions present similar

Fig. 13. Widespread tussock grasslands, central Otago, New Zealand. *Chionochloa flavescens* in foreground.

difficulties. Elsewhere the tree limit is more sharply defined either by rain-forest species of *Nothofagus* (mainly *N. solandri* Oerst. var. *cliffortioides* Poole and *N. menziesii* Oerst.) or, where the beech forest is absent or depressed, by species of subalpine scrub *(Olearia, Senecio, Dracophyllum, Dacrydium)* with general floristic and physiognomic similarities to the New Guinea subalpine scrubs (Fig. 12).

Precipitation ranges from about 40 inches up to 400 inches (Wraight, 1964), depending on locality, and includes moderate to heavy snow, which persists for several months. Mean monthly temperatures in lower alpine situations range from about 50°F in January to 25°F in July, with annual values of about 40°F. As in Australia, minimum temperatures are not low by "alpine" standards, but there is a high frost frequency, with up to 200 freeze-thaw cycles per annum (Appendix 1).

The vascular flora of more than 200 species is derived mainly from Cosmopolitan and New Zealand elements (Appendix 2). Hemicryptophytes and chamaephytes are the main life forms (Appendix 3). The native fauna is virtually lacking in larger vertebrates, as in the other mountains of the Australasian Region; the insect fauna, however, appears to be fairly rich (Anon., 1965a).

The most widespread plant communities are tall tussock grasslands dominated by species of *Chionochloa (Danthonia sens. lat.;* Zotov, 1963) (cf. Drummond and Leatham, 1959) (Fig. 13). The associated soils have been termed high-country yellow-brown earths, gley soils, and gley podzols by New Zealand workers (McLintock, 1959). Short grassland communities dominated by sod-forming species of *Chionochloa, Notodanthonia* (Zotov, 1963), and *Poa colensoi* Hook.f. are developed more locally at higher levels (Burrows, 1962a). On stonier soils the grassland communities become increasingly rich in forbs and grade into alpine herbfields in which species of *Celmisia* and *Aciphylla* are most conspicuous; various low shrubs (e.g., species of *Dracophyllum, Hebe, Senecio,* and *Podocarpus;* Wardle, 1964) also enter the community on more rocky sites. Unstable screes support an extremely open vegetation of specialized plants (Fisher, 1952). Under the most severe conditions, i.e., near the nival zone and in very wind-exposed situations, the grassland and herbfield communities grade into fellfield (alpine barrens of McLintock, 1959) (Burrows, 1962a; Cockayne, 1928): the fellfield communities on the Old Man Range in the South Island are characterized by the cushion plants *Dracophyllum muscoides* Hook.f. and *Raoulia hectori* Hook.f. (Billings and Mark, 1961). On some of the flatter plateau mountains *Sphagnum* bogs with bog peats are developed locally in wet sites, and cushion bogs and peats *(Donatia, Phyllachne, Gaimardia,* with *Oreobolus* and *Astelia)* in the more oceanic southern areas (Cranwell, 1953; Dansereau, 1962).

Fig. 14. Accelerated erosion of tussock grassland area, Mt. Lyndon, New Zealand. (Photo by Mr. R. D. Dick.)

Despite the steepness of most of the New Zealand mountains and the deeply fractured greywackes and similar weak parent materials of which they are composed, largely stable vegetation and mature soils have been able to develop. By contrast, the present situation is one of widespread instability. From Maori times (probably commencing within the last 1000 years; Cox and Mead, 1963; Molloy et al., 1963) fires became an important influence. One of the effects was the progressive destruction of forest, particularly in marginally dry areas, with the consequent extension of species of alpine grassland (as in New Guinea) to lower altitudes. During the last 100 years of European influence these effects have been extended by the practices of burning and summer pasturing of sheep, and by the spread of feral grazing and browsing mammals, particularly red deer (cf. Howard, 1964). The alpine ecosystem itself has also suffered widespread deterioration (e.g., Gibbs et al., 1945); it now presents some of the most difficult soil-erosion problems in the world (Fig. 14).

SUBANTARCTIC ISLANDS

The Subantarctic Islands of the Australasian Region comprise some of the southern shelf islands of New Zealand (Antipodes, Auckland, Campbell, Snares) and Macquarie Island. The "alpine" or, more correctly, the "antarctic-alpine" component, above the zone of coastal or lowland scrub (where this exists), includes roughly 140 sq miles.

Despite their low latitude and often considerable elevation, the islands have a pronounced maritime climate because of the surrounding ocean and the influence of the Roaring Forties. Apart from differences in day length, there is little seasonal variation in climate. It is almost continuously cool, wet, and windy, with little sunshine. On Campbell Island, about 500 ft below scrubline, mean monthly temperatures range from about 50°F in January to 30°F in July, and the daily range is also small. The yearly average is about 45°F (Marshall, 1909). Corresponding data for Macquarie Island, which is treeless, are 43°F (January), 37°F (July), and 40°F (year) (Taylor, 1955). These cool maritime conditions result in a different frost climate from that experienced above treeline in Australia and New Zealand. The frequent daily freeze-thaw cycles tend to be replaced by fewer cycles of longer duration (Appendix 1).

The vascular alpine flora of the islands as a whole comprises about 100 species, the number decreasing roughly in proportion to the size of the island and its latitude. Macquarie Island supports only about 30 species. Their affinities are still mainly Cosmopolitan, with New Zealand types next in importance and a strong development of the old Antarctic element (Appendix 2). Hemicryptophytes, with chamaephytes, are best represented (Appendix 3). There is a rich vertebrate fauna, particularly of birds and seals, but these are essentially marine species with little impact on the terrestrial ecosystems, except for locally concentrated mechanical disturbance and dunging during the breeding season. Insects, mites, and ticks are the dominant terrestrial groups (Gressitt, 1963).

In the New Zealand shelf islands the alpine communities occur above low forest or scrub, in which one or more species of the following genera are dominant, as in parts of New Zealand: *Metrosideros, Olearia, Senecio, Neopanax, Dracophyllum, Coprosma* (Chilton, 1909; Cockayne, 1928). On Macquarie Island, where there are no trees, the alpine vegetation commences at sea level. Five main communities can be recognized. The two most important, on relatively steep or well drained and gentle or poorly drained sites, respectively, are: tall tussock grassland dominated by species of *Poa* (mainly *P. foliosa* Hook.f. and *P. litorosa* Cheesem.) and *Chionochloa antarctica* (Hook.f.) Zotov, sometimes mixed with species of *Coprosma, Dracophyllum, Cassinia,* and other low shrubs; and herbfields characterized by large-leaved perennial rosette forbs, particularly species of *Pleurophyllum* and *Stilbocarpa* (Fig. 15). Both communities accumulate acid peat. On flat, ground-water sites there are fens (*Juncus scheuchzeroides* Gaud. on Macquarie Island), and bogs of mosses (e.g., *Breutelia pendula* Mitt., *Sphagnum falcatum* Besch.) and cushion plants (*Gaimardia* and *Phyllachne,* with *Coprosma, Astelia,* and *Oreobolus*), the latter having affinities with the "cushion heaths" of Tasmania. Upland sites on Macquarie Island that are continually

Fig. 15. West coast of Macquarie Island, showing herbfield community of *Pleurophyllum hookeri* on poorly drained flat and tussock grassland of *Poa foliosa* on steeper slopes. Both communities accumulate acid peat.

Fig. 16. Extensive fellfield of *Azorella selago* on windswept plateau of Macquarie Island.

exposed to cold wet winds carry fellfield vegetation on largely mineral soils, in which the cushion plant *Azorella selago* Hook.f. and the mosses *Rhacomitrium crispulatum* H. f. and W. and *Dicranoweisa antarctica* Par. are characteristic species (Fig. 16).

Since the early 1800's, most of the Subantarctic Islands have been visited by sealers, who introduced several herbivorous and carnivorous animals and alien plants. Commercial sheep grazing was also carried out on Campbell Island for many years (Wilson and Orwin, 1964). On Macquarie Island, where rabbits are well established, and on Campbell Island, where there are still sheep, there has been extensive deterioration of grassland and herbfield vegetation, with invasion by introduced plants (and the native *Crysobactron rossii* Hook. f. on Campbell Island) and more or less complete stripping of the associated peats on steep sites (Costin and Moore, 1960; Wilson and Orwin, 1964) (Fig. 17). These ecosystems have been shown to be especially vulnerable to disturbance (Costin and Moore, 1960; Holdgate and Wace, 1961), and further deterioration seems inevitable where feral herbivores occur.

Additional information is available from the works of Chilton (1909), Cockayne (1928), Taylor (1955), Godley (1960), and Oliver and Sorensen (1951). Data on other Subantarctic Islands are summarized by Wace (1960), Holdgate (1964), and Holdgate and Wace (1961). Further south, on ice-free areas of the Antarctic continent and adjacent islands, the vegetation is reduced to a sparse lichen fellfield.

Fig. 17. Erosion of grassland and herbfield peats, Macquarie Island, initiated by rabbit grazing. Rabbits were first introduced by sealers in the 1880's.

DISCUSSION

The ecosystems just considered present a discontinuous series extending between the tropics and the antarctic region over a latitudinal range of about 50 degrees. The altitude-latitude relationships are illustrated in Fig. 18. At about 53°S the alpine environment (here more correctly an antarctic-alpine environment) commences at sea level, and there is a fairly linear relationship at least to latitude 37°S, where alpine conditions commence at about 6000 ft. The lack of alpine environments farther north, until New Guinea, obscures the nature of the relationship at lower latitudes; it appears to be slightly curvilinear, although not to the same extent as in the Northern Hemisphere (cf. Daubenmire, 1954). Between latitudes 53°S and 35°S there is an increase of about 360 ft in the lower limit of the alpine environment for each degree decrease in latitude; this is also similar to the situation in the Northern Hemisphere (Daubenmire, 1954). In the Northern Hemisphere, however, the alpine ecosystems commence at much higher altitudes and latitudes; for example, the treeline at latitude 39° is at about 11000 ft in Colorado, compared with 5000 ft in New Zealand; and northern treelines occur about 10 to 20° closer to the pole. These differences are related to the generally more oceanic climates of the Australasian areas and the resultant lower summer temperatures, as discussed below.

ALPINE ECOSYSTEMS 75

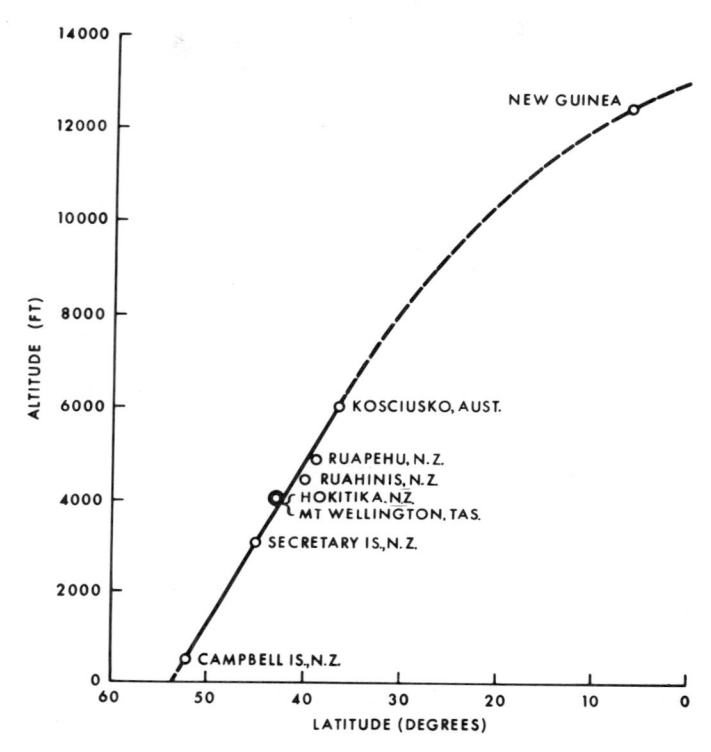

Fig. 18. Altitude of Australasian treelines in relation to latitude.

The wide geographical range of the environments under consideration implies a diversity of physical conditions. For example, in the equatorial mountains of New Guinea there are no distinct seasons, except those of a diurnal nature, with sharply contrasting day and night temperatures; precipitation is high, but snow is uncommon and nonpersistent; and there are only moderate winds. In the middle latitudes of Australia and New Zealand there is a distinct seasonal pattern of day length, temperature, and snow cover; precipitation is high, winds are strong to moderate, and there is a sharp contrast between day and night temperatures. The subantarctic environments have a distinct seasonal pattern of day length, but only slight seasonal and daily variations in temperature that is consistently low; precipitation is high with variable amounts of snow and there is much cloud and sustained strong to moderate wind. It is therefore difficult to perceive unifying climatic features except that precipitations are generally high and temperatures low at least periodically. These conditions imply considerable freeze-thaw activity with superficial solifluction.

Closer examination of the temperature factor (Appendix 1) near treeline shows little agreement between mean annual values (36 to 48°F), or between the means of the coldest months (23 to 47°F), but a fairly close correspondence of mean temperatures during the growing season (47 to 50°F; mean 49.3 ± 0.4). Considering the Australasian Region as a whole, a mean temperature of about 50°F for the warmest month seems to be the best single climatic parameter for defining the lower limit of the various alpine ecosystems (cf. Wardle, 1965, and Zotov, 1938, 1953, in New Zealand), as it does in many other parts of the world (Daubenmire, 1954).

These temperature conditions are effective in inhibiting the development of tree vegetation of widely different forms (e.g., rain forest and dense scrub in New Guinea, New Zealand, and the Subantarctic Islands; open sclerophyll woodland and scrub in Australia), and of diverse taxonomic and physiological groups (e.g., broad-leaved evergreens in Australia, conifers in parts of New Guinea, and deciduous types in parts of Tasmania). Why arboreal vegetation, but not low shrubby and herbaceous types, is unsuccessful under these conditions has not been adequately explained; Daubenmire (1954) and Wardle (1965) consider some of the possibilities. According to Daubenmire (1954), "The most promising autecologic theory to explain timberline is that it represents a point on the scale of diminishing heat supply where solar energy is adequate only to meet the annual requirements for respiration plus the requirement for foliage renewal, with a result that none is left to permit the development and maintenance of a large mass of non-productive cells as comprise the stem and root system of a normal tree." Wardle (1965), while apparently accepting the heat-deficiency theory in principle, points out, however, that the differentiation between trees and lower growth forms that takes place at timberline occurs at the seedling stage and is related to the plant's ability to develop winter-hardy (or protected) shoots.

Despite long and distant geographic separation, the vascular floras show a convergence of life forms (Appendix 3) with a preponderance of perennial herbs and dwarf semiwoody plants (hemicryptophytes and chamaephytes), as in alpine and arctic regions of the Northern Hemisphere (e.g., Raunkiaer, 1934). Following Raunkiaer (1934), it has been customary to assume that the life forms of plants are a response to the unfavorable season and that at high altitudes and latitudes the most successful plants are those in which the renewal buds are best protected from winter cold—hence the predominance of hemicryptophytes and chamaephytes with renewal buds in or just above the soil surface. Cryptophytes (geophytes, helophytes, and hydrophytes), with renewal buds below soil or water surfaces, should be even more successful, but for some reason this situation does not occur. An alternative explanation, following the heat-deficiency theory of treelines, is that the distribution of other forms of plants is not only limited by winter cold but also by shortage of energy (or some correlated factor) during the growing season. The most successful forms would be those best able to take advantage of the slightly higher daytime temperatures that are known to develop at or just above ground level (e.g., Geiger, 1965). According to this theory, the incoming energy during the day would be supplemented by energy reradiated from the ground in the case of hemicryptophytes and chamaephytes, and in addition by advected energy in the case of chamaephytes with renewal buds just above the ground. At the highest altitudes and latitudes, chamaephytes should be relatively more successful than hemicryptophytes, and available data suggest that this is so (e.g., Allan, 1937; Costin, 1954a).

Considering the geographical affinities of the vascular floras (Appendix 2), the Cosmopolitan element (including many boreal groups) is the most important, strongly supplemented in all cases except the Subantarctic Islands from the "endemic" element of the major area concerned, with a relatively small but consistent interchange of elements and contribution from old Antarctic, South American, and South African groups (cf. Costin, 1954a; Dawson, 1963; van Steenis, 1934). The recurrence of this pattern and the time required for it to develop in areas now widely separated indicate a long period of dispersal, whether by long-distance mechanisms or by former land connections. On the other hand, most of the existing alpine landscapes have only come into existence during the Quaternary (some having emerged from glaciations as recently as 10,000 to 20,000 years ago), so that the existing distribution of the alpine biota and the emergence of some present-day species must be relatively recent (cf. Fleming, 1963).

Grasslands and herbfields are the most conspicuous alpine communities in New Guinea, mainland Australia, New Zealand, and the Subantarctic Islands. Under relatively continental conditions, as in Australia and parts of New Zealand, the associated soils are organo-mineral types usually without strongly developed podsol features (e.g., apline humus soils in Australia and high-country yellow-brown earths on the eastern slopes of the New Zealand Alps). Under more oceanic conditions, as in New Guinea and the Subantarctic Islands, the soils are mainly peats or peat podsols. In rockier situations, the grasslands and herbfields are replaced by heaths (most of the Tasmanian alpine ecosystem with its preponderance of resistant dolerite falls into this category), whereas ground-water areas are characterized by "swamp" communities (moss bogs, cushion bogs, and fens) with a variety of peat, podsol, and gley soils. Under the most severe conditions for plant growth—i.e., approaching the nival limit, and where exposed to strong cold winds—the communities become very open (as fellfield) with scattered dwarf shrubs, herbs, mosses, and lichens.

Generalizations concerning the native fauna and animal communities are more difficult to make, because these aspects of the alpine ecosystems are still incompletely known. However, they do not appear to be a strongly positive feature. Excluding the Subantarctic Islands, where the larger animals form part of the marine rather than the terrestrial ecosystem, the vertebrate faunas are poor, both in species and numbers. Large grazing and browsing mammals are virtually lacking, and the vegetation is not adapted to them. In some cases (e.g., Australia) there is a rich and abundant insect fauna, but this may not be general.

In contrast to the alpine ecosystems of the Northern Hemisphere, those of the Australasian Region have evolved, until relatively recently, in the absence of man. Two main periods of human influence can be recognized. The fire-lighting activities of primitive man have affected the alpine ecosystems of New Guinea, New Zealand, and Australia, mainly in relation to adjacent subalpine vegetation. In New Guinea, there is widespread destruction of subalpine forest and scrub, and replacement by disclimax grassland (Fig. 6). Maori fires in New Zealand had similar effects, especially on the drier eastern slopes of the Southern Alps, where they may have been reinforced by unfavorable climatic change (Holloway, 1954). In Australia the treeline eucalypt vegetation is well adapted to fire, and the effects of aboriginal fire-lighting appear to have been slight. With the European period of summer grazing and burning in Australia and New Zealand and the spread of feral animals in New Zealand, the above effects have been extended, and there has been widespread deterioration of the alpine ecosystems themselves (Figs. 9 and 14). Efforts are now being made to control and repair the damage. The isolated antarctic-alpine ecosystems have no history of primitive man. They are the most vulnerable to disturbance, and the introduction of herbivores in the European period has been followed by virtual destruction of some of the grassland and herbfield vegetation and soils (Fig. 17).

What is the future of these ecosystems? At a scientific level they are the subjects of increasing research, since they stand out among the few relatively natural environments of the world, and they provide the opportunity to study and understand plant and animal responses near their environmental limits. They include areas, as in New Guinea, where there is still need for scientific exploration at a fairly broad level. Aesthetically, the alpine ecosystems are also increasing in importance, both for their wilderness value in a world where "wilderness" is fast disappearing, and for other types of recreation.

A small percentage of their primary productivity is being harvested as livestock products. Even with due regard to conservation needs, however, this utilization is likely to remain inefficient, apart from the practical management difficulties involved. Above-ground productivity is low—of the order of 0.026 to 0.052 lb/sq ft/annum (ca. 130 to 250 g/sq m), representing only 0.1 to 0.3% of the usable solar energy; and pasture quality is poor—0.1% P and 0.8% N in mature communities (Appendix 4). These values are several times lower than those reported for temperate regions (e.g., Bliss, 1962; Brougham, 1961), where management is also simpler. Higher levels of production may be possible with fertilized agronomic species, but at considerable cost (O'Connor, 1963). The era of grazing therefore seems to be drawing to a close.

At the same time, the importance of the alpine ecosystems as catchment areas is increasing, both in relation to water supply and flood control. Of the environments under discussion, those in Australia and Tasmania have been utilized most as sources of water for hydroelectric power and irrigation. Potential water values at the highest levels amount to several hundred dollars per acre per year. In New Zealand, the relation of the alpine areas to downstream aggradation and flooding is the major concern, and hydroelectric and irrigation development are increasing (cf. Costin, 1962b; Dils, 1965). In New Guinea, water from the alpine and highland areas is a major possible source of energy. Some of the Subantarctic Islands are also suitable for the development of water power, although here alternative methods may be cheaper.

Hydrological studies in Australia and New Zealand are producing useful data that will provide a basis for sound management of alpine ecosystems for water yield (e.g., Anon., 1965b; Costin et al., 1960, 1961, 1964; Costin and Wimbush, 1961). In the Australian Alps the climax herbaceous communities are the most suitable for infiltration and for erosion control, but the amount of water yield could be increased by planting trees. Above treeline, however, attempts at general afforestation would be unlikely to succeed, and present management is directed primarily toward the restoration and maintenance of the natural herbaceous cover (e.g., Costin and Wimbush, 1963a, 1963b).

This general coincidence of economic, scientific, and aesthetic interests points to the desirability of managing the alpine ecosystems largely in their natural condition, in contrast to those of most lower environments, which must be increasingly modified to meet growing economic needs.

Acknowledgments

The preparation of this review would have not been possible without assistance from the following: Dr. R. Hoogland and Messrs. E. A. Fitzpatrick, W. Goodwin, H. A. Haantjens, J. R. McAlpine, C. W. E. Moore, R. Pullen, W. Reyenga, R. Schodde, C. Totterdell, and D. J. Wimbush, CSIRO, Canberra; Dr. R. G. Robbins, Australian National University, Canberra; Dr. W. Jackson, University of Tasmania, and Dr. D. Martin, CSIRO, Hobart; Mr. J. S. Womersley, Department of Forests, Lae; Dr. A. F. Mark, University of Otago, Dunedin, Dr. P. Wardle, D.S.I.R., Christchurch, and Mr. M. J. Wraight, N.Z. Forest Service, Rangiora; Dr. L. C. Bliss, University of Illinois; Mr. H. M. Van Deusen, American Museum of Natural History, New York.

Appendix 1

Mean Annual Precipitation and Mean Monthly and Annual Temperatures[a] for Elevated and High-Latitude Localities in the Australasian Region

Locality	Source	Approx. latitude, °S	Approx. altitude, ft	Annual rainfall, inches	Jan.	Feb.	Mar.	Apr.	May	June	July	Aug.	Sept.	Oct.	Nov.	Dec.	Year
Wabag, N.G.	E. H. Fitzpatrick, CSIRO. Canberra, pers. comm.	$5\frac{1}{2}$	6800 (ca. 5700 below treeline)	ca. 100	63 (49)	63 (49)	63 (49)	63 (49)	63 (49)	62 (48)	61 (47)	61 (47)	62 (48)	62 (48)	62 (48)	63 (49)	62 (48)
Kosciusko, Aust.	Costin, 1954a	$36\frac{1}{2}$	6000 (just below treeline)	80	50	49	47	39	35	30	27	29	32	39	45	48	39
Ruapehu, N.Z.	Wardle, 1965	39	3670 (ca. 1200 below treeline)	108	53 (50)	53 (50)	50 (47)	40 (37)	32 (29)	28 (25)	26 (23)	28 (25)	29 (26)	37 (35)	41 (38)	46 (43)	39 (36)
Mt. Wellington, Tas.	Commonwealth Bureau of Meteorology, Melbourne, pers. comm.; Martin, 1939	43	4170 (just above treeline)	55	47	45	45	41	36	34	32	32	36	40	41	46	40
Old Man Ra., N.Z.	Mark, 1965, and pers. comm.	$45\frac{1}{2}$	2950 (near pre-European treeline)	42	50	50	47	44	39	34	31	37	43	44	44	49	43
Campbell Is.	Marshall, 1909	$52\frac{1}{2}$	Near sea level (ca. 500 below treeline)	55	50	50	48	44	41	40	40	40	42	43	45	49	44
Macquarie Is.	Taylor, 1955	$54\frac{1}{2}$	Near sea level ($1\frac{1}{2}$ lat. s of tree limit)	40	43	42	42	41	39	38	37	37	38	39	40	42	40

[a] Temperature values in parentheses are for treeline situations estimated from lapse rates of $2\frac{1}{2}$°F/1000 ft for New Guinea and 3°F for other areas; the New Guinea values should be regarded as tentative.

Appendix 2

Geographical Affinities of Sample Floras in the Australasian Region[a]

| Area | Source | Geographical element, % ||||||||
		Cosmopolitan	Tropical	Australian	New Zealand	Antarctic	South America	South Africa
New Guinea	van Steenis, 1934 (120 spp.)	53	26	6	6	5	3	1
Aust. mainland	Costin, 1954a (190 spp.)	46	1	30	8	8	4	3
Aust. Tasmania	Martin, 1939 (95 spp.)	34	2	44	7	6	4	2
New Zealand	Burrows, 1962b (223 spp.)	46	1	4	38	7	3	1
Subantartic Islands	Chilton, 1909 (113 spp.)	51	2	8	24	10	5	0

[a] Values shown are approximate only.

Appendix 3

Life-Form Composition of Sample Floras in the Australasian Region[a]

| Area | Source | Life form, % |||||
		Nanophanerophyte	Chamaephyte	Hemicryptophyte	Cryptophyte	Therophyte
New Guinea	Hoogland, 1958 (39 spp.)	13	23	64	0	0
Aust. mainland	Costin, 1954a (184 spp.)	1	31	41	18	9
Aust. Tasmania	Martin, 1939 (89 spp.)	20	35	28	14	3
New Zealand	Burrows, 1962b (219 spp.)	9	28	55	7	1
Subantartic Islands	Allan, 1937 (151 spp.: alpines + spp. of coastal scrub	11[b]	18	58	9	4

[a] Values shown are approximate only.
[b] Also includes small trees.

Appendix 4

Annual Above-Ground Productivity of Alpine Communities in Australia and New Zealand

Community	Productivity lb/sq ft	Productivity g/sq m	Efficiency, %	Source of information
Poa caespitosa grassland,[a] Kosciusko, Aust.	0.026	127	0.14	A. B. Costin, unpubl. ms.
Chionochloa rigida - C. pallens grassland, Craigieburn Ra., N.Z.	ca. 0.034	ca. 166	—	M. J. Wraight, pers. comm.
Celmisia viscosa herbfield, Rock & Pillar Ra., N.Z.	0.052	254	0.33	L. C. Bliss and A. F. Mark, pers. comm.
Dracophyllum muscoides fellfield, Rock & Pillar Ra., N.Z.	0.026	127	0.16	L. C. Bliss and A. F. Mark, pers. comm.

[a] 0.1% P, 0.8% N in mature grassland

REFERENCES

Allan, H. H., 1937, A consideration of the "biological spectra" of New Zealand: J. Ecol., v. 25, pp. 116-152.

Anonymous, 1965a, Insects of tussock grasslands: Rev. Tussock Grasslands and Mountain Lands Inst. (N.Z.), No. 8, pp. 26-27.

―――― 1965b, Infiltration in mountain soils: Rev. Tussock Grasslands and Mountain Lands Inst. (N.Z.), No. 8, p. 27.

Archbold, R., A. L. Rand, and L. J. Brass, 1942, Results of the Archbold Expeditions. No. 41. Summary of the 1938-1939 New Guinea Expedition: Am. Museum Natl. Hist. Bull., v. 79, pp. 197-288.

Australian Academy of Science, 1957, A report on the condition of the high mountain catchments of New South Wales and Victoria: Canberra, 62 pp.

Billings, W. D., and A. F. Mark, 1961, Interactions between alpine tundra vegetation and patterned ground in the mountains of southern New Zealand: Ecology, v. 42, pp. 18-31.

Bliss, L. C., 1962, Net primary production of tundra ecosystems, *in* Die Stoffproduktion der Pflanzendecke, *in* H. Lieth (ed.): Stuttgart, Fischer, 156 pp.

Brass, L. J., 1941, The 1938-1939 Expedition to the Snow Mountains, Netherlands, New Guinea: J. Arnold Arboretum, v. 22, pp. 271-342.

―――― 1964, Results of the Archbold Expeditions. No. 86. Summary of the Sixth Archbold Expedition to New Guinea (1959): Am. Museum Natl. Hist. Bull., v. 127, pp. 149-215.

Brougham, R. W., 1961, Factors limiting pasture production: Proc. New Zealand Soc. Animal Product., v. 21, pp. 33-46.

Bulmer, S., 1964, Radiocarbon dates from New Guinea: J. Polynesian Soc., v. 73, pp. 327-328.

―――― and R. Bulmer, 1964, The pre-history of the Australian New Guinea Highlands: Am. Anthropologist, v. 66, pp. 39-76.

Burrows, C. J., 1962a, Vegetation types of high mountain grasslands: Proc. New Zealand Ecol. Soc., No. 9, pp. 8-13.

―――― 1962b, The flora of the Waimakariri Basin: Trans. Roy. Soc. New Zealand Botan., v. 1, pp. 195-216.

Chilton, C. (ed.), 1909, The subantarctic islands of New Zealand: Wellington, Govt. Printer, 848 pp.

Cockayne, L., 1928, The vegetation of New Zealand (3rd ed.): Weinheim-Bergstr., Cramer, 456 pp.

Common, I. F. B., 1954, A study of the ecology of the adult Bogong moth, *Agrotis infusa* (Boisd.) (Lepidoptera: Noctuidae), with special reference to its behaviour during migration and aestivation: Australian J. Zool., v. 2, pp. 223-263.

Corner, E. J. H., et al., 1962-63, Royal Society Expedition to North Borneo 1961: Proc. Linn. Soc. London, v. 175, pp. 9-56 (reports).

Costin, A. B., 1954a, A study of the ecosystems of the Monaro region of New South Wales: Sydney, Govt. Printer, 860 pp.
_____ 1954b, The species factor in ecology: Australian J. Sci., v. 17, pp. 82-83.
_____ 1957, The high mountain vegetation of Australia: Australian J. Botan., v. 5, pp. 173-189.
_____ 1959, Vegetation of high mountains in Australia in relation to land use, *in* Biogeography and Ecology in Australia, A. Keast, R. L. Crocker, and C. S. Christian (eds.): Monographiae Biologicae, v. 8, 640 pp.
_____ 1962a, The soils of the High Plains: Proc. Roy. Soc. Victoria, v. 75, pp. 291-299.
_____ 1962b, Some impressions of a visit to parts of the South Island: Tussock Grasslands and Mountain Lands Inst. (N.Z.), Spec. Publ. No. 2, 16 pp.
_____, L. W. Gay, D. J. Wimbush, and D. Kerr, 1961, Studies in catchment hydrology in the Australian Alps. III. Preliminary snow investigations: Australia CSIRO Div. Plant Ind. Tech. Paper No. 15, 31 pp.
_____, and D. M. Moore, 1960, The effects of rabbit grazing on the grasslands of Macquarie Island: J. Ecol., v. 48, pp. 729-732.
_____, and D. J. Wimbush, 1961, Studies in catchment hydrology in the Australian Alps. IV. Interception by trees of rain, cloud, and fog: Australia CSIRO Div. Plant Ind. Tech. Paper No. 16, 16 pp.
_____ 1963a, Reaction of species to adverse conditions in the Snowy Mountains: Australia CSIRO Div. Plant Ind. Field Sta. Rec., v. 2(2), pp. 19-30.
_____ 1963b, Hastening secondary succession in the Snowy Mountains with natural herbaceous mulch: Australia CSIRO Div. Plant Ind. Field Sta. Rec., v. 2(2), pp. 31-34.
_____, D. J. Wimbush, and R. N. Cromer, 1964, Studies in catchment hydrology in the Australian Alps. V. Soil moisture characteristics and evapotranspiration: Australia CSIRO Div. Plant Ind. Tech. Paper No. 20, 20 pp.
_____, D. J. Wimbush, and D. Kerr, 1960, Studies in catchment hydrology in the Australian Alps. II. Surface run-off and soil loss: Australia CSIRO Div. Plant Ind. Tech. Paper No. 14, 23 pp.
Cox, J. E., and C. B. Mead, 1963, Soil evidence relating to postglacial climate on the Canterbury Plains: Proc. New Zealand Ecol. Soc., No. 10, pp. 28-38.
Cranwell, L. M., 1953, An outline of New Zealand peat deposits: Wellington, Govt. Printer, Proc. Seventh Pacific Sci. Congr., v. 5, pp. 186-208.
Dansereau, P., 1962, New Zealand revisited: Garden J., v. 12, pp. 12, 55, 108, 144, 185, 217, 227.
Daubenmire, R., 1954, Alpine timberlines in the Americas and their interpretation: Indianapolis, Ind., Butler Univ. Botan. Studies, v. 11, pp. 119-136.

David, T. W. E., 1950, The Geology of the Commonwealth of Australia: London, Edward Arnold, 1365 pp.
Dawson, J. W., 1963, Origins of the New Zealand alpine flora: Proc. New Zealand Ecol. Soc., No. 10, pp. 12-15.
Dils, R. E., 1965, Watershed management in New Zealand: Tussock Grassland and Mountain Lands Inst. (N.Z.), Spec. Publ. No. 4, 28 pp.
Directorate of Industrial Development, 1954, Economic Resources of Tasmania (3rd ed.): Davies, Hobart, 25 pp.
Drummond, H. M., and E. H. Leatham, 1959, Bibliography of New Zealand tussock grasslands: D.S.I.R. (N.Z.) Bull., No. 132, 41 pp.
Elder, N. L., 1959, Vegetation of the Kaweka Range: Trans. Roy. Soc. New Zealand, v. 87, pp. 1-18.
Fisher, F. J. F., 1952, Observations on the vegetation of screes in Canterbury: J. Ecol., v. 40, pp. 156-167.
Fleming, C. A., 1963, Age of the alpine biota: Proc. New Zealand, Ecol. Soc., No. 10, pp. 15-18.
Geiger, R., 1965, The climate near the ground: Cambridge, Mass., Harvard Univ. Press, 611 pp.
Gibbs, L. S., 1914, A contribution to the flora and plant formations of Mount Kinabalu: J. Linn. Soc. (Botan.), v. 42, pp. 1-240.
Gibbs, H. S., J. D. Raeside, J. K. Dixon, and A. J. Metson, 1945, Soil erosion in the high country of the South Island: D.S.I.R. (N.Z.), Bull., No. 92, 72 pp.
Godley, E. J., 1960, The botany of Southern Chile in relation to New Zealand and the Subantarctic: Proc. Roy. Soc. New Zealand, v. B152, pp. 457-475.
Good, R., 1963, On the biological and physical relationships between New Guinea and Australia, *in* Pacific Basin Biogeography: Honolulu, Bishop Museum Press, 561 pp.
Gressitt, J. L., 1963, Insects of Antarctica and Subantarctic Islands, *in* Pacific Basin Biogeography: Honolulu, Bishop Museum Press, 561 pp.
Haantjens, H. A., E. Reiner, and R. G. Robbins, 1958, Lands of the Goroka-Mt. Hagen area, New Guinea: Australia CSIRO Div. Land Res. Reg. Surv., Rept. No. 58-1, 177 pp.
Hedberg, O., 1951, Vegetation belts of the East African mountains: Svensk Botan. Tidskr., v. 45, pp. 140-202.
Holdgate, M. W., 1964, Terrestrial ecology in the maritime Antarctic, *in* Biologie antarctique, R. Carrick (ed.): Paris, Hermann, 651 pp.
Holdgate, M. W., and N. M. Wace, 1961, The influence of man on the floras and faunas of southern islands: Polar Record, v. 10, pp. 475-493.
Holloway, J. T., 1954, Forests and climate in the South Island of New Zealand: Trans. Roy. Soc. New Zealand, v. 82, pp. 329-410.
Hoogland, R. D., 1958, The alpine flora of Mount Wilhelm (New Guinea): Dr. J. H. Lam Jubilee, Suppl. IV, Blumea, v. 2, X, pp. 220-238.

Howard, W. E., 1964, Introduced browsing mammals and habitat stability in New Zealand: J. Wildlife Management, v. 28, pp. 421-429.
Jacobs, M., 1958, Contribution to the botany of Mount Kerintji and adjacent area in West Central Sumatra. I. Ann. Bogor., v. 3, pp. 45-79.
Lane-Poole, G. E., 1925, The forest resources of the Territories of Papua and New Guinea: Melbourne, Govt. Printer, 209 pp.
McLintock, A. N., 1959, A descriptive atlas of New Zealand: Wellington, Govt. Printer, 109 pp.
Manley, G., 1953, Climate and the British scene: London, Collins, 314 pp.
Mark, A. F., 1965, Central Otago: Vegetation and mountain climate: New Zealand Geograph. Soc. Misc. Ser., No. 5, pp. 69-91.
_____, and G. T. S. Baylis, 1963, Vegetation studies on Secretary Island, Fiordland: New Zealand J. Botan., v. 1, pp. 215-220.
Marshall, P., 1909, The meteorology of Campbell Island, in The Subantarctic Islands of New Zealand, C. Chilton (ed.): Wellington, Govt. Printer, 848 pp.
Martin, D., 1939, The vegetation of Mt. Wellington, Tasmania. The plant communities and a census of the plants: Papers Proc. Roy. Soc. Tasmania (June), pp. 97-124.
Molloy, B. P. J., C. J. Burrows, J. E. Cox, J. A. Johnston, and P. Wardle, 1963, Distribution of subfossil forest remains, eastern South Island, New Zealand: New Zealand J. Botan., v. 1, pp. 68-77.
Mulvaney, D. J., 1963, Archaeology in Australia: Current Anthropol., v. 4, p. 357.
_____ 1964, The Pleistocene colonisation of Australia: Antiquity, v. 38, pp. 263-267.
O'Connor, K., 1963, The establishment of grasses in humid tussock grassland regions: Rev. Tussock Grasslands and Mountain Lands Inst. (N.Z.), No. 5, pp. 1-4.
Oliver, R. L., and J. H. Sorensen, 1951, Botanical investigations on Campbell Island: Cape Expedition Ser. Bull., No. 7, Wellington, D.S.I.R., 38 pp.
Perry, R. A., M. J. Bik, E. A. Fitzpatrick, H. A. Haantjens, J. R. McAlpine, R. Pullen, R. G. Robbins, G. K. Rutherford, and J. C. Saunders, 1965, General report on lands of the Wabag-Tari area, Territories of Papua and New Guinea, 1960-1961: Australia CSIRO Land Res. Ser. No. 15, Melbourne, CSIRO, 141 pp.
Raunkiaer, C., 1934, The life-forms of plants and statistical plant geography: New York, Oxford Univ. Press, 632 pp.
Reiner, E., 1960, The glaciation of Mt. Wilhelm: Geograph. Rev., v. 50, pp. 491-503.
Richards, P. W., 1952, The tropical rain forest: Cambridge, 450 pp.
Robbins, R. G., 1961, The montane vegetation of New Guinea: Tuatara, v. 8, pp. 121-133.

Rutherford, G. K., 1964, The tropical alpine soils of Mt. Giluwe, Australian New Guinea: Can. Geograp., v. 8, pp. 27-33.
Senn, G., 1925, The upper limit of forests in Java: J. Manchester Geograph. Soc., v. 41, pp. 1-10.
Taylor, B. W., 1955, The flora, vegetation and soils of Macquarie Island: A.N.A.R.E. Repts., B, 2, 1, Melbourne, Antarctic Div., Dept. External Affairs, 192 pp.
Troll, C., 1958, Structure soils, solifluction, and frost climates of the earth: U.S. Army Snow Ice Permafrost Res. Estab., Transl., 43, 121 pp.
van Steenis, C. G. G. J., 1934, On the origin of the Malaysian mountain flora. Part 1. Facts and statements of the problem: Bull. Jardin Botan. Buitenzorg, v. 13(2), pp. 135-262.
―――― 1935, On the origin of the Malaysian mountain flora. Part 2. Altitudinal zones, general considerations and renewed statement of the problem: Bull. Jardin Botan. Buitenzorg, v. 13(3), pp. 129-417.
―――― 1958, Vegetation map of Malaysia: Haarlem, Joh. Enschéde en Zonen.
Wace, N. M., 1960, The botany of the southern oceanic islands: Proc. Roy. Soc. New Zealand, v. B152, pp. 475-490.
Wardle, P., 1962, Subalpine forest and scrub in the Tararua Range: Trans. Roy. Soc. New Zealand, v. 1, pp. 77-89.
―――― 1964, Facets of the distribution of forest vegetation in New Zealand: New Zealand J. Botan., v. 2, pp. 352-366.
―――― 1965, A comparison of alpine timberlines in New Zealand and North America: New Zealand J. Botan., v. 3, pp. 113-135.
Webb, L. J., 1964, An historical interpretation of the grass balds of the Bunya Mountains, South Queensland: Ecology, v. 45, pp. 159-162.
Wilson, P. R., and D. F. G. Orwin, 1964, The sheep population of Campbell Island: New Zealand J. Sci., v. 7, pp. 460-490.
Wraight, M. J., 1963, The alpine and upper montane grasslands of the Wairau River Catchment, Marlborough: New Zealand J. Botan., v. 1, pp. 351-376.
―――― 1964, Ecology and state of the alpine grasslands of Westland: Proc. New Zealand Grassland Assoc., pp. 90-94.
Zotov, V. D., 1938, Some correlations between vegetation and climate in New Zealand: New Zealand J. Sci. Tech., v. 19, pp. 474-487.
―――― 1953, Some factors determining distribution of plants in New Zealand: Proc. Seventh Pacific Sci. Congr., v. 5, pp. 156-159.
―――― 1963, Synopsis of the grass subfamily Arundinoideae in New Zealand: New Zealand J. Botan., v. 1, pp. 78-136.

5

Comparison of Some North American and Eurasian Alpine Ecosystems

J. MAJOR AND S. A. BAMBERG
Department of Botany
University of California
Davis, California

Abstract

Alpine ecosystems are so varied in vegetation, soils, climate, and flora that the alpine zone can be defined only physiognomically. It includes the landscapes above the treeline and below the snowline. Even in regions so arid that mountain summit vegetation has a steppe or desert aspect, trees occur along water courses at lower elevations.

The following factors may be said to determine the nature of any ecosystem: regional climate, soil parent material, relief, the biota (including man), fire, and duration of plant succession and soil development. Fire is negligible in alpine ecosystems. The effects of relief, soil parent material, man, and time can be standardized to specific levels by proper choice of sites. The differentiating factors, then, are regional climates and regional floras and faunas.

Alpine floras and faunas of the northern hemisphere all contain a proportion of more or less circumpolar species plus endemic species. The circumpolar species allow quantitative comparisons to be made between areas; the endemics, however, allow only qualitative comparisons. The proportion of endemics increases to the south.

The figures representing regional climates of different alpine regions are very diverse and are less informative ecologically than water and heat regimes. Alpine ecosystems are microthermal, with a potential evapotranspiration of ca. 200 to 400 mm of water a year, and heat is adequate only during a brief summer period. Water relations are more varied. Snowmelt usually produces a water excess, and even summer may show no water deficit. In summer-dry climates, however, there are water deficits of up to 80 mm a month. Such dry apline areas may not only have a vegetation of steppe or even desert physiognomy but even contain normally lowland xerophytic species as well.

The objective of this paper is to compare in a preliminary way the botanical aspects of some alpine ecosystems in certain high mountains of the northern hemisphere. If we know what present ecological conditions are, and what factors determine them, presumably we can understand the historical development of these systems during the Quaternary.

From the Alps of Europe as a specific mountain range, "alpine" has taken a wider, generic meaning. We shall use the word, uncapitalized, in this wider sense.

Ecosystems in the alpine belt of the high mountains are so varied in vegetation, soils, climate, and flora that the alpine belt can be defined only physiognomically. It includes the landscapes above the forest line and below the snowline. No unity other than physiognomy exists in such areas, although certain floristic and climatic features occur throughout.

Even in regions too xeric for zonal vegetation of trees, watercourses provide local habitats for trees. In the arid Great Basin of western North America, for example, sagebrush (*Artemisia tridentata* Nutt.) steppe may extend from valley slopes to summits clearly in the alpine belt. However, trees occur along the streams (*Populus angustifolia* James), and in local centers of snow accumulation or in water-seepage sites on north slopes aspen groves (*Populus tremuloides* Michx.) occur. The endemic *Populus pamirica* Kom. and such endemic birches of the section *Albae* as *Betula pamirica* Litw. and *B. murgabica* V. Vassil. are found in similar sites in the even more arid Pamir of Central Asia (Lukanenkova and Sidorov, 1961a, 1961b; Gusev, 1959), although the high-altitude vegetation there is of strictly desert aspect. The southeastern Altai also lacks a forest belt, and the zonal steppe of the valleys extends up to steppelike mountain meadows and mountain tundra (Mikhailov, 1961, p. 88). The plant communities that include tree species in these arid regions are nonzonal, hydrophytic formations in zonal vegetation of desert or steppe.

One can make a similar technical distinction between some arctic tundras and the alpine vegetation of arctic mountains. Thus along foothill watercourses on the north slope of the Brooks range in Alaska the tree *Populus balsamifera* L. is the northernmost local outpost of this life form (Wiggins and Thomas, 1962, pp. 137, 375). The slopes of the Brooks Range, then, are occupied by alpine vegetation. *Larix dahurica* Turcz. similarly grows farther north than any other tree, to about 74°30'N in the Katanga River basin of northern Siberia (Sochava, 1956, pp. 250, 268). It is not clear whether the favorable effects of drainage or snow accumulation are responsible for tree distributions so far north.

All these woody plants at their upper or northern limits may have a shrub life form, although under more favorable conditions they do exist as trees. For example, at the mouth of the Laen River *Larix dahurica* at its northern limit is technically a chamaephyte, i.e., a low shrub <10 cm in height, growing in a typical tundra; 35 to 40 km to the south the species forms krummholz, with individual stems up to 1 1/2 to 2 m tall (Polozova, 1961).

Above the alpine zone is a nival belt, also best described physiognomically as vegetation not forming a closed sward and occurring in the favorable microhabitats of a snow (or ice) landscape (Reisigl and Pitschmann, 1958, 1959). Snow and ice accumulate from year to year as a zonal phenomenon, and plant growth is possible only in the favorable spots, which become less common with increasing altitude.

LANDSCAPES AND ECOSYSTEMS

Our scale of consideration is not landscapes but ecosystems. Landscapes are geographical units, whereas ecosystems (or biogeocenoses) are ecological units (Major, 1958, p. 352). The latter have obvious advantages in comparing environments.

Different mountain landscapes are too different to compare as wholes. We have no bases for such comparisons. For example, the rounded, ice-topped mountains of northern Scandinavia, Wales, and New England contrast with the pyramidal Alpine forms on the metamorphic rocks of Graubunden, or the limestone benches of Glarus, the gneissic horns of the central Alps, and the granitic needles of Chamonix. In America the contrasts carry to the broad-shouldered peaks of Colorado; the great cirque floors of the Uintas; the smallness of scale of the Wasatch; the ruggedness of the Wind Rivers; the spectacular upthrusts of the Tetons; the ice-shrouded summits of coastal British Columbia; the light-colored bare granite of the Sierra Nevada of California; the bright colors, soft forms, and shrinking ice tongues of the Alaska Range; and the great scree slopes of the Brooks Range. The "goltsy" of the Urals and the desert landscapes of the eastern Pamirs bring further variation.

However, in detail we can find snow flushes, a bit of cliff or windswept ridge, a fertile meadow—all of which have some similarity in many ecological features as well as physiognomy. Specifically, we can find flat, well-drained vegetation and soils formed over sodic rocks, with normal snow accumulation, ungrazed by domestic livestock, lying midway between the treeline and snowline; such limited ecosystems may be comparable.

FACTORS DETERMINING ECOSYSTEMS

A comparison of alpine ecosystems is most practically made with the factors that are thought to determine these ecosystems and not with the results of the interactions of these factors, namely, vegetation and soils.

The following independent factors may be said to determine the nature of any ecosystem (Jenny, 1941; Major, 1951; Crocker, 1952; Billings, 1952): regional climate; soil parent material; aspects of relief including local climate, ground water, and snow accumulation; fire; the biota, including flora, fauna, and man; and time elapsed in autogenic development of the ecosystem (plant succession and soil development).

By proper selection of sites, certain of these factors can be eliminated as not being functionally related to the differences between the plant aspects of ecosystems in different alpine regions. These are fire, relief, soil parent material, man, and time. By elimination, then, we conclude that differences between alpine ecosystems can be ascribed to differences in floras (and faunas) and in regional climates.

Factors cannot cause differences in vegetation (and soil) if they are constant (or absent) or if their variations cause no significant changes in the dependent aspects of the ecosystems (Jenny, 1946). This last method is, of course, not available to us a priori; its use demands data or an accepted theory.

FIRE

Fire is not an independent factor in alpine ecosystems. It may be used by man to extend continuous meadow communities of the alpine zone down into the subalpine zone. It may naturally cause such a local extension for a short period of time (decades) (Aulitzky et al., 1961, p. 43; Stahelin, 1943), or, by exposing the soil to catastrophic erosion, it may produce habitats within the forest belt suitable for particular alpine plants adapted to bare scree and talus or to the crevices and niches of bare rock (Grabherr, 1936). In general fire is at a zero level.

RELIEF

Relief differences are extremely marked both within and among mountain landscapes. However, we can choose one kind of relief position for all our comparisons. In general we shall choose flat areas, well drained (if this is zonally possible, as in nonpermafrost areas), with a normal amount of snow accumulation. The effects of relief will depend partially on the levels of the other factors in the ecosystem, notably regional climate.

If an ecosystem difference in vegetation or soil cannot be demonstrated to follow an observable difference in relief, the partial effect of the relief difference is nil, and it can be neglected.

SOIL PARENT MATERIAL

Most mountain ranges contain a variety of soil parent materials, so the flora can be an independent factor—i.e., not limited by a specialized kind of rock that allows only certain kinds of plants to occur in the area. The scale of variety must be commensurate with the scale of plant-dispersal distances.

Plant ecologists must regard the lithological variety of rock types with respect to plant nutrition and soil formation. Meaningful separations are based on calcareous versus sodic (siliceous), poor versus rich (in Ca, Mg, Fe), or the presence of ultrabasics and young volcanics. We standardize on sodic rocks, which form the core of so many mountain ranges. In pedology, soils formed over calcareous rocks have been universally regarded as nonzonal.

MAN

Man has been of minor importance in some alpine areas. His actions have expanded some by pushing down the treeline (Aulitzky et al., 1961; Grabherr, 1936; Stahelin, 1943). In the western U.S. grazing by domestic sheep and cattle has drastically changed the nature of the vegetation and caused soil losses even in the alpine zone (Ellison, 1954, 1960; Johnson, 1961; Strickler, 1961). Unfortunately, there seem to be no descriptions from the Alps of the effects on alpine vegetation and soils of the extermination and later local introduction of large herbivores. The chamois *(Rupicapra rupicapra)* and ibex *(Capra ibex ibex)* were removed from most of their natural range. Recent reintroductions have been unaccompanied by the predators necessary to keep populations balanced to their habitats' grazing capacity. We can eliminate these anthropogenic effects by selecting climax areas and not degraded ones.

DURATION OF PLANT SUCCESSION AND SOIL FORMATION

This factor can be standardized to climax or zonal conditions. That is, in a graph plotting an appropriate vegetation property against time, with all other factors held at a constant level, the slope of the curve approaches zero. The condition of zero slope is climax or zonal. This seems to be the only case where we can use a theory to eliminate one factor from consideration.

It is necessary to describe the constant conditions carefully. Braun-Blanquet and Jenny (1926; Braun-Blanquet, 1951, pp. 452-485) suggested a classically simple successional scheme for ecosystems developed on limestone in the perhumid climate of the alpine belt in the continental central Alps, namely, that the most thoroughly leached and therefore most acid soils are the oldest and support the oldest vegetation. Climax or zonal vegetation is the acidicole Curvuletum. Wlodek et al. (1931) and Ellenberg (1953; 1963, p. 520) concluded that the Curvuletum did not develop exclusively from the limestone that underlay its acid, humus-rich soil but from a mixture of rock moved by glaciers and solifluction on to the limestone. The solum developed from materials not evident in the bedrock beneath it.

Additionally, the vegetation and soils described by Braun-Blanquet and Jenny (1926) and arranged by them into a successional series are, according to Ellenberg, formed not from solid rock but from clastic. They form a regosol series and not a lithosol one. The difference is important, for the time necessary to develop a soil and its attendant vegetation on the clastic material of a regosol is very much less than on the solid rock of a lithosol. The rapid regosol soil formation and plant succession in montane ecosystems found by Crocker and his students (Dickson and Crocker, 1953, 1954; Crocker and Major, 1955; Crocker and Dickson, 1957) are matched in the Alps by Braun-Blanquet's (1951, pp. 486-490) and Lüdi's (1945) results in subalpine ecosystems. Time zero to climax spans only a few hundred years.

Plant succession on a lithosol takes place by spread of plants from cracks and crevices in the rock and may involve no disintegration of the bedrock at all but simply the accumulation of wind-blown fine particles. On bedrock that still retains its glacial polish, we have seen deep meadow soils in the subalpine belt of the Swiss Tessin, ericad mats 20 cm thick in arctic Swedish Lappland, and even a subalpine forest near Lake Atwood in the Uinta Mountains of Utah.

Unfortunately, the actual parent materials of most alpine soils are unknown. The chemical and mineralogical criteria suggested by Barshad (1964) have not been applied.

Welten (1958) suggested that the alpine soils of the Schynigeplatte in Switzerland that he studied were with one exception built up, not weathered down. Soils not subject to deposition were too shallow to support zonal vegetation.

Frost churning of alpine soils does not everywhere prevent plant succession in high-altitude environments. A cyclic development of vegetation and soil is described by Billings and Mooney (1959), and Watt (1947) has generalized the idea. It is not necessary that the climax vegetation occupy most of a geographical area for its recognition to be useful. We are interested in the differences between areas of rapid change (seral) on new soil parent materials (such as fresh moraines or landslips) and areas of equilibrium (climax) between vegetation plus soil and the environment.

FAUNA

The general occurrence of a circumpolar faunistic element common to most high mountains makes the resulting ecosystems similar, but striking faunistic lacunae and endemism make various alpine ecosystems qualitatively different. Some specific niches may be unfilled in particular mountains. Principles discussed below under Flora apply there.

FLORA

Certainly floras (the kinds of plants available) differ among various alpine areas. Of all the factors that determine and differentiate ecosystems, this floristic factor is most neglected. Floristic differences between ecosystems are problems of disjunct distributions. Data to describe and compare the floristic factor therefore come from taxonomic monographs and local floras, but both habitually neglect the orographic nature of many disjunct distributions as well as the ecological and historical reasons for them.

Disjunction in plant ranges are frequently so cursorily dismissed as to be inaccurately described on the basis that in the long course of (inadequately described) time any improbable event of disseminule migration, ecesis, and reproduction can happen once, and once is enough. The argument eliminates consideration of floristic problems, but the problems remain. Stebbins suggests that the rare constipated seagull and the uncommon slovenly plover can account for a great number of known plant disjunctions. Their role in colonizing with plants oceanic islands and areas on their migration routes must certainly be very great. However, it must also be limited, or else areas of most similar ecology, such as the lands with mediterranean climates on five continents and alpine areas throughout the globe, could not now be occupied by distinctively different floras (e.g., Major and Bamberg, 1967).

For example, in the forest region of eastern Pite Lappmark in northern Sweden, 35 isolated mountains rising above timberline were investigated floristically (Wistrand, 1962). These peaks, now alpine islands rising to 873 m above the timberline at 600 m, are now isolated by the surrounding forests. They probably lost their alpine floras during the postglacial hypsithermal interval (Wistrand, 1962, p. 169), for few of their alpine plants now occur in the lowland forests. They have therefore been recolonized by alpine plants within the last few thousand years. They now show an extraordinary diversity in their alpine floras. For 27 alpine species tabulated from 35 peaks, the distribution of frequencies over individual mountains is approximately normal, with an average of 8.8 species, range of 18 to 2, and standard deviation of 3.7. The vegetation of these isolated habitats must differ because their floras differ, regardless of the ecological differences that can be demonstrated.

Alpine floras and faunas of the northern hemisphere all contain a proportion of more or less circumpolar species that are common in varying degrees to the high mountains throughout this area. However, they also contain often highly constructive (edificator) (Braun-Blanquet, 1951, p. 451) or dominant species derived from adjacent and lowland biogeographic regions. Very often the constructive value in alpine ecosystems of the latter group of endemic species is greater than that of the former. The circumpolar species allow quantitative comparisons to be made between different mountain areas; the other group of endemics presents qualitative differences that are very difficult to evaluate in their effects on the ecosystems concerned. The proportion of endemics increases to the south.

For example, the Sierra Nevada of California contains 615 alpine species of vascular plants (Munz and Keck, 1959): 16.8% are endemic to this range; 11.2% are found also in the Great Basin, Cascade, and Coast ranges within California; 16.1% extend from the Sierra Nevada through the Cascades and Coast Ranges of the Pacific Northwest as far as southern Alaska; 41.3% are found as far as the Great Basin and Rocky Mountains; 3.9% extend into the boreal vegetation and mountains of eastern North America; and 10.7% are more or less circumpolar. Thus 28.0% are limited to California and 44.1% to California and the Pacific Northwest. Fully 85.4% present no floristic possibility of correlating the alpine vegetation of the Sierra Nevada with mountain ranges outside western North America. Also, within California an additional 52 species occur only in the alpine belt of mountains outside the Sierra Nevada.

In the Swiss Alps, H. and M. Brockmann-Jerosch (Schröter, 1926, pp. 1135-1139) classified 420 alpine species of vascular plants into 7.4% vertical ubiquists that, according to the examples mentioned (cf. also Wikus, 1958), are mostly circumpolar; 4.4% also in northern Europe; 37.5% also in the central and southern European mountains; 15.4% only in the Alps; 22.5% also in the Arctic and Altai; 8.2% only in the Arctic in addition to the Alps; and 4.8% only additionally in the Altai. The Arctic groups include the circumpolar plants (ca. 75% of the arctic 30.7%, or about 25% over-all). Thus >57% of the species are exclusively European.

Using the Brockmann-Jerosch categories, Wikus (1958) found some interesting differences in the flora of the Dolomites of East Tirol compared to the Swiss Alps. Among 293 species, including some mosses and lichens, she found an increase to 17.1% for species limited to the Alps, a slight decrease to 34.6% for central and southern European species, a considerable increase to 12.0% for Eurasian species, and a slight decrease for the "circumpolar" remainder, with 29.1% versus 34.9% for the Swiss Alps in this category.

The limited possibilities of directly applying the highly developed study of vegetation from the Swiss Alps to even nearby mountain ranges are apparent from the figures giving the proportion of the 420 Swiss alpine species also in these ranges: Carpathians 49.5%, Pyrenees 59.0%, Caucasus 25.9%, Urals 22.1%, Altai 27.6%, Himalayas

15.0%, western Arctic (Europe to eastern North America) 29.4%, and eastern Arctic (Urals eastward to Pacific North America) 28.5%. The total in common with the Arctic is 57.9%.

Already we can see one difficulty in comparisons of floras based on purely geographical analyses—namely, the geographical generalizations used by different students are entirely different for various geographical regions. Another difficulty is the continuous nature of plant areas, which show few distinct lines between quite different floras. And finally, comparison of mere numbers may conceal more of biological interest than it reveals. Still, we can hardly continue to ignore the floristic reason for differences among vegetation in different regions if we wish to describe comparatively and to account for the fascinating pattern of vegetation on the earth.

Floristic data for the Caucasus are provided by Grossgeim (1936). The alpine flora is not separately treated as such, so we concentrate on 5 high mountain regions of the 18 into which Grossgeim divides the Caucasian isthmus (Table 1). Note that the numbers of species are not linearly proportional to the areas of the regions.

Grossgeim classifies the distributional areas of Caucasian plants into seven types: Tertiary relics; boreal, including Arctic and European; steppe, including pannonic (Hungarian plain), pontic (Ukraine), and sarmatic to the east; xerophytic, split into the mountains of the Mediterranean, Asia Minor, and central Asia; desert, including Turanian, Iranian, and Saharan; Caucasian; and adventive. Table 2 shows

TABLE 1

High-Mountain Regions of the Caucasus, with Data on Their Vascular Floras

Region	Area km^{2*}	Ratio	No. of spp., no. ratio	No. of spp./ 1000 km^2	Endemism, %
Caucasus Main Range: north slope	70,740	6.5	1861, 1.56	26.3	20.0
Mountainous Dagestan	18,810	1.7	1545, 1.30	82.1	17.1
Central Trans- caucasia	32,400	3.0	2522, 2.12	77.9	15.0
Southern Trans- caucasia: mountains of southern Georgia	10,890	1.0	1190, 1.00	109.3	9.9
Mountainous Armenia	21,510	2.0	1766, 1.48	82.1	10.0

From Grossgeim (1936) with misprints* corrected.

TABLE 2

Classification of Areas of Geographical Distribution of Some
Regional Caucasian Floras

Region	Geographical classes, %								
	Boreal	Tertiary	Steppe	Mediterranean	Asian	Desert	Caucasus	Adventive
Caucasus, north slope	38.2	12.7	5.6	13.2	9.7	0.1	20.0	0.5
Mountainous Dagestan	34.7	3.6	6.3	20.0	12.8	0.8	20.9	0.9
Central Transcaucasia	31.1	6.8	4.1	20.0	16.6	0.9	16.8	1.7
Southern Transcaucasia	37.1	4.4	2.4	12.7	33.4	0.4	9.1	0.9
Mountainous Armenia	19.9	2.4	3.9	18.1	43.7	2.4	8.4	1.2

Grossgeim, 1936, p. 68.

the distribution of the five regional floras in these classes. The uniqueness of each region is immediately apparent. No two "geographical spectra" are alike, and Grossgeim has an excellent discussion of the differences (1936, pp. 69-81). Similarity of floras is related mainly to physical contiguity and paths of migration. For example, the Mediterranean area has contributed by way of the Crimea around the Caucasus from the north; Central Asian plants have come through the Iranian mountains south of the Caspian sea.

Abramov (1953) has more recently considered the flora of southern Ossetia, a part of Grossgeim's central Transcaucasian region. Vascular plants number 1609 species and bryophytes 352. The partition of the species among the vegetation belts is interesting. Of the vascular plants, 833 are in the subalpine belt, 707 in the alpine, and 165 in the subnival. The bryophytes have 214, 204, and 70 species in these respective belts. The alpine vascular flora is therefore somewhat richer than that of the Sierra Nevada of California and 68% richer than that of the Swiss Alps. The geographical areas of the species according to vegetation belts are given in Table 3. The three belts have 139, 180, and 54 of the 286 southern Ossetian endemics.

Numbers of locally distributed species increase with altitude, and numbers of more widely distributed species decrease. The holarctic

TABLE 3

Classification of Areas of Geographical Distribution of Vascular Plants of Southern Ossetia Found in High-Mountain Vegetation

Belt	Holarctic	Palearctic	European	Atlantic	Mediterranean	Pannonic	Pontic	Sarmatic	Asia Minor	Central Asia	Caucasus	Colchic	Others
Subalpine	12.0	20.4	7.8	0.1	10.2	0.8	1.2	0.2	16.2	1.1	20.8	8.8	0.4
Alpine	11.3	15.1	5.4	0.1	7.4	0.9	0.4	0.4	18.4	1.7	30.4	7.9	0.6
Subnival	9.7	4.2	3.2	0.0	4.2	0.0	0.0	0.0	24.3	4.2	44.8	5.4	0.0

Abramov, 1953, pp. 18-19.

and palearctic elements decrease from the subalpine (32.4%) through the alpine (26.4%) to the subnival (13.9%) belts. The Mediterranean-European element similarly decreases from 18.1% through 12.9% to 7.4%. On the other hand, the proportion extending from Asia Minor through the Caucasus to Central Asia increases from 38.1% through 50.5% to 73.3% upward through these three altitudinal belts. The Colchic element behaves as the more widely distributed species, decreasing with altitude.

The bryophytes contrast with the vascular plants in geographical distribution (Table 4). Most have a very wide distribution.

Hultén (1950) has made a very detailed analysis of the distribution of the Scandinavian flora. Of the 1857 plants classified into 48 types of distribution areas, about 1450 are mountain plants. Of the 180 arctic-montane plants that are therefore exclusively alpine to the south, Hulten describes 6.1% as arctic-montane only in Europe and 15.6% more in Eurasia; 63.3% are circumpolar, but 25.0% are not in the mountains of central Europe while 38.3% are; 15.0% are amphiatlantic. Of the 63.3% more or less circumpolar plants, only 48.9% of the total 180 have continuous distributions in Siberia, where the rest have large gaps. The boreal plants are similarly limited in areal distribution, so there are only limited possibilities of floristically correlating Scandinavian boreal vegetation with that in other parts of the world.

A similarly detailed discussion could be given of the floristic relationships of the Pamir (Ikonnikov, 1961), the northern Tien Shan

TABLE 4

Classification of the Areas of Geographical Distribution of
the Bryophytes of Southern Ossetia Found in
High-Mountain Vegetation

Belt	Geographical classes, %							
	Bipolar	Cosmopolitan	Holarctic	Palearctic	European	Mediterranean	Asia Minor	Caucasus
Subalpine	23.0	1.6	60.4	5.9	2.7	5.9	0	0.5
Alpine	21.7	1.1	62.3	9.2	1.7	4.0	0	0.0
Subnival	21.0	1.6	59.7	9.7	4.8	0.0	0	3.2

Abramov, 1953, p. 19.

(Rubtsov, 1956), Altai (Kuminova, 1960), and the Carpathians (Pax, 1898, p. 233), among others.

It is concluded that the floras of the Pamir (Ikonnikov, 1961), Tien-Shan (Krasnov, 1888), Caucasus (Fedorov, 1952), and Alps (Scharfetter, 1938, p. 269) have minimal relationship to other mountain floras. They have formed by differentiation in place to a much greater degree than by migration (principally during the glacials). Ovchinnikov (1941) emphasizes the indigenous nature of the cryophile flora of the mountains of Central Asia. It is not arctic and therefore probably not circumpolar, but it has been formed in place and is therefore limited in areal distribution. It distinguishes the vegetation of Central Asia qualitatively from vegetation that is otherwise similar ecologically.

A second conclusion is that floristic relationship is directly proportional to physical contiguity. For example, for the mountains of southern Siberia, Mikhailov (1961, p. 47) mentions that, of the 300 plant species known from the high mountain belts of the Altai, almost 40% appear also in the tundra zone of northern Siberia. This figure increases to 50% for the Sayan and to 60% in the Stanovoi ranges. The floristic similarity to the northern tundra is directly proportional to direct connection with the arctic tundra through more or less continuous mountain ranges.

The literature contains descriptions of the flora and vegetation of specific mountains that also support the above conclusions. Among these areas are the continental and arctic mountain Sokuidakh (900 m elevation at 71°20'N, 127°45'E near the mouth of the Lena River), whose closest analogous flora is in the Taimyr Peninsula north of 75°N (Yurtsev, 1959); the cold deserts at the upper limit of vegetation in northern Eurasia (Kuvaev, 1961); and the Urals, with their rich complement of endemic and relict species (Gorchakovsky, 1963, 1954; Igoshina, 1960; Khokhriakov, 1959).

REGIONAL CLIMATE

Regional climate is obviously a factor that differentiates ecosystems, and the other ecological factors discussed above operate within a regional climatic framework. We shall attempt some answers to these questions: Do alpine climates differ? How do they differ? Of what importance are these differences to the plant and soil aspects of ecosystems?

Descriptions of climate are not always ecologically satisfying. For our purposes we regard climates as consisting of moisture and heat regimes. The moisture regime we describe as the yearly course of the calculated balance between water income to the ecosystem (precipitation) and outgo from it (actual evapotranspiration). The heat regime is expressed in units of water usable by the ecosystem, and it is represented by Thornthwaite's potential evapotranspiration (an exponential function of temperatures above freezing) (Thornthwaite, 1948; Thornthwaite, et al., 1957; Major, 1963). An excess of water income over outgo produces a water surplus that in alpine climates in winter accumulates as snow and in summer leaches soils. A deficit means water is used from soil storage, insofar as excess water has been stored in the soil.

"Water surplus" is subject to some misunderstanding. This is the seasonal amount of precipitation over and above any amounts that can be evaporated, transpired, or stored in the soil. It therefore represents runoff. It is, of course, not overland runoff but simply watershed yield of water. Its amount provides a check on the calculations. Patton (1956) used equivalence of calculated water surplus and gaged watershed yields as an absolute check on the validity of the Thornthwaite scheme calculations in California. The check was good. Penman (1959) used the discrepancies between measured and calculated runoffs from the Spergelgraben and Rappengraben studied by Burger in Switzerland to question the precipitation-runoff relationships measured on these two watersheds. The matter is discussed further by Major (1963).

Climatic data for alpine stations are uncommon. We have diagrammed moisture and heat regimes for 116 stations that lie near timberline or between timberline and snowline, according to Hermes (1955), Frenzel (1960), Murzaev (1958), Zabirov (1955), Mikhailov (1961), and Ladygina (1962), plus personal observations. The primary

TABLE 5

Comparative Data for Some Alpine Climatic Stations

Station	Latitude, °N	Longitude	Elevation, m	Timberline, m	Snowline, m	Precipitation, mm	Temperature, °C	Potential evapo-transpiration, mm	Actual evapo-transpiration, mm	Water surplus, mm	Water deficit, mm	Continentality
Ak-Kem, Altai, Siberia, USSR	49°55'	86°38'E	2058	2100	2800	471	−4.8	351	346	125	5	23.7
Aragatz, Armenia, USSR	40°30'	44°15'E	3228	2700	3900	862	−1.9	318	295	567	23	19.0
IV Cantonieri, Stelvio Pass, Italy	46°31'	10°28'E	2545	2150	3000	1114	−2.0	332	332	782	0	13.9
Corona, Colorado	40°01'	105°43'W	3553	3300	4600	1051	−2.3	298	272	779	26	18.4
Ellery Lake, California	37°56'	119°14'W	2930	3150	4550	760	2.6	397	236	523	161	14.3
Fedchenko Glacier, Tadzhikistan, USSR	38°53'	72°14'E	4169	3600	4600	798	−7.1	153	153	687	0	18.3
Gartok, western Tibet	31°45'	80°20'E	4602	4250	6000	88	−0.7	350	88	0	262	20.8
Krestovoi Pass, Caucasus, USSR	42°30'	44°27'E	2380	2200	3500	1695	−3.6	394	394	1301	0	18.2
Mt. Rainier, Paradise, Washington	46°47'	121°44'W	1690	1800	2500	2963	3.6	453	436	2527	17	11.5
Mt. Washington, New Hampshire	44°16'	71°18'W	1910	1500	—	1940	−2.7	334	334	1606	0	20.6
Myn Dzhilki, Tien-Shan, USSR	43°00'	77°09'E	3036	2450	3600	734	−2.7	308	308	414	0	15.2
Pamir Biol. Sta., near Murgab, Tadzhikistan, USSR	38°10'	73°57'E	3864	3800	5100	66	−0.9	387	66	0	321	28.0
Tien-Shan Observatory, USSR	42°00'	78°13'E	3672	3000	4100	292	−7.5	212	202	90	10	22.1
White Mts. (alpine), California	37°35'	118°15'W	3800	3350	4800	368	−2.4	274	180	188	94	13.8
Wonder Lake, Alaska	63°28'	150°52'E	610	700	2300	515	−4.6	380	346	169	34	25.7

data of monthly average precipitation and temperatures have come from U.S. Weather Bureau summaries or yearly records, Köppen and Geiger's Handbuch der Klimatologie, pertinent papers such as Narinyan (1960), Giacomini and Pignatti (1955), and Sveshnikova (1962), or regional climatologies (Chelpanova, 1963; Zanina, 1961; Vitvitskii, 1960; Orlova, 1963). Calculated potential evapotranspiration and precipitation for certain stations were taken from Mather's compilations (1963). In all cases we have computed water balances by assuming a possible soil storage of 100 mm available water, unequally available as it is used (Thornthwaite et al., 1957; Major, 1963). A sampling of our data is given in Table 5 and Figs. 1 to 11.

The first conclusion from our data is that enormous climatic variability exists in Northern Hemisphere alpine environments. Water relations are extremely variable. Some variability can be associated with variations in absolute altitude of the alpine belt with latitude.

Alpine climates can be classified as humid or arid. Most are humid. Examples are Krestovoi Pass (Fig. 2) in the main range of the Caucasus, Stelvio Pass (Fig. 3) of the Alps, the northern slope of the Tien-Shan (Myn-Dzhilki), and Mount Washington (Fig. 4) in the eastern U.S. The same pattern of calculated excess of precipitation over need of the ecosystem for water (based on monthly average data of the climatic elements) holds throughout the Alps, the Caucasus main range east to Dagestan, Great Britain, the Urals, many mountain areas of southern Siberia, coastally influenced Alaska, the Aleutians, and most of Scandinavia.

Such areas are characterized by considerable summer precipitation. Surplus summer water (up to 200 mm a month in maritime

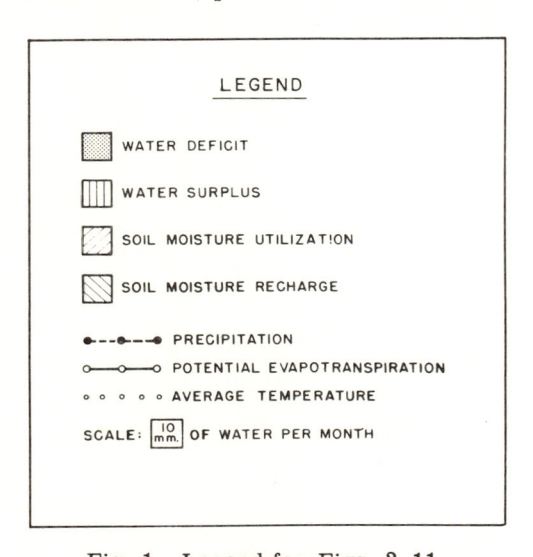

Fig. 1. Legend for Figs. 2-11.

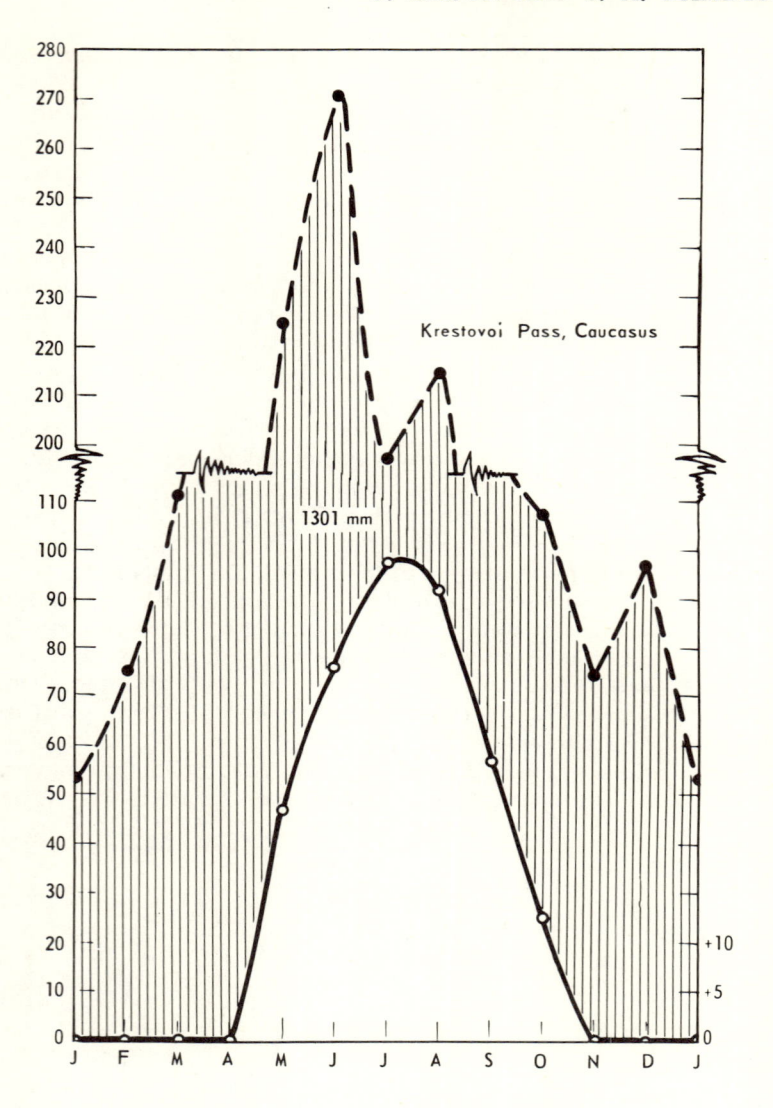

Fig. 2. Climatic diagram for the Krestovoi Pass in the Main Range of the Caucasus, east of the highest peaks. Months are on the abscissa, millimeters of water on the left ordinate, temperature in degrees centigrade on the right ordinate. Note the break in the ordinate scale. See Fig. 1 for the legend, Table 4 for a pertinent description, and the text for discussion.

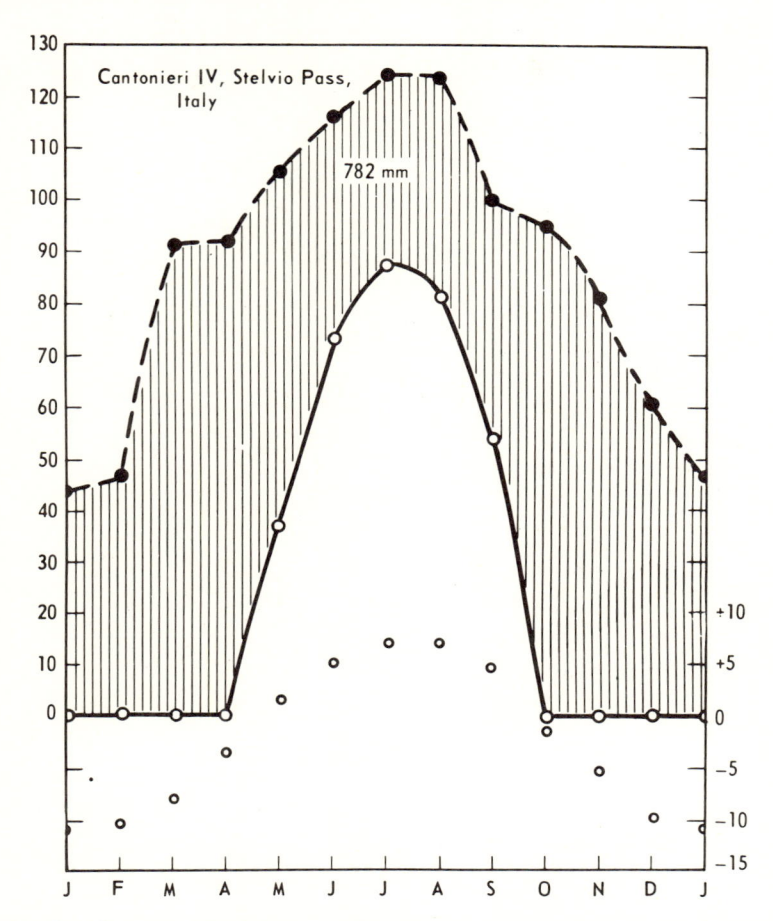

Fig. 3. Climatic diagram for Cantonieri IV, just below the Stelvio Pass, in Italy between the Ortler and the Engadine. Details as in Fig. 2.

areas) leaches the soils. Snowmelt adds to such surpluses in summer.

Because monthly potential evapotranspirations in the alpine belt reach 80 to 100 mm water use in July, monthly precipitation less than this amount will result in use of soil-stored water and some drought (water deficit). An example is Mount Rainier, Washington (Fig. 5), where need and demand for water are just out of phase. At Mount Rainier an average low of about 43 mm precipitation in July is 55 mm below potential evapotranspiration. The slight summer drought contrasts with excess winter precipitation of 2527 mm.

At Ak-Kem in the central Altai (Fig. 6) the need and demand curves almost coincide. Moisture conditions for plants, on the average, should be as favorable as at Mount Rainier, although the former

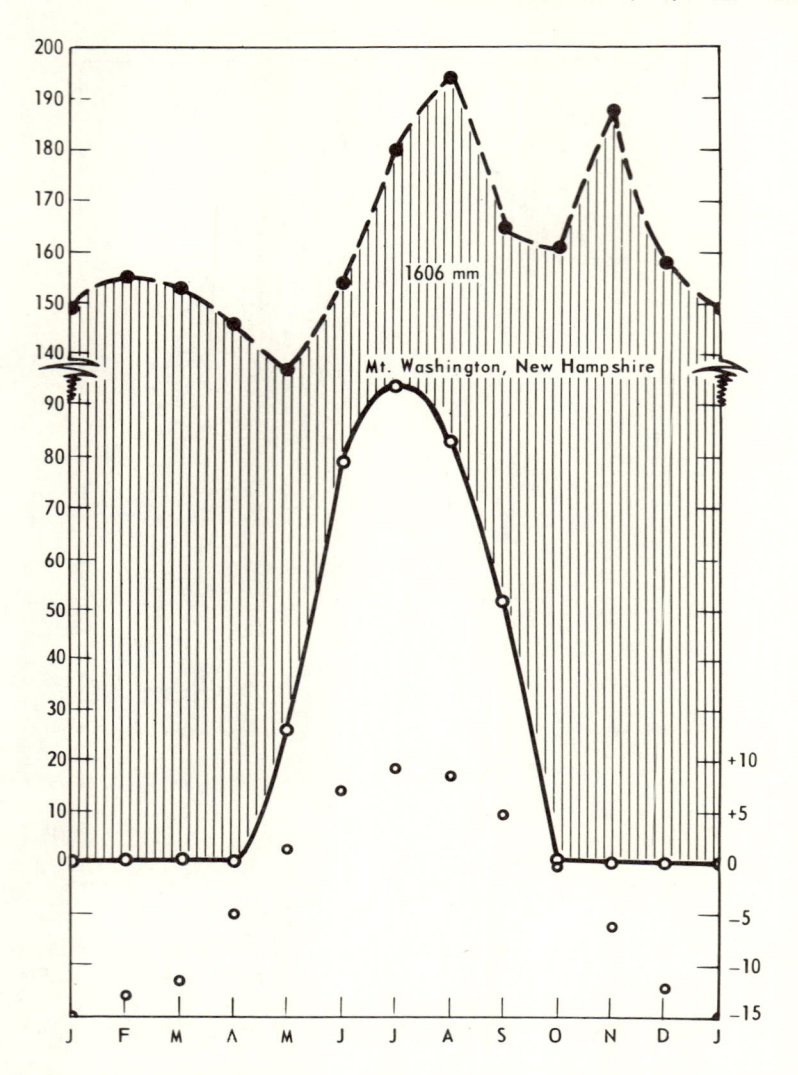

Fig. 4. Climatic diagram for the summit of Mt. Washington, New Hampshire, the highest peak in the Presidential Range. Details as in Fig. 2. Note the break in the ordinate scale.

station has only 471 mm precipitation as against the latter's 2963 mm. The nearby station Kara-Tyurek at 2755 m elevation has a July mean temperature of 6.4°C and a January mean of -17.1°. In these high, glaciated mountains precipitation is said to equal 1900 to 2600 mm/year (Mikhailov, 1961, pp. 79, 81). Such temperatures and precipitation would eliminate any water deficit and in fact assemble a water surplus of at least 1600 mm/year.

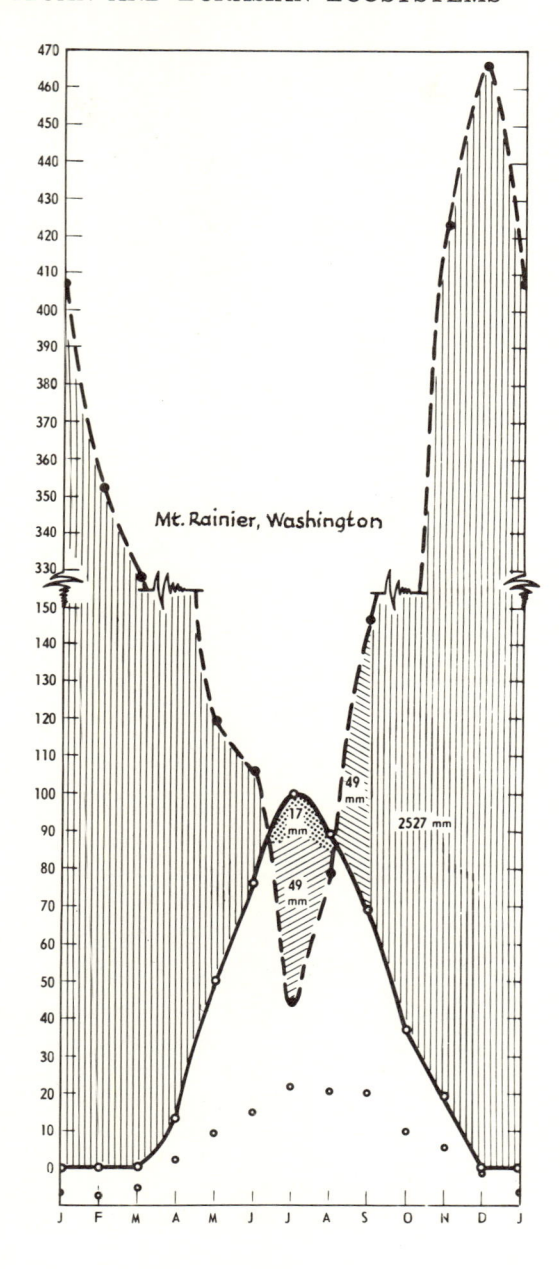

Fig. 5. Climatic diagram for Paradise in the subalpine zone on the isolated Mt. Rainier in the Cascade Range of Washington. Details as in Fig. 2. Note the break in the ordinate scale.

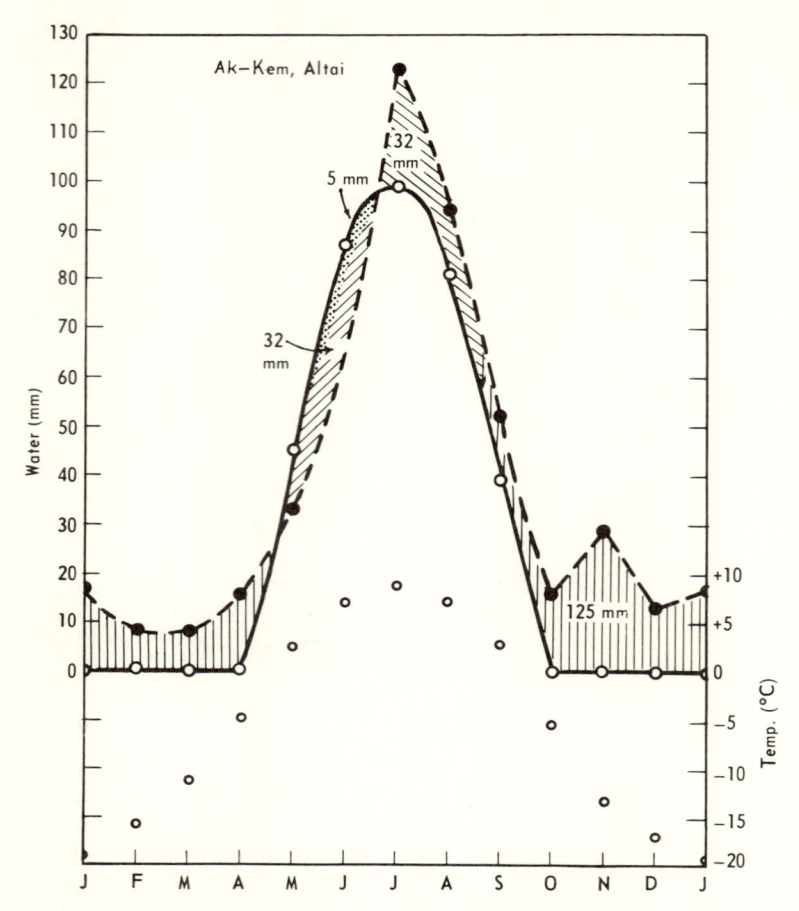

Fig. 6. Climatic diagram for Ak-Kem in the high, glaciated, central Altai of southwestern Siberia. Details as in Fig. 2.

Increasing amounts of summer drought are evident in Transcaucasia (Mount Aragatz, Fig. 7), continental valleys of Scandinavia, Central Asia, and the western U.S. Both mediterranean and dry, continental climates produce summer drought. The Rocky Mountains have slight summer drought (Corona, Colorado, Fig. 8) and the Sierra Nevada considerable (Ellery Lake). The summer drought in the desert White Mountains of the southwestern Great Basin (Fig. 9) is interrupted by summer thundershowers, as is also true, of course, in the Rocky Mountains.

The alpine area of the White Mountains is an arid region. Of the total average yearly precipitation of 395 mm, only 71 mm (18%) comes during the 3 summer months (Pace, 1963). In half the summer months of record, <10 mm of precipitation falls. Winter winds are strong,

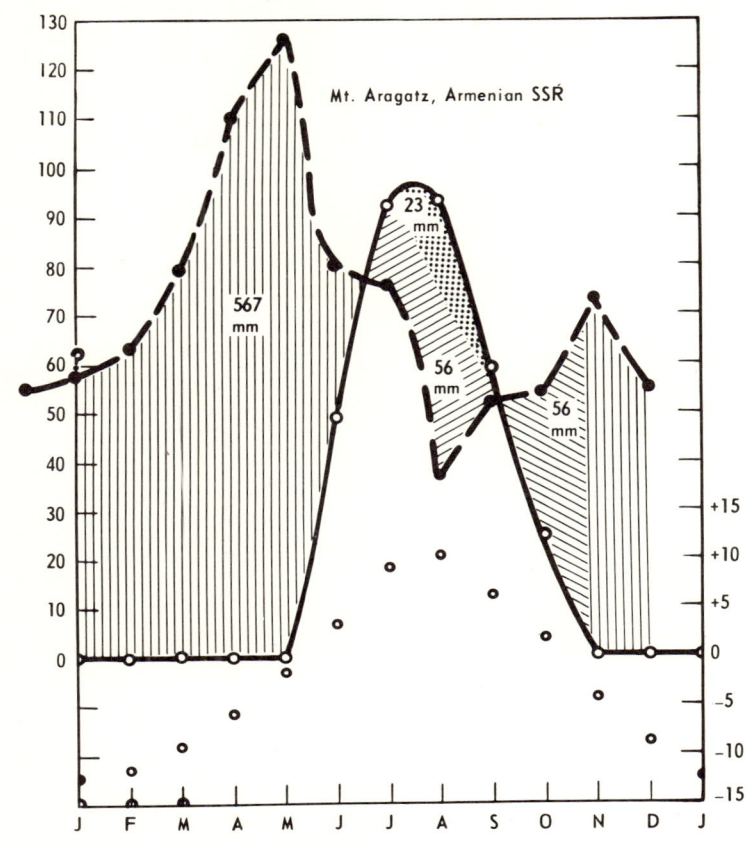

Fig. 7. Climatic diagram for the alpine belt on isolated Mt. Aragatz, Armenia, USSR. Details as in Fig. 2.

and snow is drifted so that large areas get little water from the 339 mm of precipitation (86%) that comes as snow. Only during July to September does rain occur, and then it forms <75% of the total precipitation in those months. In spite of this aridity our calculations indicate a runoff of 188 mm a year in the alpine belt (51% of precipitation). Overland runoff is certainly slight or nonexistent, particularly from areas underlain by dolomite, but water yield from the alpine part of the watershed is not. Streams are perennial between roughly 9500 and 6500 ft (2800 to 1980 m), and there are many springs in the range. A notable group occurs at 11,800 ft (3600 m) east of Mount Hogue (White Mountain Peak quadrangle, California, U.S. Geological Survey topographic map, 1/62,500, 1962). Arctic aridity is evident on the north slope of Mount McKinley (Wonder Lake).

Aridity increases markedly from the northern, outer ranges of the Pamir (Fedchenko Glacier, Fig. 10) to the interior ranges of

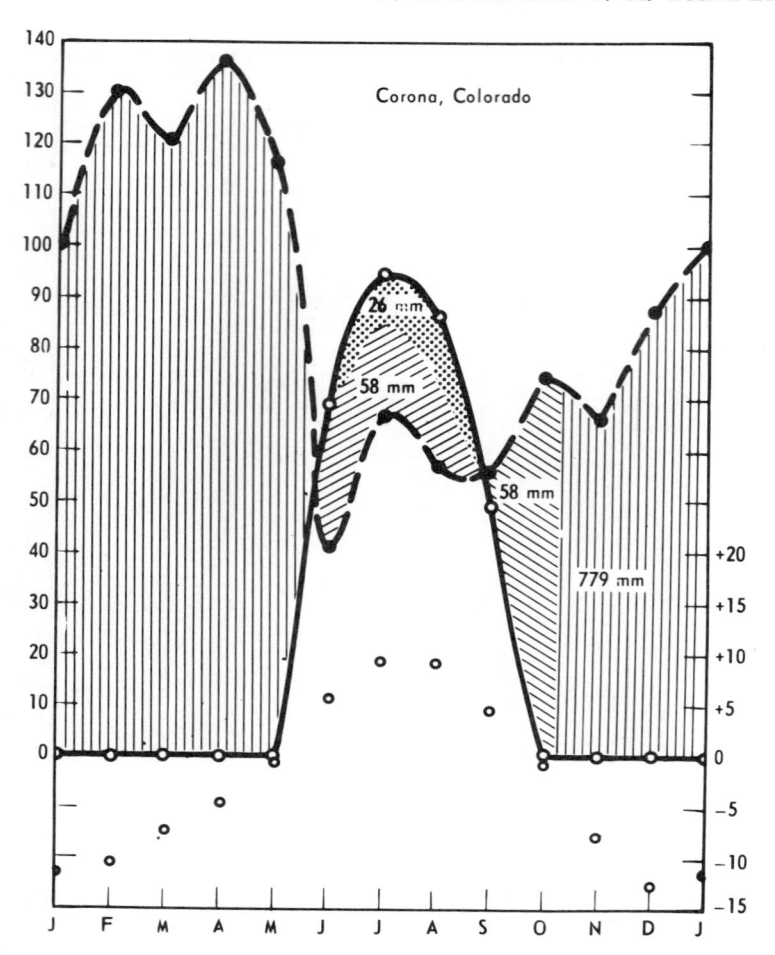

Fig. 8. Climatic diagram for Corona on the west side of the Front Range of Colorado in the Rocky Mountains. Details as in Fig. 2.

Central Asia. The Tien-Shan Observatory is sufficiently colder than the outer range Myn-Dzhilki, so the difference in precipitation of 292 versus 734 mm is expressed not as increased drought but as increase in water storage, mostly as winter snow (90 versus 414 mm). Continental, arid, and extreme alpine climates are at Gartok in western Tibet and especially the Pamir Biological Station (Fig. 11). In these areas plant growth is strictly limited by precipitation as low as 66 mm/year. Summer water deficits here are up to 90 mm/month, and the vegetation assumes a desert or steppe aspect and even contains species of normally lowland xerophytes [e.g., *Eurotia ceratoides* (L.) C.A.M.] in the neighborhood of such American mesophytic alpine species as *Oxyria digyna* (L.) Hill, *Smelowskia calycina* (Steph.) C.A.M.,

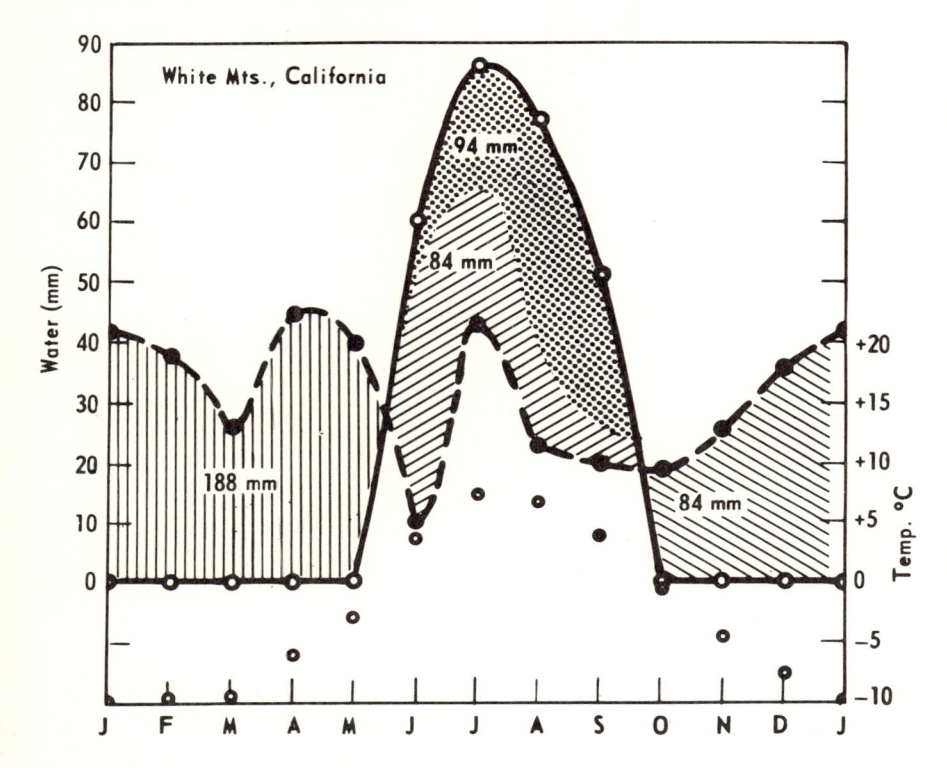

Fig. 9. Climatic diagram for the alpine belt in the White Mountains, a Great Basin range of eastern California that is separated only by the Owen's Valley from the Sierra Nevada. Details as in Fig. 2.

and a low form of *Dasiphora fruticosa* (L.) Rydb. Zonal vegetation and soils are both of desert aspect (Krivonogova, 1960; Ladygina, 1960).

Most alpine areas show some water accumulation as snow that becomes suddenly and totally available with summer. Local spots may therefore have a humid climate suitable for mesophytic alpine plants even in arid mountains. Too much snow accumulation, of course, eliminates the growing season. On the other hand, the lack of winter snow cover in the arid mountains of Central Asia is a most unfavorable situation for plants.

Thermal conditions in alpine belts are more uniform than moisture conditions. They are microthermal, with potential evapotranspiration from 150 to possibly 400 mm of water a year. Available heat is concentrated in a 2- to 5-month summer growing season. Although positive temperatures may occur over a longer period, winter snow accumulation delays the beginning of plant activity. Of course, the short summer growing season can be interrupted by freezing

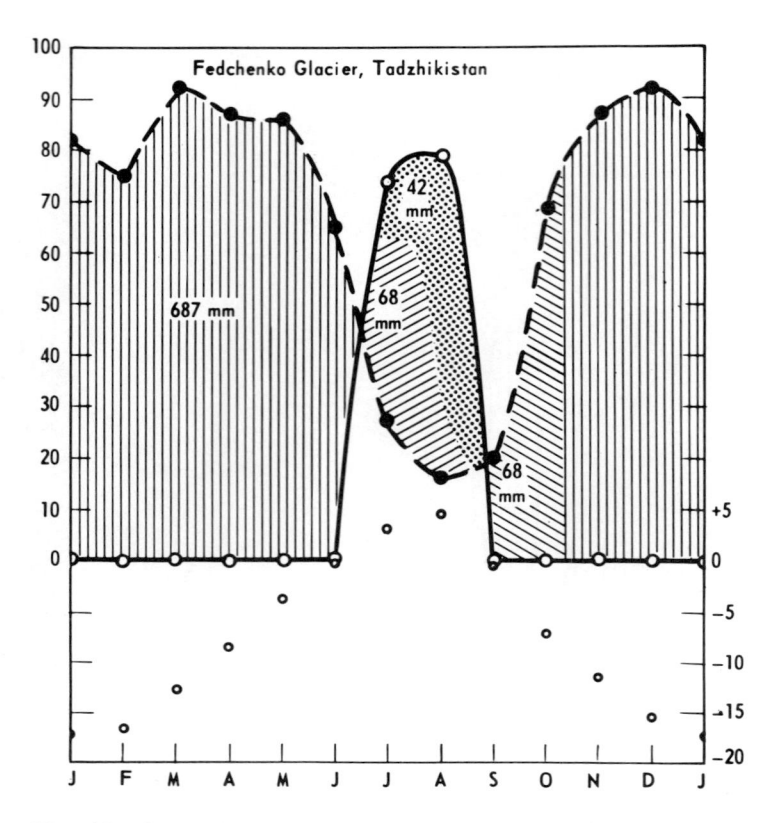

Fig. 10. Climatic diagram for the alpine belt at the Fedchenko Glacier, which extends northward from the transverse (north-south) Akademiia Nauk Range on the boundary between the Altai, dissected western, and erosion-filled eastern Pamir. Details as in Fig. 2.

temperatures. In general we believe it is the heat regime that distinguishes the alpine belt.

Actual evapotranspiration, a suggested measure of plant productivity (Major, 1963), is always low in alpine areas. It cannot be greater than potential evapotranspiration and is often limited by deficient precipitation to a figure well below the potential. Its lower limit is the amount of precipitation.

Water deficit or seasonal drought is quite general in alpine climates. It can assume any value less than the difference between potential evapotranspiration and precipitation.

Water surpluses are usually large. They can be zero in arid regions, although snow accumulation usually appears at least partially as water surplus. Maximum figures are the differences between precipitation and actual evapotranspiration.

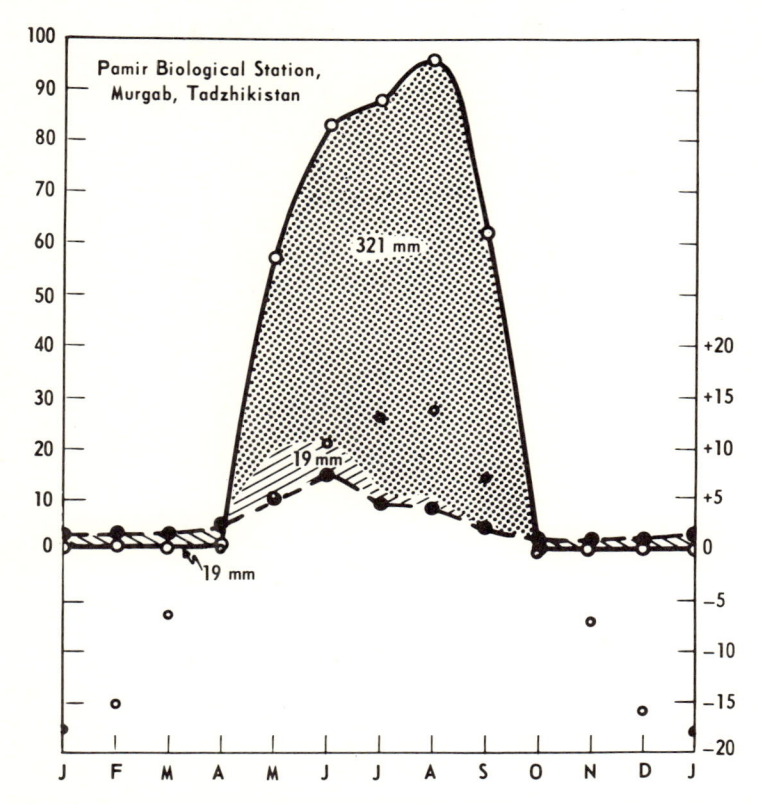

Fig. 11. Climatic diagram for the Pamir Biological Station in the high, cold, very arid eastern Pamir near Murgab. Details as in Fig. 2.

VARIATIONS IN MOUNTAIN ZONATIONS

We have no space to present the results of the interactions of the above ecological factors to form the wide variety of mountain zonations actually known. However, alpine vegetation is not homogeneous, and neither are the mountain zonations of which the alpine belt is a part. The work of Stanyukovich (1955), Grebenshchikov (1957), and Mikhailov (1961) can serve as a splendid introduction to this topic.

Acknowledgment

The authors appreciate National Science Foundation support for this study.

REFERENCES

Abramov, I. I., 1953, Analysis of the flora of southern Ossetia (in Russian): Leningrad Gos. Ord. Lenina Univ. im A. A. Zhdanov, 22 pp. (abstract of dissertation).

Aulitzky, H., A. Czell, G. Fromme, I. Neuwinger, H. Schiechtl, and R. Stern, 1961, Beschreibung des Gurglertales (hinterstes Oetztal in Nordtirol), *in* Oekologische Untersuchungen in der subalpinen Stufe zum Zwecke der Hochlagenaufforstung, Teil 1: Mitt. Forstl. Bundes-Versuchsanst. Mariabrunn, v. 59, pp. 33-52.

Barshad, I., 1964, Soil development, *in* Chemistry of the Soil (2nd ed.), F. E. Bear (ed.): New York, Reinhold, pp. 1-70.

Billings, W. D., 1952, The environmental complex in relation to plant growth and distribution: Quart. Rev. Biol., v. 27, pp. 251-265.

_____, and H. A. Mooney, 1959, An apparent frost hummock-sorted polygon cycle in the alpine tundra of Wyoming: Ecology, v. 40, pp. 16-20.

Braun-Blanquet, J., 1951, Pflanzensoziologie (2nd ed.): Berlin, Springer, 631 pp.

_____, and H. Jenny, 1926, Vegetationsentwicklung und Bodenbildung in der alpinen Stufe der Zentralalpen: Denkschr. Schweiz. Naturforsch. Ges., v. 63, pp. 183-349.

Chelpanova, O. M., 1963, Central Asia, vol. 3, *in* Climates of the USSR (in Russian): Leningrad, Gidrometeorol., 447 pp.

Crocker, R. L., 1952, Soil genesis and the pedogenic factors: Quart. Rev. Biol., v. 27, pp. 139-168.

_____, and B. A. Dickson, 1957, Soil development on the recessional moraines of the Herbert and Mendenhall Glaciers, southeastern Alaska: J. Ecol., v. 45, pp. 169-185.

_____, and J. Major, 1955, Soil development in relation to vegetation and surface age at Glacier Bay, Alaska: J. Ecol., v. 43, pp. 428-448.

Dickson, B. A., and R. L. Crocker, 1953, 1954, A chronosequence of soil and vegetation near Mt. Shasta, California, I and II: J. Soil Sci., v. 4, pp. 123-154; III, v. 5, pp. 173-191.

Ellenberg, H., 1953, Führt die alpine Vegetations- und Bodenentwicklung auch auf reinen Karbonatgesteinen zum Krummseggenrasen *(Caricetum curvulae?):* Ber. Deut. Botan. Ges., v. 66, pp. 241-246.

_____ 1963, Vegetation Mitteleuropas mit den Alpen, *in* Einführung in die Phytologie, Bd. IV, Teil 2, H. Walter (ed.): Stuttgart, Ulmer, 945 pp.

Ellison, L., 1954, Subalpine vegetation of the Wasatch Plateau, Utah: Ecol. Monographs, v. 24, pp. 89-184.

_____ 1960, The influence of grazing on plant succession of rangelands: Botan. Rev., v. 26, pp. 1-78.

Fedorov, A. A., 1952, History of the high mountain flora of the Caucasus in the Quaternary Period (in Russian): Mater. Chetv. Periodu, v. 3.

Frenzel, B., 1960, Die Vegetations- und Landschaftszonen Nord-Eurasiens während der letzten Eiszeit und während der postglazialen Wärmezeit. I. Allgemeine Grundlagen: Akad. Wiss. Lit. (Mainz) Abhandl. Math.-Nat. Kl. 1959, v. 13, pp. 935-1099.

Giacomini, V., and S. Pignatti, 1955, Flora e vegetazione dell'alta Valle del Braulio con speciale riferimento ai pascoli d'altitudine: Mem. Soc. Ital. Sci. Nat. Museum Civico Storia Nat. Milano, v. 11, pp. 1-194.

Gorchakovsky, P. L., 1954, The high mountain vegetation of Yaman-Tau, the highest peak of the southern Urals (in Russian): Botan. Zh., v. 39, pp. 827-841.

_____ 1963, Endemic and relict elements in the flora of the Urals and their origin (in Russian), *in* Materialy po istorii flory i rastitelnosti SSSR, Tr. Botan. Inst., Akad. Nauk SSSR Ser., v. 4, pp. 285-375.

Grabherr, W., 1936, Die Dynamik der Brandflächenvegetation auf Kalk- und Dolomitböden des Karwendels: Beih. Botan. Centralbl., v. 55B, pp. 1-94.

Grebenshchikov, O., 1957, Vertical vegetation zones in the mountains of the eastern part of Western Europe (in Russian): Botan. Zh., v. 42, pp. 834-854.

Grossgeim, A. A., 1936, Analysis of the flora of the Caucasus (in Russian): Tr. Botan. Inst. Akad. Nauk SSSR, Azerb. Filial, v. 1, 260 pp.

Gusev, U. D., 1959, On the upper limit of trees and woody scrub in the mountainous Badakhshansk Autonomous Region (in Russian): Botan. Zh., v. 44, pp. 1158-1162.

Hermes, K., 1955, Die Lage der oberen Waldgrenze in den Gebirgen der Erde und ihr Abstand zur Schneegrenze: Kölner Geograph. Arb., v. 5, pp. 1-277.

Hultén, E., 1950, Atlas över växternas utbredning i norden: Stockholm, Generalstabens Litografiska Anstalts Förlag, 512 pp.

Igoshina, K. N., 1960, Features of the vegetation of some mountains in the Urals as related to the character of the rocks (in Russian): Botan. Zh., v. 45, pp. 533-546.

Ikonnikov, S. S., 1961, Composition and properties of the flora of the Pamir (in Russian): Izv. Akad. Nauk Tadzh. SSR Otd. Sel'skokhoz. i Biol. Nauk, v. 1, pp. 43-53.

Jenny, H., 1941, Factors of Soil Formation: New York, McGraw-Hill, 281 pp.

_____ 1946, Arrangement of soil series and types according to functions of soil forming factors: Soil Sci., v. 61, pp. 375-391.

Johnson, W. M., 1961, The ecology of alpine and subalpine ranges in Wyoming as related to use by game and domestic sheep: Wyoming Univ. Publ., v. 25, pp. 81-82.

Khokriakov, A. P., 1959, New localities for the relict calcicole flora of the northern Urals (in Russian): Botan. Zh., v. 44, pp. 1727-1730.

Krasnov, A. N., 1888, On the history of development of the flora of the southern part of the eastern Tian Shan (in Russian): Zap. R. G. O. po Obshchestva Geograph., v. 19 (not seen, cited from Ikonnikov, 1961).

Krivonogova, M. B., 1960, Cushion and spiny-cushion plants, their geographical distribution and basic properties: Akad. Nauk SSSR, Probl. Botan., v. 5, pp. 243-253.

Kuminova, A. V., 1960, Vegetation of the Altai (in Russian): Izv. Sibirsk. Otd. Akad. Nauk SSSR, Ser. Biol., 450 pp.

Kuvaev, V. B., 1961, The altitudinal belt of cold, stony deserts in the mountains of northern Eurasia (in Russian): Botan. Zh., v. 46, pp. 337-347.

Ladygina, G. M., 1960, On the altitudinal distribution and some questions of the dynamics of the deserts of the Mountainous Badakhshansk Autonomous Region (in Russian): Akad. Nauk SSSR, Probl. Botan., v. 5, pp. 254-264.

_____ 1962, Contribution to knowledge of the vegetation of the Fedchenko Glacier region (valley of the Kaind River) (in Russian): Botan. Zh., v. 47, pp. 381-388.

Lüdi, W., 1945, Besiedlung und Vegetationsentwicklung auf den jungen Seitenmoränen des grossen Aletschgletschers: Zürich, Ber. Geobot. Forsch. Inst. Rübel, 1944, pp. 35-112.

Lukanenkova, V. K., and L. F. Sidorov, 1961a, Recurring features in the distribution of the upper limits of shrub growth in the region of contact of anterior and central Asia in the mountains of the USSR: Botan. Zh., v. 46, pp. 1294-1298.

_____ 1961b, On the upper limits of shrub growth in the mountains of the USSR (in Russian): Botan. Zh., v. 46, pp. 201-207.

Major, J., 1951, A functional, factorial approach to plant ecology: Ecology, v. 32, pp. 392-412.

_____ 1958, Plant ecology as a branch of botany: Ecology, v. 39, pp. 352-363.

_____ 1963, A climatic index to vascular plant activity: Ecology, v. 44, pp. 485-498.

_____, and S. A. Bamberg, 1967, Some Cordilleran plants disjunct in the Sierra Nevada of California, and their bearing on Pleistocene ecological conditions: this volume.

Mather, J. R., 1963, Average climatic water balance data of the continents. II. Asia (excluding USSR): Drexel Inst. Tech., Publ. Climatol., v. 16, pp. 1-262; III. USSR: v. 16, pp. 263-378.

Mikhailov, N. I., 1961, The mountains of southern Siberia (in Russian): Moskow, Gos. Izd. Geograf. Lit., 238 pp.

Munz, P. A., and D. D. Keck, 1959, A California flora: Berkeley, Univ. Calif. Press, 1681 pp.

Murzaev, E. M. (ed.), 1958, Central Asia, its physico-geographical characteristics (in Russian): Moscow, Akad. Nauk SSSR.

Narinyan, S. G., 1960, On the ecology and phenology of the alpine cover of Mt. Aragatz (Armenian SSR) (in Russian): Akad. Nauk SSSR. Probl. Botan., v. 5, pp. 195-217.

Orlova, V. V., 1963, Western Siberia, vol. 4, in Climates of the USSR (in Russian): Leningrad, Gidrometeorol. Izd., 360 pp.

Ovchinnikov, P. N., 1941, *Sibbaldia tetrandra* Bge. and the question of the origin of the cryophile vegetation of Central Asia (in Russian): Soviet. Botan., v. 1941, pp. 145-152.

Pace, Nello, 1963, Climatological data summary for the decade 1 January 1953 through 31 December 1962 from the Crooked Creek Laboratory (10,150 feet) and the Barcroft Laboratory (12,470 feet): Berkeley, Univ. Calif. White Mountain Res. Sta.

Patton, C. P., 1956, A quantitative assessment of the Thornthwaite classification of 1948: Ann. Assoc. Am. Geograph., v. 46, pp. 268-269 (abstract).

Pax, F., 1898, Grundzüge der Pflanzenverbreitung in den Karpathen, in Vegetation der Erde, A. Engler and O. Drude (eds.): Leipzig, W. Engelmann, 269 pp.

Penman, H. L., 1959, Notes on the water balance of the Spergelgraben and Rappengraben: Mitt. Schweiz. Anstalt Forstl. Versuchswesen, v. 35, pp. 99-109.

Polozova, T. G., 1961, On some northern stations of *Larix dahurica* Turcz. and *Alnaster fruticosus* Ldb. at the mouth of the Lena River, in Materialy po Rastitelnosti Yakutia (in Russian): Akad. Nauk USSR, Vses. Obshch. Yakutskoe Otd., pp. 291-294.

Reisigl, H., and H. Pitschmann, 1958, Obere Grenzen von Flora and Vegetation in der Nivalstufe der zentralen Oetztaler Alpen (Tirol): Vegetation, v. 8, pp. 93-128.

_____ 1959, Zur Abgrenzung der Nivalstufe: Phyton, v. 8, pp. 219-224.

Rubtsov, N. I., 1956, The flora of the northern Tien Shan and its geographical relationships (in Russian): Botan. Zh., v. 41, pp. 23-42.

Scharfetter, R., 1938, Das Pflanzenleben der Ostalpen: Wien, Deuticke, 419 pp.

Schröter, C., 1926, Das Pflanzenleben der Alpen (2nd ed.): Zürich, Raustein, 1288 pp.

Sochava, V. B., 1956, Larch forests, in Vegetation of the USSR, E. M. Lavrenko and V. B. Sochava (eds.) (in Russian): Moscow, Akad. Nauk SSSR, pp. 249-318.

Stahelin, R., 1943, Factors influencing the natural restocking of high altitude burns by coniferous trees in the Central Rocky Mountains: Ecology, v. 24, pp. 19-30.

Stanyukovich, K. V., 1955, Basic types of zonation in the mountains of the USSR (in Russian): Izv. Vses. Geogr. Obshch., v. 87, pp. 232-243.

Strickler, G. S., 1961, Vegetation and soil condition changes on a subalpine grassland in eastern Oregon: U.S. Dept. Agr. Forest Service, Pacific Northwest Forest Range Expt. Sta. Res. Paper, v. 40, 46 pp.

Sveshnikova, V. M., 1962, Water regime of the plants and soils of the high mountain deserts of the Pamirs (in Russian), Izv. Akad. Nauk Tadzh. Otd. Sel'skokhoz. i Biol. Nauk, v. 9, pp. 1-247.

Thornthwaite, C. W., 1948, An approach toward a rational classification of climate: Geograph. Rev., v. 38, pp. 55-94.

───, J. R. Mather, and D. B. Carter, 1957, Instructions and tables for computing potential evapotranspiration and the water balance: Drexel Inst. Tech. Publ. Climatol., v. 10, pp. 183-311.

Vitvitskii, G. N., 1960, Climates of Asia outside the USSR (in Russian): Moscow, Gos. Izd. Geogr. Lit., 399 pp.

Watt, A. S., 1947, Pattern and process in the plant community: J. Ecol., v. 35, pp. 1-22.

Welten, M., 1958, Pollenanalytische Untersuchung alpiner Bodenprofile: historische Entwicklung des Bodens and säkulare Sukzession der örtlichen Pflanzengesellschaften, *in* Festschrift Werner Lüdi, M. Welten and H. Zoller (eds.): Zürich, Veroff. Geobot. Inst. Rübel, v. 33, pp. 253-274.

Wiggins, I. L., and J. H. Thomas, 1962, A flora of the Alaskan Arctic slope: Arctic Inst. No. Amer., Spec. Publ., No. 4, 426 pp.

Wikus, E., 1958, Die Vegetation der Lienzer Dolomiten (Osttirol): Arch. Botan. Biogeograph. Ital., v. 34, pp. 157-184.

Wistrand, G., 1962, Pite Lappmarks kärlväxtflora med särskild hänsyn till skogslandet och de isolerade fjällen: Acta Phytogeogr. Suecica, v. 45, pp. 1-241.

Wlodek, J., K. Strzemienski, and E. Ralski, 1931, Untersuchungen über die Böden der Mischassoziationen im Gebiete der Czerwone Wierchy und Bielskie Zstry (Tatra-Gebirge): Bull. Acad. Polon. Sci. Lettr., Ser. B, Sci. Nat., v. 1930, pp. 103-122.

Yurtsev, B. A., 1959, The high mountain flora of Mt. Sokuidakh and its place in the mountain flora of arctic Yakutia (in Russian): Botan. Zh., v. 44, pp. 1171-1177.

Zabirov, P. D., 1955, Glaciation of the Pamir (in Russian): Moscow, Gos. Izd. Geogr. Lit., 372 pp.

Zanina, A. A., 1961, Caucasus, v. 2, *in* Climates of the USSR (in Russian): Leningrad, Gidrometeorol. Izd., 290 pp.

ARCTIC AND ALPINE ENVIRONMENTS (H. E. Wright, Jr., and W. H. Osburn, eds.), 119-136, ©1967 Indiana University Press

6
Distribution of Alpine Plants in Northern Japan

M. TATEWAKI
Botanical Institute
Faculty of Agriculture
Hokkaido University
Sapporo, Japan

Abstract

The alpine flora of northern Japan is well represented by that of Hokkaido, the northern large island of Japan, which is located at the intersection of three routes: the northern, from the Asiatic Continent through Sakhalin, the northeastern, from the Bering Sea region through the Kuriles, and the southern, from Honshu, the main island of Japan. Among the problems of distribution of alpine plants in northern Japan, the endemic, the disjunctive, and the young volcanic elements are treated in the present paper phytogeographically.

Endemic elements. The number of higher plants indigenous to the alpine belt of Hokkaido are estimated to be about 400 species. They are mainly composed of alpine and boreal-alpine plants. Among them, the endemic species number about 40, most of which occur in the Central Mountains System. Endemism is rare on recent volcanoes, and it is restricted mainly to those built of special rocks or to old volcanoes. According to analysis of plant distribution, the distinct endemic species have been extraordinarily reported from mountains composed of ultrabasic rocks such as Mt. Apoi and Mt. Yubari. They include derivatives of continental genera such as *Callianthemum*, *Lagotis*, *Hypochoeris*, etc.

Disjunctive elements. This type of distribution is found in mountains composed of ultrabasic rocks, thus showing the same tendency of distribution as the endemic species. A fine representative exists in Mt. Yubari, composed of serpentinite, slate, and schalstein. The distinct examples of the disjunctive alpine plants are here restricted and are all considered to be relic elements with respect to migrational routes. An important key to analyzing the distribution is given by the disjunctive species in the alpine flora of the Daisetsu Massif, the highest range (about 2000 m), situated in the center of Hokkaido and consisting of various volcanoes in different ages of formation.

Young volcanic elements. There are many interesting problems of plant distribution on volcanoes, relating to volcanic age, activity, geographical position, and situation, especially whether or not they are isolated. The young volcanoes that are still now active, such as Mts. Komagatake, Tarumai, Tokachi, Asahi, and Meakan, have a rather low number of alpine species. It is noticeable that there are few endemic species, whereas Northern Asiatic Pacific and circumpolar elements are abundant.

The alpine flora of northern Japan is well represented by that of Hokkaido, the large northern Japanese island, an important and interesting phytogeographic area because it is located at the intersection of three routes: the northern, from the Asiatic Continent through Sakhalin; the northeastern, from the Bering Sea region through the Kurils; and the southern, from Honshu, the main island of Japan. Of unknown importance is the land-bridge connection with Eurasia in the past.

In an earlier paper the writer described the alpine plants in Hokkaido and the physiography, history of botanical research, and general view of plant communities in the alpine zone (Tatewaki, 1963). The present paper treats the distribution of the alpine plants of Hokkaido, especially the endemic and disjunctive plants and the plants that grow on the young volcanic mountains.

PHYSIOGRAPHY

Hokkaido extends from lat. 41°24'N to 45°31'N, and from long. 139°45'E to 145°49'E. It is almost rhombic in outline, with a fishtail-shaped extension called the Oshima Peninsula on the southwest and two small bifurcate arms called the Shiretoko and Nemuro Peninsulas at the east end. At most 386 km from north to south or from west to east, it has an area of 77,900 sq km. Separated on the south from Honshu by the Tsugaru Strait and on the north from Sakhalin by the Soya Strait, Hokkaido is surrounded by the Sea of Japan on the west, the Sea of Ochotask on the north, and the Pacific Ocean on the south. Because Hokkaido is situated at the conjunction of the elongate lines projected from the mainland of Japan, Sakhalin, and the Kurils, the distribution of the alpine plants is very important with respect to the mainland flora.

Physiographically and geologically Hokkaido may be divided into four parts. The northwestern and the central parts are distinctly separated from the southwestern by a median depression (now deeply buried under alluvial deposits) extending from the Ishikari plain to the vicinity of Tomakomai on the Pacific coast. The eastern part is not sharply delimited from the central.

Southwestern Part

The whole surface of southwestern Hokkaido is mountainous, although high peaks are not numerous. It consists of late-Tertiary rocks, the so-called Hidaka group (Paleozoic), and various plutonic and volcanic rocks. The Hidaka group is represented in the mountain group of the Matsumae district at the southwestern side. On the eastern side, however, many active and extinct volcanoes belonging to the extension of the Nasu Range stretch from south to north, e.g., Mt. Komagatake (1140 m); Mt. Makkarinupuri (1895 m), Mt. Nisekowan (1309 m), Mt. Usu (725 m), Mt. Tarumai (1024 m), and Mt. Eniwa (1320 m). The highest peak is Mt. Makkarinupuri (also known as Yezofuji). The alpine flora of this mountain is protected by the natural-monument regulation.

Central Part

The Central Mountain System (the so-called Yezo Mountain System) forms the backbone of the main island, trending north-northwest from near Cape Erimo to Cape Soya. These complex mountains are made up partly of the Paleozoic and Mesozoic sediments and partly of plutonic and volcanic rocks. The six mountain groups are defined from south to north, viz. the Apoi Massif, the Hidaka Range, the Yubari Range, the Central Highland, the Uryu Massif, and the Kitami Range.

The Hidaka Range, in the southern part of the Yezo Range, contains comparatively high peaks, a few of which exceed 1900 m. It is composed mostly of rocks of the Hidaka group and of granite. The summits are densely covered with straggling dwarf pine, and its alpine flora is comparatively poor in species. Slight traces of glaciers were recently discovered, although there are no glaciers at present in this district.

The Apoi Massif, a disjunctive small mountain group, is situated west of the southernmost Hidaka Range. It is composed of Mesozoic peridotite connected to the northwest with the Yubari Range. Only Mt. Apoi (881 m) and Mt. Pinneshiri (958 m) are prominent. In spite of the rather low altitude, the Apoi Massif has a wonderful alpine flora, including many endemic and rare plants. At present it is protected by the natural-monument regulation.

The north-south Yubari Range is located northwest of the Hidaka Range and on the southwestern side of the Central Highland. It is made partly of serpentinite, with peaks towering to an elevation of 1900 m. The alpine meadows of the Yubari Range are well known in Japan as a vast treasury of alpine plants; they thus have great significance to the phytogeographer.

The Uryu Massif is an elongated serpentine district in the western part of the central Hokkaido. Mt. Shiratori (776 m) has the representative alpine flora.

The Central Highland, the highest mountain group in northern Japan, contains the highest peaks (about 2000 m elevation) in Hokkaido. Alpine meadows and bogs are plentiful, with many interesting boreal plants. Nowhere in northern Japan are there more extensive alpine meadows so rich in species. Volcanic rocks in this group are composed of liparite, andesite, basalt, and their pyroclastic equivalents. The Central Highland consists of about 20 main peaks, among which Mt. Asahi (2290 m) and Mt. Tokachi (2077 m) are the representative volcanoes.

The Central Mountain System forks and becomes gradually lower to the north in the Kitami Ranges, which consists partly of Paleozoic rocks. The highest peak of the cluster, Mt. Horonupuri (839 m), has an interesting alpine flora.

Farther northwest is the Kabato Massif, composed mainly of the Hidaka group in the southern part and of Pleistocene andesite in the northern part. Mts. Matsuneshiri (1100 m) and Kumaneshiri (971 m) are located in the former part, and Mts. Shokanbetsu (1491 m) and Hamamasu (1258 m) in the latter.

Off the northern end of Hokkaido, the isolated islands of Rishiri and Rebun are one of the northern treasuries of alpine and subalpine species. Rishiri is a typical volcanic island with a peak (Mt. Rishiri, 1718 m); it is composed mainly of Pleistocene andesite and its pyroclastics. Rebun, on the contrary, is generally hilly with altitudes of 200 to 300 m (except Mt. Rebun, 490 m); it consists mainly of Cretaceous and especially late-Tertiary rocks.

Eastern Part

Eastern Yezo is composed of low hills or uplands of Tertiary and Mesozoic formations with subordinante amounts of the Hidaka group. In the northeastern part, a chain of extinct volcanoes at the southwest end of the Kuril volcanic belt runs eastward to the Shiretoko Peninsula. Mt. Iwo (1563 m), Mt. Rausu (1661 m), Mt. Shari (1545 m), Mt. Oakan (1371 m), and Mt. Meakan (1510 m) are well known and are composed mostly of andesitic rock. Among them, the alpine flora of Mt. Oakan and Mt. Meakan in the Akan National Park has been protected. The alpine vegetation is different on each peak, one of which is volcanic and the other active.

FLORISTIC COMPOSITION OF ALPINE PLANTS IN HOKKAIDO

Higher plants (Pteridophyta, Gymnospermae, and Angiospermae)

DISTRIBUTION OF ALPINE PLANTS

indigenous to the alpine zone include not only the alpine or the arctic-alpine plants but also the subalpine, bog, swamp, and aquatic plants. They belong to about 440 species and 60 families in total, among which 225 species and 42 families are considered to be alpine and arctic-alpine. This paper will discuss only the last two groups.

Scientific names follow mostly Ohwi (1957, 1965).

According to Engler's systematic arrangement of the families, the number of genera and species of alpine plants of Hokkaido is shown in Table 1. Genera with three or more species are as follows:

3 species: *Lycopodium, Minuartia, Hypericum, Phyllodoce, Vaccinium, Primula, Gentianella, Lagotis, Veronica, Saussurea, Taraxacum, Luzula, Deschampsia*
 4 species: *Stellaria, Trollius, Potentilla, Astragalus, Gentiana*
 5 species: *Polygonum, Saxifraga, Oxytropis, Viola, Pedicularis*
 6 species: *Salix*
 8 species: *Juncus*
16 species: *Carex*

Analysis of Distribution Types

Wide-ranging elements (46 spp.)

Cosmopolitan (5 spp.): *Lycopodium selago, Botrychium lunaria, Deschampsia flexuosa, Trisetum spicatum, Carex pyrenaica.* Except for *Deschampsia flexuosa*, these species are not found in new volcanoes.

Circumpolar (41 spp.): *Lycopodium alpinum, Selaginella selaginoides, Botrychium lanceolatum, Athyrium alpestre, Juniperus communis* var., *Oxyria digyna, Polygonum bistorta, Polygonum vivaparum, Minuartia verna* var., *Ranunculus acris* var., *Sagina saginoides, Dryas octopetala* var., *Potentilla fruticosa, Potentilla nivea, Sibbardia procumbens; Diapensia lapponica* var., *Arctous alpinus* var., *Ledum palustre* var., *Loiseleuria procumbens, Phyllodoce caerulea, Vaccinium uliginosum, Vaccinium vitis-idaea, Empetrum nigrum* var., *Androsace lehmanniana, Pinguicula vulgaris* var., *Linnaea borealis, Juncus filiformis, Juncus triglumis, Luzula parviflora, Agrostis borealis, Deschampsia caespitosa* var., *Hierochloe alpina, Phleum alpinum, Sparganium angustifolium, Sparganium hyperboreum, Carex bipartita, Carex capillaris, Carex vaginata, Eriophorum scheuchzeri, Kobresia bellardii, Scirpus caespitosus.*

Northern Pacific elements (125 spp.)

Northern Pacific (19 spp.): *Stellaria ruscifolia, Geum calthaefolium, Geum pentapetalum, Sanguisorba stipulata, Cassiope lycopodioides, Harrimanella stelleriana, Phyllodoce aleutica, Primula cuneifolia, Fauria crista-galli, Lagotis glauca, Pedicularis chamissonis* var.,

TABLE 1
Number of Genera and Species of Alpine Plants on Hokkaido

Family		No. of genera	No. of species
Lycopodiaceae		1	3
Selaginellaceae		1	1
Ophioglossaceae		1	2
Polypodiaceae		2	2
Pteridophyta	4	5	8
Pinaceae		1	1
Cupressaceae		1	1
Gymnospermae	2	2	2
Salicaceae		1	6
Betulaceae		2	2
Polygonaceae		3	7
Caryophyllaceae		6	12
Ranunculaceae		7	11
Guttiferae		1	3
Papaveraceae		2	2
Cruciferae		5	6
Crassuraceae		1	2
Saxifragaceae		2	6
Rosaceae		8	13
Leguminosae		3	11
Geraniaceae		1	1
Rhamnaceae		1	1
Violaceae		1	5
Onagraceae		1	2
Umbelliferae		4	5
Archichlamydeae	17	49	95
Diapensiaceae		1	1
Ericaceae		10	15
Empetraceae		1	1
Primulaceae		2	4
Gentianaceae		4	9
Boraginaceae		2	2
Scrophulariaceae		4	12
Orobanchaceae		1	1
Lentibulariaceae		1	1
Caprifoliaceae		1	1
Vallerianaceae		1	1
Campanulaceae		1	2
Compositae		11	16
Sympetalae	13	40	66

Family	No. of genera	No. of species
Liliaceae	4	5
Juncaceae	2	11
Gramineae	9	14
Sparganiaceae	1	2
Cyperaceae	4	20
Orchidaceae	1	2
Monocotyledoneae 6	21	54

SUMMARY

Systematic group	No. of families	No. of genera	No. of species
Archichlamydeae	17	49	95
Sympetalae	13	40	66
Dicotyledoneae	30	89	161
Monocotyledoneae	6	21	54
Angiospermae	36	110	215
Gymnospermae	2	2	2
Pteridophyta	4	5	8
Total	42	117	225

Veronica stelleri var., *Campanula chamissonis*, *Campanula lasiocarpa*, *Arnica unalascensis*, *Taraxacum trigonolobum*, *Tofieldia coccinea*, *Juncus mertersianus*, *Platanthera chorisiana*.

Northern Asiatic Pacific (19 spp.): *Hypericum kamtschaticum*, *Draba ussuriensis*, *Saxifraga renifromis*, *Sorbus sambucifolia*, *Viola crassa*, *Tilingia ajanensis*, *Arcterica nana*, *Bryanthus gmelini*, *Gentiana jamesii*, *Gentianella auriculata*, *Pentstemon frutescens*, *Saussurea riederi* var., *Juncus beringensis*, *Juncus kamtschatcensis*, *Luzula oligantha*, *Carex hakkodensis*, *Carex scita* var., *Carex stenantha*, *Platanthera makinoi*.

Japanese (44 spp.): *Salix reinii*, *Polygonum nakaii*, *Polygonum weyrichii*, *Arenaria katoana*, *Arenaria merckioides*, *Stellaria nipponica* var., *Aquilegia japonica*, *Pulsatilla nipponica*, *Trollius hondoensis*, *Cardamine nipponica*, *Draba japonica*, *Macropodium pterospermum*, *Sedum ishidae*, *Boykinia lycoctonifolia*, *Alchemilla japonica*, *Potentilla matsumurae*, *Potentilla miyabei*,* *Sorbus pseudogracilis*, *Oxytropis japonica* var., *Epilobium dielsii*, *Epilobium foucaudianum*, *Bupleurum nipponicum* var., *Peucedanum multivittatum*, *Phyllodoce nipponica* var.,

---
*Northern Japanese, occurring mainly in Hokkaido, southern Sakhalin, and the southern Kurils.

Gentiana nipponica, Gentianella takedae, Swertia cuspidata, Eritrichium nipponicum var., *Mertensia pterocarpa* var., *Pedicularis apodochila, Pedicularis koidzumiana,* Veronica schmidtiana, Anaphalis alpicola, Crepis hokkaidoensis,* Senecio kawakamii,* Tofieldia okuboi, Juncus fauriensis, Agrostis flaccida, Poa hakusanensis, Poa hayachinensis, Carex flavocuspis, Carex kabanovii,* Carex oxyandra, Carex urostachys.*

Endemic elements (43 spp.)

The endemic elements are explained in the next chapter.

Asiatic elements (36 spp.)

Eastern Asiatic (25 spp.): *Pinus pumila, Alnus maximowiczii, Polygonum ajanense, Trollius riederianus, Dicentra peregina, Saxifraga laciniata, Saxifraga merckii, Astragalus adsurgens, Astragalus membranaceus, Astragalus secundus, Hedysarum vicioides, Bupleurum triadiatum, Rhododendron aureum, Patrinia sibirica, Taraxacum platypecidum, Allium maximowiczii, Zygadenus sibiricus, Juncus potaninii, Juncus triceps, Anthoxanthum nipponicum, Carex eleusinoides, Carex melanocarpa, Carex tenuiformis, Carex vanheurckii, Scirpus maximowiczii.*

Eastern Asiatic - western North American (8 spp.): *Saxifraga cherlerioides* var., *Spiraea betulifolia, Geranium erianthum, Rhododendron camtschaticum, Gentiana glauca, Boschniakia rossica, Artemisia arctica, Artemisia trifurcata* var.

Asiatic - western N. American (3 spp.): *Minuartia arctica, Minuartia macrocarpa* var., *Gentiana algida* var.

Eurasiatic elements (11 spp.)

Eurasiatic (4 spp.): *Cryptogramma crispa, Rumex montanus, Silene repens* var., *Hedysarum hedysaroides.*

Eurasiatic - western North American (6 spp.): *Anemone narcissiflora, Viola repens, Pedicularis oederi, Pedicularis verticillata, Lloydia serotian, Luzula wahlenbergii.*

Eastern North America - Eurasiatic - western North American (1 sp.): *Sedum rosea.*

North American elements (7 spp.)

North American - eastern Asiatic (4 spp.): *Lycopodium sitchense Arabis lyrata* var., *Vaccinium ovalifolium, Calamagrostis purpurascens.*

Western European - North American - eastern Asiatic (3 spp.): *Stellaria calycantha, Deschampsia atropurpurea* var. *Carex livida.*

ENDEMIC ELEMENTS

Floristic Composition

Endemic Species. The alpine plants of Hokkaido include 43 endemic species in 17 families (Table 2), or about 20% of all the plants. This large number of plant species is unusual in the North Pacific islands. Besides the endemic varieties mentioned below, the following alpine varieties of normally nonalpine species may be added to the alpine flora, although they are excluded from the alpine species in the present paper. They are *Viola brevistipulata* W. BECKER var. *hidakana* S. WATANABE, *Coelopleurum lucidum* FERNALD var. *trichocarpum* HARA, *Swertia tetrapetala* PALL. var. *yezo-alpina* HARA, *Cirsium pectinellum* A. GRAY var. *alpinum* KOIDZ., *Erigeron thunbergii* A. GRAY var. *glabratus* A. GRAY, *Ixeris dentata* NAKAI var. *alpicola* OHWI and *Fritillaria camtschatcensis* KER-GAWL. var. *alpina* TATEWAKI ET S. KAWANO.

Endemic Varieties. The endemic varieties of the alpine plants in Hokkaido are enumerated here (C, central part; R, Rishiri and Rebun; SW, southwestern part).

Arenaria katoana MAKINO var. *lanceolata* TATEWAKI Mt. Apoi (C)

Silene repens PERS. var. *apoiensis* HARA Mt. Apoi (C)

Stellaria nipponica OHWI var. *yezoensis* HARA Mt. Apoi (C)

TABLE 2

Number of Endemic Species in Hokkaido

Family	No. of genera	No. of species	Family	No. of genera	No. of species
Salicaceae	1	5	Primulaceae	1	2
Betulaceae	1	1	Gentianaceae	1	1
Caryophyllaceae	2	2	Scrophulariaceae	2	3
Ranunculaceae	3	5	Compositae	6	7
Guttiferae	1	2	Sympetalae 4	10	13
Papaveraceae	1	1			
Crassulaceae	1	1	Dicotyledoneae		
Saxifragaceae	1	1	16	26	41
Leguminosae	2	5	Gramineae	2	2
Rhamnaceae	1	1			
Violaceae	1	3	Monocotyledoneae		
Umbelliferae	1	1	1	2	2
Archichlamydeae			Angiospermae		
12	16	28	17	28	43

Aruncus dioicus FERN. var. *subrotundatus* HARA Mt. Apoi (C)
Potentilla matsumurae WOLF var. *apoiensis* (NAKAI) Mt. Apoi (C)
Sanguisorba stipulata RAFIN. var. *riishirensis* HARA (R) (C)
Oxytropis japonica MAXIM. var. *sericea* KOIDZ. Daisetsu Mts. (C)
Viola brevistipulata W. BECKER var. *hidakana* S. WATANABE Hidaka Ranges (C)
Bupleurum nipponicum KOSO-POLIANSKY var. *yesoense* HARA Mt. Apoi (C)
Coelopleurum lucidum FERNALD var. *trichocarpum* HARA (C)
Peucedanum multivittatum MAXIM. var. *linearilobum* TATEWAKI Mt. Apoi (C)
Tilingia ajanesis REGEL var. *angustissima* KITAGAWA Mt. Apoi (C)
Gentiana algida PALL. var. *igarashii* MIYABE ET KUDO Daisetsu Mts. (C)
Mertensia pterocarpa TATEWAKI ET OHWI var. *yezoensis* TATEWAKI ET OHWI (C)
Veronica yezo-alpina TAKEDA var. *angustifolia* TATEWAKI Mt. Apoi (C)
Cirsium pectinellum A. GRAY var. *alpinum* KOIDZ. Daisetsu Mts. (C)
Erigeron thunbergii A. GRAY var. *angustifolius* HARA Mt. Apoi (C)
Saussurea riederi HERD. var. *kudoana* (TATEWAKI ET KITAMURA) Mt. Apoi (C)
Saussurea yanagisawae TAKEDA var. *vestita* KITAMURA (C)
Deschampsia caespitosa BEAUV. var. *levis* OHWI Mt. Yubari (C)
Hierochloe pluriflora KOIDZ. var. *intermedia* OHWI (SW)
Carex scita MAXIM. var. *riishirensis* KUEKENTH. (C)
Hosta rectifolia NAKAI var. *atropurpurea* (NAKAI) Daisetsu Mts. (C)

Distribution of Endemic Species

The distribution of the endemic species in the southwestern, central, and eastern parts of Hokkaido is shown in Table 3. The islands of Rishiri and Rebun, situated near the northwestern end of the main island, have a flora closely related to that of Sakhalin and are added as a fourth group.

As is shown in Table 3, 37 species (86%) of the 43 endemic species are found in the central part; of these, 3 species occur in the southwestern part, 1 in the eastern part, 3 in the islands of Rishiri and Rebun, and 28 in the various massives and ranges of the Central Mountain System.

A large number of alpine plants has been reported on Mt. Yubari, Mt. Apoi, and the Daisetsu Mountains of the Central Mountain System.

The former two mountains, composed of ultrabasic rocks, are rich in so-called serpentine plants. Mt. Yubari is partly composed of serpentinite and Mt. Apoi of peridotite. The distinct disjunctive genera in Japan, such as *Callianthemum* and *Hypochoeris*, are each represented by endemic species in Mt. Apoi. The endemic elements of the Daisetsu Mountains, derivatives partly of the Asiatic element and partly the Northern Pacific element, are restricted to relatively older volcanoes in the Daisetsu Group. The endemism rarely occurs in volcanoes of recent activity. There is only one endemic species in this category, *Viola kitamiana*, which is closely related to *Viola crassa* (the Northern Asiatic Pacific element).

DISJUNCTIVE DISTRIBUTION

Thirty-nine species of the disjunctive distribution are limited to one mountain or a small group of mountains (Table 4). They rarely grow on volcanoes of recent origin. Only four species are found in the southwestern part. Such species as *Astragalus adsurgens*, *Gentianella auriculata*, and *Taraxacum platypecidum* occur only on Mt. Ohira, the limestone mountain. In the Rishiri-Rebun part, there are only six species; all except *Anthoxanthum nipponicum* have been reported in Sakhalin but are not found in the main island of Hokkaido.

The best example of a disjunctive group of alpine plants is in the central part, referred to as "the backbone" of Hokkaido. It includes 29 species, or 74% of the disjunctive species. Mt. Yubari and Mt. Apoi, the ultrabasic rock formation, have three and two species, respectively. In the northern part, only one species, *Androsace lehmanniana*, occurs in Mt. Horonupuri, which is made of Paleozoic rocks.

The Central Highland, the "Roof of Hokkaido," including the Daisetsu Mountains, is particularly rich in disjunctive species, with 23 (59%) of the total. One migrational route came from the northeast through the Kurils and the other from the continent through Sakhalin. The following species are found in the Kurils but not in Sakhalin: *Minuartia macrocarpa* var., *Stellaria calycantha*, *Gentiana glauca*, *Pedicularis oederi*, *Pedicularis verticillata*, *Artemisia trifurcata* var., *Taraxacum trigonolobum*, *Luzula parviflora*, *Deschampsia atropurpurea* var., *Phleum alpinum*, *Carex bipartita*, *Carex eleusinoides*, *Carex livida*, *Kobresia bellardii*, and *Juncus triceps*.

On the other hand, the following two species are found only in Sakhalin and not in the Kurils: *Carex kabonovii* and *Eriophorum scheuchzeri* var. The species found in Sakhalin and also the Kurils are *Sibbaldia Procumbens*, *Juncus triglumis*, and *Carex vaginata*, whereas those found neither in Sakhalin nor Kurils are *Gentiana algida* and *Juncus potaninii*. The latter was once collected by H. Koidzumi in Mt. Kamuimetokunupuri, but it has not been found in recent surveys. The rich disjunctive elements in the Central Highland are caused by

TABLE 3

Distribution of Endemic Species

	Rishiri and Rebun	South-western part	Eastern part	Apoi Massif	Hidaka Range	Yubari Range	Central Highland	Mashike Massif	Uryu Massif	Kitami Massif	Entire area
							Central part				
Salix hidaka-montana	.	.	.	.	+	.	.	.	.	.	.
S. hidewoi	.	+	.	.	.	.	.	.	.	.	+
S. paludicola	.	.	+	.	.	.	.	.	.	.	+
S. pauciflora	.	.	.	.	.	.	+	.	.	.	+
S. yezoalpina	+	.	.	.	.	.	+	.	.	.	+
Betula apoiensis	.	.	.	+	.	.	.	.	.	.	+
Melandryum hidaka-alpinum	.	.	.	.	+	.	.	.	.	.	+
Stellaria pterosperma	.	.	.	.	.	.	+	.	.	.	+
Aconitum yamazakii	.	.	.	.	.	.	+	.	.	.	+
A. yuparense	.	+	.	.	.	+	.	.	.	.	+
Callianthemum miyabeanum	.	.	.	+	.	.	.	.	.	.	+
Trollius citrinus	+	.	.	.	+	.	.	.	.	.	+
T. pulcher	+	.	.	.	.	.	.	.	.	.	.
Hypericum samaniense	.	.	.	+	.	.	.	.	.	.	.
H. tatewakii	.	.	.	.	.	.	.	.	.	+	+
Papaver fauriei	+	.	.	.	.	.	.	.	.	.	+
Thlaspi japonicum	+	+	.	.	.	.	.	.	.	.	.
Saxifraga nishidae	.	.	.	.	.	+	.	.	.	.	+
Astragalus yamamotoi	.	+	.	.	.	.	.	.	.	.	.

DISTRIBUTION OF ALPINE PLANTS

Species									Total
Oxytropis hidaka-montana	.	.	.	.	.	.	.	.	
O. kudoana	.	.	.	.	.	+	.	.	
O. rishiriensis	+	.	.	.	.	+	.	.	
O. shokanbetsuensis	.	.	.	.	.	.	.	+	
Rhamnus ishidae	.	.	.	+	.	.	+	.	
Viola alliariaefolia	.	.	+	.	.	.	.	.	
V. kitamiana	.	.	.	.	.	+	.	.	
V. yubariana	.	.	.	+	.	+	.	.	
Angelica stenoloba	.	.	+	.	.	.	.	.	
Primula kamuiana	.	.	.	.	.	.	.	.	
P. yuparensis	.	.	.	.	.	+	.	.	
Gentianella yuparensis	.	.	.	.	.	+	.	.	
Lagotis takedana	.	.	.	.	.	+	.	.	
L. yezoensis	.	.	.	+	.	.	.	.	
Veronica yezo-alpina	.	.	.	.	+	.	.	+	
Erigeron miyabeanus	.	.	.	.	+	.	.	+	
Hypochoeris crepidioides	.	.	+	.	.	.	.	.	
Leontopodium miyabeanum	.	+	.	.	.	.	.	.	
Saussurea chionophylla	.	.	.	.	+	.	.	.	
S. yanagisawae	.	+	.	.	.	.	.	+	
Scorzonera rebunensis	+	.	.	.	.	.	+	.	
Taraxacum yuparense	.	.	.	+	+	.	.	.	
Elymus yubaridakensis	.	.	.	.	+	.	.	+	
Hierochloe pluriflora	.	.	.	.	+	.	.	+	
Total	6	6	2	8	9	13	7	1	2	37

TABLE 4

Disjunctive Elements

Species	Mountains[a]	Distribution type
Botrychium lanceolatum	Mt. Rishiri (R)	Circumpolar
Polygonum nakaii	Mt. Apoi (C)	Japanese
Minuartia macrocarpa var.	Daisetsu Mts. (C)	Asiatic→western North American
Sagina saginoides	Mt. Rishiri (R)	Circumpolar
Stellaria calycantha	Daisetsu Mts. (C)	Western European←North American→Eastern Asiatic
Alchemilla japonica	Mt. Yubari (C)	Japanese
Sibbaldia procumbens	Daisetsu Mts. (C)	Circumpolar
Astragalus adsurgens	Mt. Ôhira (SW)	Eastern Asiatic
Bupleurum nipponicum var.	Mt. Apoi (C)	Japanese
Androsace lehmanniana	Mt. Horonupuri (C)	Circumpolar
Gentiana algida var.	Daisetsu Mts. (C)	Asiatic-western North American
G. glauca	Daisetsu Mts. (C)	Eastern Asiatic-western North American
Gentianella auriculata	Mt. Ôhira (SW)	Northern Asiatic Pacific
G. takedae	Mt. Yôtei (SW)	Japanese
Lagotis glauca	Mt. Futanami (R)	Northern Pacific
Pedicularis koidzumiana	Mt. Rishiri (R)	Northern Japanese
P. oederi	Daisetsu Mts. (C)	Eurasiatic→western North American
P. verticillata	Daisetsu Mts. (C)	Eurasiatic→western North American
Artemisia trifurcata var.	Daisetsu Mts. (C)	Eastern Asiatic-western North American
Taraxacum platypecidum	Mt. Ôhira (SW)	Eastern Asiatic
T. trigonolobum	Daisetsu Mts. (C)	Northern Pacific
Zygadenus sibiricus	Mt. Rishiri (R)	Eastern Asiatic
Juncus mertensianus	Daisetsu Mts. (C)	Northern Pacific
J. potaninii	Mt. Kamuimetoku (C)	Eastern Asiatic
J. triceps	Daisetsu Mts. (C)	Eastern Asiatic
J. triglumis	Daisetsu Mts. (C)	Circumpolar
Luzula parviflora	Daisetsu Mts. (C)	Circumpolar
Anthoxanthum nipponicum	Mt. Rishiri (R)	Eastern Asiatic
Deschampsia atropurpurea var.	Daisetsu Mts. (C)	Western European←North American→Eastern Asiatic
Phleum alpinum	Daisetsu Mts. (C)	Circumpolar
Carex bipartita	Daisetsu Mts. (C)	Circumpolar
C. capillaris	Mt. Yubari (C)	Circumpolar
C. eleusinoides	Daisetsu Mts. (C)	Eastern Asiatic
C. kabanovii	Daisetsu Mts. (C)	Northern Japanese
C. livida	Daisetsu Mts. (C)	Western European←North American→Eastern Asiatic
C. melanocarpa	Mt. Yubari (C)	Eastern Asiatic
C. vaginata	Daisetsu Mts. (C)	Circumpolar
Eriophorum scheuchzeri var.	Daisetsu Mts. (C)	Circumpolar
Kobresia bellardii	Daisetsu Mts. (C)	Circumpolar

[a] SW, southwestern part; C, central part; R, Rishiri and Rebun Islands.

the climatic changes and the volcanic activities in eastern Hokkaido and the southern Kurils during the Quaternary Period.

ALPINE PLANTS CHARACTERISTIC FOR GEOLOGIC FORMATIONS

Mountains of Ultrabasic Rock

Mountains of ultrabasic rock provide a good example of the present problem. Only one species, *Anaphalis alpicola,* is limited to ultrabasic mountains such as Mt. Apoi, Mt. Yubari, and Mt. Shiratori. *Selaginella selaginoides, Arenaria kotoana,* and *Draba japonica* are found on Mt. Yubari and some pre-Cretaceous rocks in the Hidaka Range. In a similar manner *Potentilla fruticosa* occurs on Mt. Apoi and Mt. Horonupuri. *Allium maximowiczii* is only on the serpentine mountains such as Mt. Yubari and Mt. Shiratori and also on the limestone of Mt. Ohira. *Eritrichium nipponicum* var. occurs in the mountains of ultrabasic rocks of the main island of Hokkaido and the Cretaceous rock district of the island of Rebun.

Limestone Mountains

The limestone flora is known to have a characteristic plant distribution. The endemic and the disjunctive elements of Mt. Ohira were described above. *Silene repens* was reported only on this mountain, although var. *apoiensis* occurs on the peridotite of Mt. Apoi. *Crepis hokkaidoensis, Lloydia serotina,* and *Carex tenuiformis* occur on Mt. Ohira. *Swertia tetrapetala* var. *yezo-alpina* is not truly alpine; although it occurs under alpine conditions on Mt. Ohira in southeastern Hokkaido, it commonly is found in the plains and meadows of eastern and northern Hokkaido.

Old Volcanoes

Another remarkable phytogeographic group, not strictly disjunctive in distribution, is found scattered in the mountains of the pre-Tertiary formations or old volcanoes (Table 5). All these species are found in the Central Mountain System, the most important position for the distribution of alpine plants of Hokkaido. The distribution of the characteristic alpine plants in these mountain groups in this category is shown in Table 5.

Dryas octopetala var. and *Potentilla nivea* occur in the old volcanoes as well as the ultrabasic rock mountains and the limestone mountain. *Saxifraga laciniata* (Eastern Asiatic element) and *Sparganium angustifolium* (circumpolar element) are found only in Mt. Yubari

TABLE 5

Characteristic Elements of the Old Volcanoes

	Rishiri and Rebun	South-western part	Eastern part	Apoi Massif	Hidaka Range	Yubari Range	Central Highland	Mashike Massif	Kitami Massif	Entire area
Cryptogramma crispa	+	.	.	.	+	+	.	.	.	+
Oxyria digyna	+	.	.	.	.	.	+	.	+	+
Minuartia arctica	+	.	+	.	+	.	+	.	.	+
Pulsatilla nipponica	+	.	.	.	+	+	+	.	+	+
Saxifraga laciniata	.	.	.	.	.	.	+	.	.	+
Dryas octopetala var.	+	+	.	.	+	+	+	.	+	+
Potentilla nivea	+	+	.	.	.	+	.	.	.	+
Astragalus secundus	+	.	.	.	.	.	+	.	.	+
Hedysarum hedysaroides	.	.	+	.	+	+	+	.	+	+
Viola repens	.	.	+	.	.	.	+	.	.	+
Bupleurum triradiatum	+	.	.	.	+	+	+	+	.	+
Gentiana jamesii	.	.	.	.	.	+	+	.	.	+
Swertia cuspidata	.	.	.	.	+	+	+	.	.	+
Pedicularis apodochila	+	.	+	.	+	.	+	.	.	+
Crepis hokkaidoensis	+	+	+	.	.	.	+	+	+	+
Senecio kawakamii	+	+	.	.	+	+	+	.	+	+
Lloydia serotina	.	+	.	.	.	.	+	.	.	+
Tofieldia okuboi	.	+	.	.	+	+	+	.	.	+
Sparganium angustifolium	.	.	.	+	.	.	.	+	.	+
Carex tenuiformis	+	.	.	+	+	.	+	.	+	+
C. vanheurokii	.	.	.	.	.	+	+	.	.	+
Scirpus maximowiczii	.	.	+	.	+	+	+	.	.	+
Platanthera makinoi	.	.	.	.	+	+	+	.	.	+

and the Daisetsu Mountains. Most of them are found on pre-Quaternary formations, and fewest on the extinct volcanoes.

Active Volcanoes

The active volcanoes in northern Japan are in general barren of vegetation, but they have some stepping-stone-like communities. Only a few alpine plants are found on still-active volcanoes such as Mt. Koma, Mt. Tarumai, Mt. Asahi, Mt. Meakan, Mt. Iwo, etc. (Table 6), whereas about twice this number are generally found on the old volcanoes.

The circumpolar type has 7 species, the Japanese 6, and the Northern Asiatic Pacific 5. Besides these, *Dicentra peregrina* and *Potentilla miyabei* are sometimes found. *Gaultheria miqueliana,* not an alpine plant, is most common and often forms pure societies in the new volcanic area. In northern Japan and the Southern Kurils, the rather rare species *Arenaria merckioides* is distributed only on new

TABLE 6

Common Species of Active Volcanoes

Species	Distribution type
Salix reinii	Japanese
Alnus maximowiczii	Eastern Asiatic
Polygonum ajanense	Eastern Asiatic
P. viviparum	Circumpolar
P. weyrichii	Japanese
Spiraea betulifolia	Eastern Asiatic-western North American
Viola crassa	Northern Asiatic Pacific
Tilingia ajanensis	Northern Asiatic Pacific
Arcterica nana	Northern Asiatic Pacific
Cassiope lycopodioides	Northern Pacific
Ledum palustre var.	Circumpolar
Loiseleuria procumbens	Circumpolar
Vaccinium uliginosum	Circumpolar
V. vitis-idaea	Circumpolar
Empetrum nigrum var.	Circumpolar
Pentstemon frutescens	Northern Asiatic Pacific
Campanula lasiocarpa	Northern Pacific
Agrostis flaccida	Japanese
Deschampsia flexuosa	Cosmopolitan
Carex flavocuspis	Japanese
C. oxyandra	Japanese
C. stenantha var.	Northern Asiatic Pacific
C. urostachys	Japanese
Juncus filiformis	Circumpolar

volcanoes. In northeastern Hokkaido it has been found on Mt. Meakan and on Mt. Rausu.

Acknowledgments

The writer expresses his hearty thanks to Dr. H. Takeda for his kind advice, to Profs. J. Suzuki and T. Ishikawa for advice on the geology, and to Prof. Kimura (Tohoku University), Drs. Y. Satake and J. Ohwi (Tokyo Science Museum), Prof. H. Hara (Tokyo University), and Prof. S. Kitamura (Kyoto University) for their help. He also thanks Dr. K. Ito and Mr. M. Toyama (Hokkaido University) for their assistance in the preparation of this paper.

REFERENCES

Ohwi, J., 1957, Flora of Japan, 1st ed. (in Japanese): Tokyo, Shibundô, 1383 pp.
———— 1965, Flora of Japan, rev. ed. (in Japanese): Tokyo, Shibundô, 1560 pp.
Tatewaki, M., 1963, Alpine plants in Hokkaido (in Japanese): Tohoku Univ., Sci. Rept., Ser. 4, v. 29, pp. 165-188.

ARCTIC AND ALPINE ENVIRONMENTS (H. E. Wright, Jr., and W. H. Osburn, eds.), 137-141, ©1967 Indiana University Press

7
Main Features of the Fauna and Ecology of the Alpine Vertebrates of the USSR

R. P. ZIMINA
Institute of Geography
Academy of Sciences
Moscow, USSR

Abstract

The population of vertebrates in the mountainous regions of the USSR is characterized by a poor specific composition of the fauna, a low number of individuals, and a small biomass. There is a predominance of species consuming vegetative parts of plants, mostly rodents and ungulates and their predators. The majority of the alpine-belt inhabitants are nocturnally active. The snow cover stays on for about 9 months. During the winter the majority of alpine rodents hibernate (marmots, ground squirrels, and Tien-Shan Zapodids hibernate more than 8 months a year); pikas and voles lay in large amounts of supplies for the winter. The majority of carnivores, ungulates, and some birds are characterized by a vertical migration. In the majority of high-mountain regions of the USSR, poikilothermic amphibians and reptiles are extremely rare, their highest occurrence being in the mountains of Middle Asia. All high-mountain reptiles living higher than 3800 m are ovoviviparous.

Since 1948 I have studied the main patterns of vertical distribution and ecological characteristics of the fauna, especially mammals and birds, in several different mountain systems — the Tien-Shan, Pamir, Caucasus, Balkan ranges, and Carpathians.

The southern part of the Soviet Union is bordered by gigantic mountain belts such as the Carpathians, Krimea, the Caucasus, Pamir, Tien-Shan, Altai and the mountains of Siberia and the Far East. In all these mountains strong dissection and great contrasts of altitude (from 300 to 7500 ft) are characteristic. Also, the nature of alpine regions displays essential changes latitudinally, and the animal populations change as well.

First, of tremendous importance in the determination of the natural characteristics and faunal composition of alpine regions is the geographical position of the mountain country. Different geographical variants of alpine landscapes depend in part upon the position of the mountain area within a given geographical zone and in part upon its elevation.

The classical alpine meadows are developed in mountain systems of the relatively warm and moist oceanic type (such as the Carpathians and West Caucasus). These richly developed meadows, called "alpine carpets," are dominated by large flowering plants such as *Viola*, *Gentiana*, and *Primula*. In mountains of relatively cold and arid conditions (continental type), we find the dry steppes of the Trans-Baikal mountains, mountain tundra of the Siberian systems, cool deserts of the Tien-Shan and Pamir, and so on (Stanukovitch, 1960; Lavrenko, 1964).

The nature of the vertical distribution of animals and their genetic relation to the various centers of faunal origin are quite different in the mountains of Soviet Middle Asia and Siberia from those in the mountains of south-European mountains. In the European mountains, faunistic elements characteristic of broad-leaved forests are richly represented at all altitudes; Mediterranean and alpine elements of Near Eastern origin are also common. The faunistic composition in the mountain belts of Middle Asia is quite different. In the Kopet Dag some relation to the Trans-Caucasian mountains may be observed. But to the east, with the increasing altitude of the Pamir and Tien-Shan, the role of European and Mediterranean elements quickly decreases, and a larger number of species typical of the steppes and deserts of Asia appear. The Alpine species here are of Central Asian origin. Thus the faunal complex of Middle Asian mountains has, in all species of animals and in all vertical zones, a clear relation to the fauna of steppes and deserts (Zimina, 1964a).

Finally, very important for the general faunal composition of mountain countries is the position of these countries with respect to centers of origin of specific faunistic types. For instance, Alpine mammals can be combined into groups of life forms, such as high-mountain voles and mountain ungulates, which possess the same adaptability to stony ground and severe climatic conditions of great altitudes. However, in different mountain systems these animals belong to different systematic groups originating from separate centers of origin. Such are Central Asiatic alpine pika *(Ochotona macrotis)* and the East Siberian pika *(Ochotona hyperborea)*, the silver vole *(Alticola argentatus)* from Tien-Shan and snow vole of the European mountains (subgenus *Chionomys*), and the Central Asiatic ibex *(Carpa sibirica)* from Tien-Shan, compared with the chamois *(Rupicapra rupicapra)* and *(Capra caucasica)* of the Caucasus.

The interpenetration of "eastern" and "western" alpine elements with one another can be observed along the whole distance from Central Asia to Europe and accounts for much of the heterogeneity of the Alpine fauna. The elements of the eastern complex are ecologically more plastic and extend over a larger area.

Only a few very highly specialized organisms are adapted to life in the Alpine regions. Among the alpine inhabitants the dominant species are those (mostly rodents and ungulates) that consume only vegetative parts of plants, and their predators. For instance, in the high ranges of the Tien-Shan and Pamir, marmots, voles, hares, and pikas — all herbivores — predominate. Seventy percent of the mammalian population consumes vegetative parts of plants, the only plentiful food in high mountains. Other foods such as seeds and fruits, insects, arachnids, worms, and mollusks have less importance, because they are present only in small amounts or are available only during a short period of the year.

In alpine regions many species use rock outcrops and debris for protection. Life among debris and sometimes among large rock accumulations has resulted in the appearance of a whole series of adaptations. For instance, many animals living in such habitats have a characteristic grey color that makes them nearly invisible among the rocks. Rapid and agile movement over the rocks is associated with the special construction of extremities, and for many species the ability to take large jumps or to squeeze through narrow spaces is an adaptation for protection from predators.

It is very interesting to note that a large number of animals, nocturnally active in other parts of their ranges, are active here during the day. At night, when the temperature often falls below freezing, there are no flying insects, and the occasional reptiles and common mouselike rodents hide. No species of small mammal in the alpine region is active throughout the night. For this reason predators such as ermine, altai weasel *(Mustela altaica)*, fox, and badger hunt during the day.

In winter, living conditions for inhabitants of high mountain regions are extremely hard. The thickness and the duration of snow cover are different in various altitudinal zones. The duration of snow cover is about 3 months in the foothill areas and up to 9 to 10 months in the high-altitude regions — longer even than in northern parts of the Soviet Union, where the snow cover is most extensive. In the highest regions snow cover prevents animals from moving about and getting food. Generally the winter is the hardest period in the life of inhabitants of high mountains, and only those that are well adapted to the severe weather survive. Adaptations differ among various animals. Some alpine rodents consuming vegetative parts of plants hibernate during the winter (marmots, ground squirrels, zapodids, and others hibernate more than 8 months a year). Some store large amounts of food for the winter period (pika, voles of the genera *Alticola* and *Chionomys,* and others). A large number of ungulates and carnivores, and some birds characteristically migrate vertically in response to the duration and extent of snow cover, or else they concentrate on high plateaus without snow cover (as in the Pamir) (Zimina, 1964a).

To conclude my general discussion of mountain animal life, I should like only to stress that the role of radiation is not the same in mountain altitudinal zones and in the lowlands. This is a very striking factor in determining the altitude of the upper boundary of tree vegatation and the corresponding limit of animal distribution in the Alpine and subalpine belts. In mountain massifs both boundaries are subjected to gradual changes in elevation according to their geographical position, but they are associated with the absolute height of the mountains and the degree of their continentality. For example, the upper limits of forest regions occur at an altitude of about 1100 to 1600 m in the Carpathians, 2500 to 2600 m in the Caucasus, and 2800 to 3000 m in the Tien-Shan. This phenomenon is a direct effect of greater radiation in continental areas, as is indicated by the very interesting observation of Davitaia (1962) on the role of radiation heat in the existence of forests in Alpine regions, by Gursky's researches (1957) in the Alpine Khorog botanical garden in the Pamir, and by previous observations of Strelnikov (1948) on the role of the radiation factor in the life of Alpine cold-blooded animals (reptiles and insects).

According to Davitaia's data, heat resources in the atmosphere necessary for the existence of tree vegetation can be two to three times less in the mountains than on a lowland plain at the polar boundary of forests (700 to 800 degrees of active temperature in the north and only 200 to 300 degrees in the mountains).

References

Davitaia, F. F., and Melnik, Iu. S., 1962, Radiation heating of the active surface and boundary of the forest (in Russian): Moscow, Meteorology and Hydrology, No. 1, p. 3-9.

Gursky, A. V., 1957, Fundamental results of the introduction of trees in the USSR (in Russian): Moscow-Leningrad, Acad. Sci. USSR, Publ. Office, 56 pp.

Lavrenko, E. M., 1964, Types of vertical vegetation zones in the mountains of the USSR, *in* Current problems of geography (in Russian): Moscow, Publ. Office "Nauka," pp. 189-195.

Stanukovitsh, K. V., 1960, Alpine vegetation in the USSR (in Russian): Dushanbe, Publ. Acad. Sci. Tadzh. SSR, pp. 43-103.

Strelnikov, I. D., 1948, Significance of solar radiation and the effect of physico-geographical factors in the evolution of animals in different landscapes, *in* Problems of physical geography, v. 13 (in Russian): Moscow-Leningrad, Publ. Office Acad. Sci. USSR, pp. 145-155.

Zimina, R. P., 1964a, Regularities in the vertical distribution of mammals (in Russian): Moscow, Publ. Office "Nauka," pp. 25-96.
_____ 1964b, Geographical regularities of the vertical animal distribution in the southern mountains of the USSR (Carpathians, Caucasus, Tien-Shan) *in* Current problems of geography (in Russian): Moscow, Publ. Office "Nauka," pp. 196-200.

8
Origin and History of Holarctic Tundra Ecosystems, with Special Reference to Their Vertebrate Faunas

R. S. HOFFMANN AND R. D. TABER
Department of Zoology and School of Forestry
University of Montana
Missoula, Montana

Abstract

Two events have been of major importance in shaping the present distribution of tundra ecosystems: progressive cooling and drying of world climate during the Tertiary, culminating in the Pleistocene, and the Hypsithermal. Although arctic and alpine tundras have similar vegetation types, they differ markedly in climate and physical environment, as well as in vertebrate faunas, and they have different histories. Arctic tundra fauna did not appear in Europe until mid-Pleistocene, although the lowland tundra ecosystem probably developed earlier in north-central Siberia. The North American arctic lacked primary tundra species until the Wisconsin. An alpine tundra fauna evolved in the Central Asian highlands, which presently supports a rich fauna. Some species reached the Alps and the Rocky Mountains during the Pleistocene. Interglacial periods and the Hypsithermal significantly elevated timberline and exterminated relict populations in the Rocky Mountains and the Alps, in contrast to the higher, more extensive Central Asian highlands. The present depauperate alpine tundra faunas of peripheral highlands consist of a few immigrant stocks from Central Asia, plus those lowland or montane species able to tolerate alpine conditions. These periods of warmth also restricted arctic tundra to refugia; isolated glacial and interglacial refugia were of great importance in the evolution of tundra faunas.

Tundra, a word of Russian and ultimately of Lapp origin, was originally applied to the arctic plains north of the limit of forest

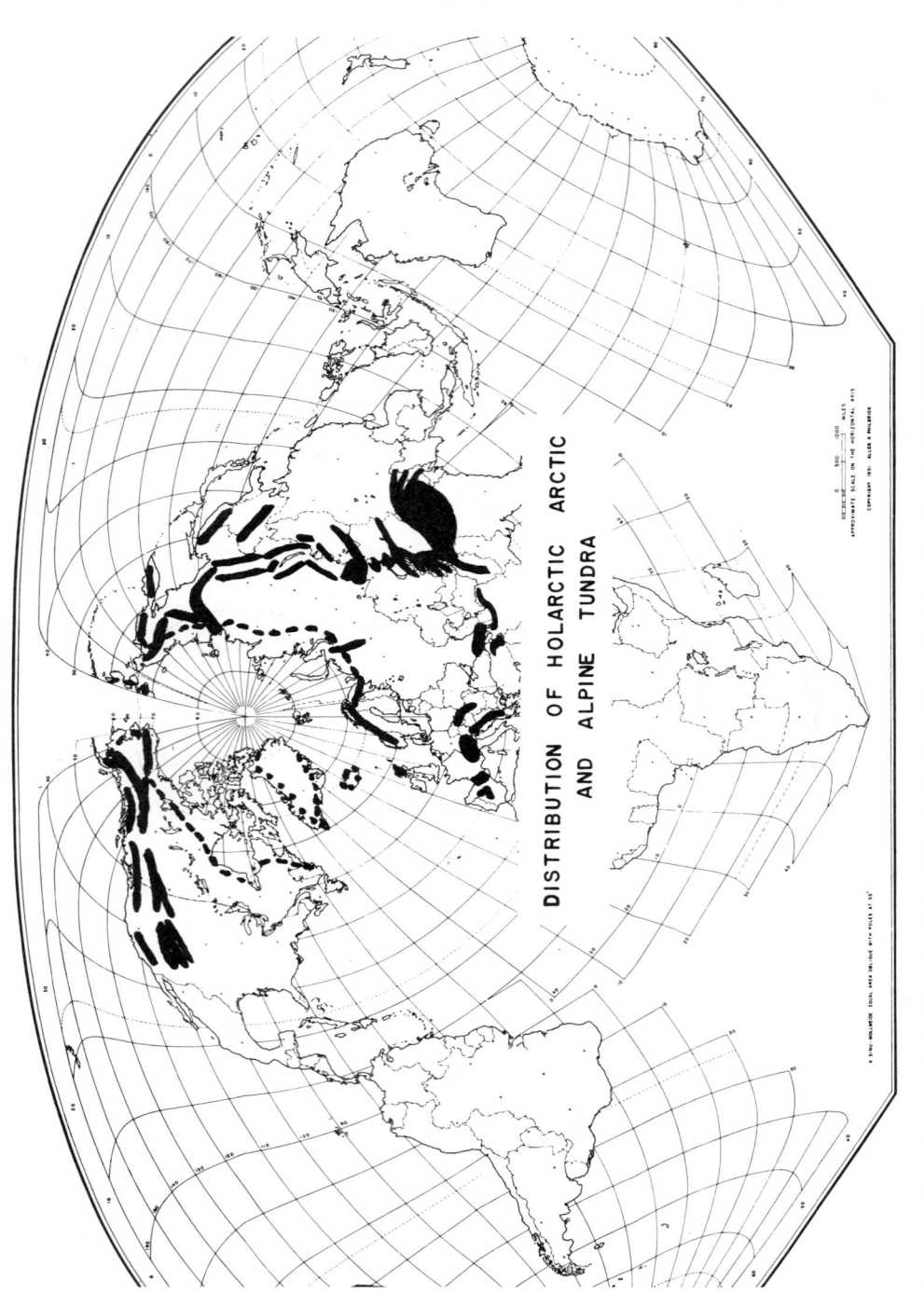

Fig. 1. Present extent of arctic and alpine tundras in the Holarctic.

growth, where there is a low plant cover of graminoids, herbs, mosses, lichens, and small shrubs. By analogy the term has been applied to alpine vegetation of similar physiognomy growing above the upper limit of montane forests, and the view that arctic and alpine tundras are essentially alike has become entrenched. Although relationships do exist, their strength differs from place to place as a result of differences in the historical development of alpine and arctic ecosystems and in the evolution of their biotas. It is the purpose of this essay to trace this development and evolution.

EVOLUTION OF TUNDRA CLIMATE

Two events have been of paramount importance in shaping the present-day distribution of tundra ecosystems: the progressive cooling and drying of world climate during the Tertiary period, culminating in the Pleistocene; and the post-Pleistocene interval of greater warmth, the Hypsithermal.

MacGinitie's (1958) and Dorf's (1960) reconstructions of Tertiary climate indicate that a tundra vegetation zone, either arctic or alpine, did not exist in the Cretaceous-Eocene period, although Arnold (1959) argues for the existence of "tundra-like" areas "a few feet wide" along mountain glaciers. Larson's suggestion (1957, p. 19) that "the cold region [i.e., tundra] covered the most elevated peaks of the Arctic and Boreal highlands only" during the early Tertiary is based on reported evidence of glaciation in the Rocky Mountains at this time, and is highly questionable. King (1958, p. 28) has concluded that the highlands were elevated at most by a few thousand feet, not enough to produce alpine conditions.

In Oligocene-Miocene time strong uplift of the entire Rocky Mountains occurred, as much as 5000 ft. Associated with this movement was a southward shift of both temperate and subtropical forest associations (MacGinitie, 1958; Dorf, 1960), and a broad belt of subarctic forest is inferred to have existed north of about 65°N lat. (Dorf, 1960). After reviewing the literature, Larson (1957) concludes that, by the Miocene, tundra occupied a considerable part of the arctic highlands. If he is correct, it seems likely that tundra may have extended southward at sufficiently high elevations in the Cordillera, in view of the high relief of the Rocky Mountains at this time. It is very unlikely, however, that any significant belt of circumpolar low tundra then existed. In the absence of any paleobotanical evidence, mid-Tertiary tundra such as Larson postulates remains unprovable.

The most rapid cooling of temperature during the Tertiary occurred during the Pliocene and culminated in the Pleistocene series of glacial fluctuations. As Larson (1957) says, "The Tertiary climatic development then consists of an expansion downhill and over the lowlands of the continually colder climates evolving in the Arctic and

Boreal highlands." At this period arctic and alpine tundra ecosystems first acquired evolutionary and zoogeographic significance. The present extent of arctic and alpine tundras in the Holarctic is schematically illustrated in Fig. 1. Alpine areas in Africa, Australasia, and South America and the very limited antarctic tundra will not be considered in this paper.

NATURE OF THE TUNDRA ECOSYSTEMS

Most ecologists have in the past considered alpine and arctic tundras to be so similar that they were combined into a single unit, the tundra biome (see Kendeigh, 1961). Although it is true that certain features of tundra climates are alike in both alpine and arctic regions, and that growth forms of tundra plants resemble each other, there are important differences between the two ecosystems. Arctic tundra is exposed to much greater differences in day length than are most alpine areas. The thin atmosphere of alpine areas influences radiation and temperature very differently than does the denser atmosphere of the arctic lowlands. Great variation in slope and exposure in alpine tundra has important effects on air movement and moisture that differ qualitatively from those found in the arctic (Bliss, 1956, p. 331).

Differences in substrate are also profound. Steep slopes and exposed rock are more common in the alpine tundra, and soils are ordinarily well drained. However, contrary to widely held opinion, alpine soils are frequently deep and well developed, and areas of impeded drainage form a characteristic though limited biotope in most alpine areas (Nimlos and McConnell, 1965). Differences in alpine and arctic tundra environments and their effects on vegetation are reviewed by Bliss (1956); as will be seen, the vertebrate faunas of the two tundra ecosystems are also very different.

RECENT TUNDRA VERTEBRATES

Alpine Tundra

This fauna can be grouped into primary, montane, and secondary species. Primary alpine species are defined as those having their major populations in alpine tundra, although individuals or small populations may occur below the forest line. Examples of such primary alpine species are the hoary marmot *(Marmota caligata)* and white-tailed ptarmigan *(Lagopus leucurus)* of the Rocky Mountains. Montane alpine species are defined as those living in the alpine tundra, but also having significant populations in ecosystems on lower slopes. Such species, however, are generally found only in mountainous areas. Examples are the bighorn sheep *(Ovis canadensis)* and Clark's

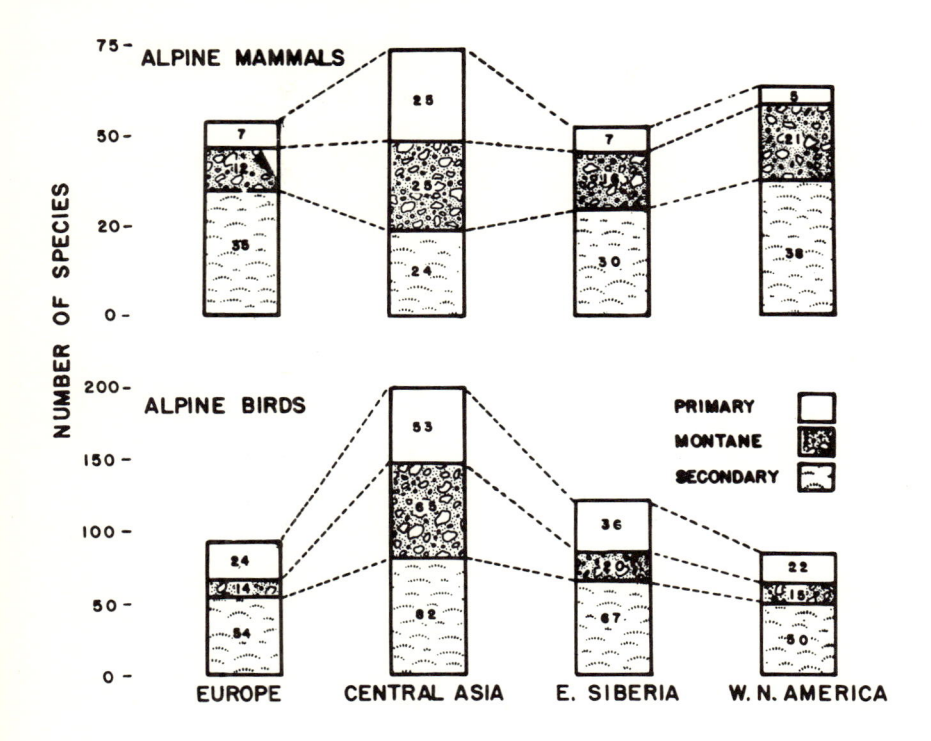

Fig. 2. Proportions of primary, montane, and secondary species in alpine fauna.

nutcracker *(Nucifraga columbiana)*. Finally, secondary alpine species, while having established alpine populations, also occur in other ecosystems, both within and outside the mountains. The white-crowned sparrow *(Zonotrichia leucophrys)* and the deer mouse *(Peromyscus maniculatus)* exemplify such widespread species.

Figure 2 shows that the proportion of primary, montane, and secondary species in an alpine fauna vary geographically, the first two occurring mostly in Central Asia. In every area, however, the species that merely penetrate the alpine tundra from below (montane and secondary alpine species) outnumber the obligate tundra species.

Arctic Tundra

Arctic birds and mammals can be divided similarly into primary and secondary tundra species. Here, too, as Fig. 3 shows, secondary forms outnumber primary. The only exception is the group of water and wading birds belonging to the order Charadriiformes, of which over half are obligate arctic tundra breeders. Larson (1957) comments on the high degree of specialization to the tundra habitat seen

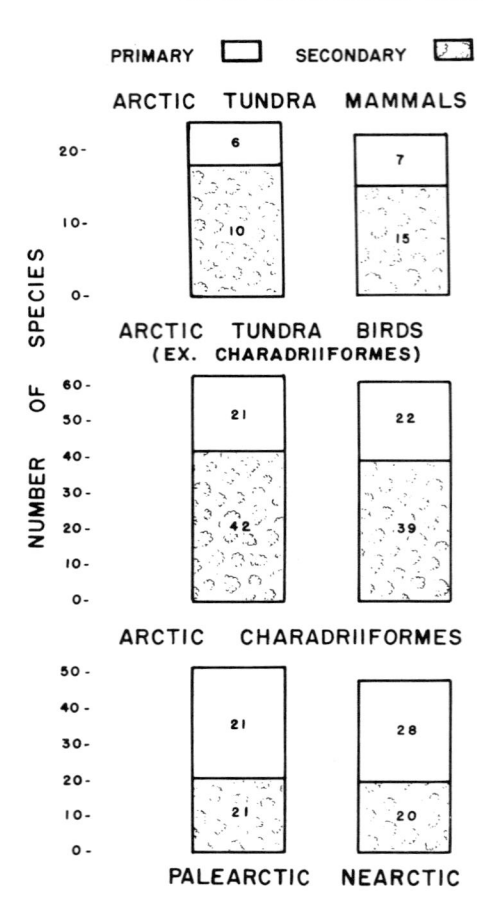

Fig. 3. Proportions of primary and secondary arctic tundra species.

in this group. He believes that the tundra species evolved from taxa that originally invaded the arctic and temperate montane highlands during the Tertiary and became adapted to the tundra environment. Thus, when the circumpolar arctic tundra developed at low altitudes during the Pliocene, these forms were able to spread onto it. Whether or not the evolution of these northern Charadrii began as early as Larson supposes, the group has the strongest tundra affinities of any of the vertebrates.

Arctic-Alpine Species

Biogeographers have long been fascinated by species with disjunct distributions. Those living in the arctic tundra, but with isolated populations in the alpine tundra south of the species' main range, are

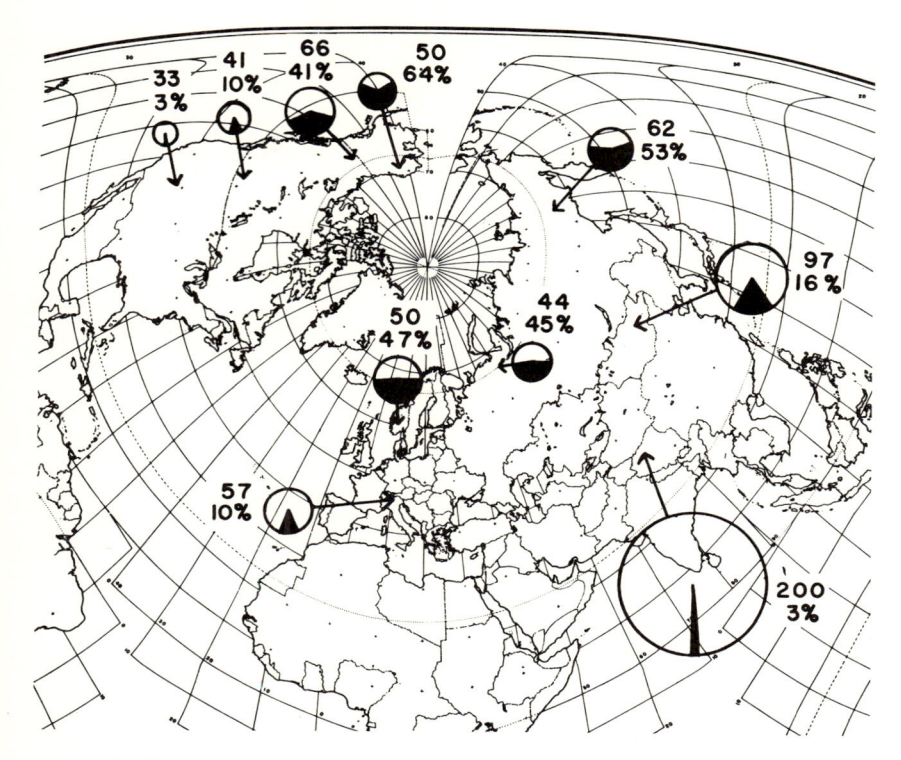

Fig. 4. Proportion of tundra birds having arctic-alpine distribution.

termed "arctic-alpine" species. Such species form a significant part of alpine tundra floras, even far to the south. For example, about one-third of the alpine plants in the Rocky Mountains from Montana to Colorado are "arctic-alpine" (Holm, 1923; Johnson and Billings, 1962). Invertebrate faunas may also have a pronounced "arctic-alpine" component; Brown (1942) found that three-quarters of the primary alpine butterflies in the Colorado Rockies were of this sort. Among tundra vertebrates, "arctic-alpine" distributions are rare in the more southerly alpine areas, and the probable reasons are discussed later in this paper. However, the proportion of alpine species that are also arctic tundra inhabitants (Figs. 4, 5) increased northward and is highest in northern Alaska, eastern Siberia, the northern Urals, and northern Scandinavia, where existing contacts between arctic and alpine tundra (see Fig. 1) permit direct movement between the two at present.

The abundance of secondary tundra (both arctic and alpine) and montane alpine species in recent faunas complicates the problem of interpreting the Pleistocene record. It is not possible to designate a fossil faunal assemblage as a component of a tundra ecosystem unless

TABLE 1

Glacial/inter-glacial stage[a]	Europe		North America				Glacial/inter-glacial stage[b]
	Lowland tundra	Alpine tundra	Beringia	Lowland tundra	Cent. N. America	Beringia	Alpine tundra	Cent. N. America	
Late Würm (III)	Alopex; Rangifer; Tichorhinus; E. primigenius; Lepus timidus; Lemmus; Dicrostonyx torquatus; Microtus gregalis	Capra; Rupicapra; Marmota; Microtus nivalis	Dicrostonyx torquatus; Lemmus; Ovibos; E. primigenius; Rangifer	Dicrostonyx torquatus; Lemmus; Ovibos; E. primigenius; Rangifer	Dicrostonyx ludsonius?; E. primigenius; Ovibos; Rangifer	Ovis nivicola	Ovis canadensis; Oreamnos; Marmota caligata; Dicrostonyx sp.[c]	Late Wisconsin
Early Würm (I,II)	Alopex; Rangifer; Ovibos; Tichorhinus; E. primigenius; Lepus timidus; Lemmus; Dicrostonys henseli (= hudsonius); I; D. torquatus; II	Capra; Rupicapra; Marmota; Microtus nivalis			Dicrostonyx hudsonius?; E. primigenius; Rangifer; Ovibos		Ovis cf. canadensis; Oreamnos?	Early Wisconsin
Eemian		Capra; Rupicapra; Marmota; Cuon				None	None	Sangamon
Riss (= Saale)	Rangifer; Ovibos; Tichorhinus; E. primigenius; "Lemmings"	Capra; Marmots[a]	Rangifer?		None	None	None	Illinoian
Hoxnian					None	None	None	Yarmouth
Mindel (= Elater)	Rangifer; Ovibos; Tichorhinus; E. cf. primigenius; Dicrostonyx	Capra	None	None	None	None	None	Kansan
Cromerian	Rangifer?; Ovibos? (= Praeovibos); E. cf. primigenius?; Dicrostonyx	None	None	None	None	None	None	Aftonian
Menapian (= Günz?)	None	None	None	None	None	None	None	Nebraskan
Waalian	None	None	None	None	None	None	None	
Eburonian	None	None	None	None	None	None	None	
Tiglian	None	None	None	None	None	None	None	
Praetiglian	None	None	None	None	None	None	None	

[a] Terminology follows Deevey (1961).
[b] Does not necessarily imply exact correlation with European stage. See Kurtén (1963) for various alternatives.
[c] Unpublished.

HOLARCTIC TUNDRA ECOSYSTEMS 151

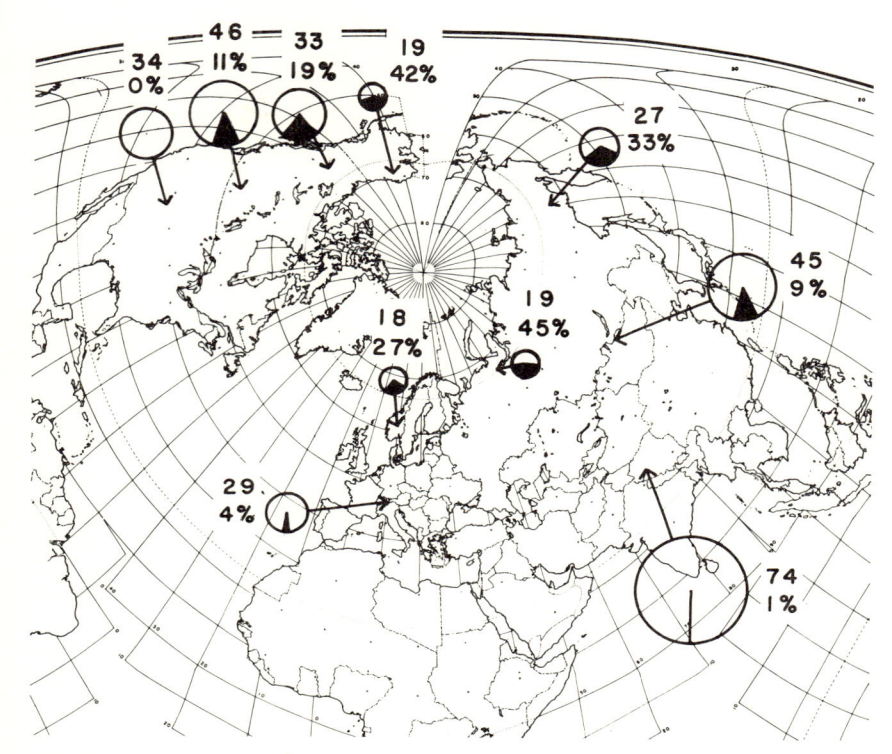

Fig. 5. Proportion of tundra mammals having arctic-alpine distribution.

primary tundra forms are present, or unless there is corroborative evidence from plant fossils.

PLEISTOCENE TUNDRA FAUNAS

The recent summaries of European Pleistocene faunas (Charlesworth, 1957; Kowalski, 1959; Zeuner, 1959; Fejfar, 1961) and those of North America by Hibbard et al. (1965) and others allow the plotting of time occurrence of the critical primary tundra species (Table 1). In addition, *Rangifer tarandus, Tichorhinus antiquitatis,* and *Elephas primigenius* have been listed, because of their importance in the tundra and loess steppe deposits.

Arctic Tundra

A number of interesting inferences can be drawn from Table 1. First, it is apparent that a typical lowland tundra fauna does not appear in Europe until the mid-Pleistocene (according to a recent stratigraphy and chronology, as reviewed by Deevey, 1961). This is the fauna of the Riss (Saale) glaciation. However, the previous glaciation, the Mindel, included the first tundra species, although the fauna as a whole was more temperate, including *Talpa, Desmana, Sciurus, Hippopotamus, Cervus,* etc. It has been suggested by some that the first indications of the lineages destined to develop into the tundra species occurred in the interglacial Cromer Forest Bed *(Rangifer, Elephas* cf. *primigenius),* but this hypothesis has been denied recently (Charlesworth, 1957; Kahlke, 1965). In any case, the first half of the Pleistocene in Europe seems to lack any species specifically adapted to either arctic or alpine tundra ecosystems. This fact led Menzbier (1923) to conclude that the tundra biota did not evolve (from a steppe fauna) until very late Pleistocene. However, in other respects his pioneering paper has been substantiated by later work. Zeuner (1959, p. 311) comments, "Generally speaking, faunas corresponding to the biotopes here distinguished [tundra and loess steppe] are typically represented in the Upper Pleistocene only, whilst in the Middle Pleistocene the distinction is less complete, and almost non-existent in the Lower Pleistocene. This is to be expected if the differentiation of the faunas is the result of climatic fluctuations. The first few glacial phases are marked chiefly by the extinction of [Pliocene] forms ...But already some newcomers from the more continental east availed themselves of the opportunity to extend their area of distribution...It is characteristic of the immigrant elements...that, at their first appearance, they are rare, and that they establish themselves only gradually, apparently as the result of the recurrence of suitable climatic phases... Thus, hundreds of thousands of years and repeated phases of particularly suitable climate appear to have been necessary to establish these immigrants in Europe." Not only adaptation of forms to the new tundra environment, but also the gradual elimination of less well adapted competitor species were probably involved in the differentiation of the fauna of the lowland tundra ecosystem. Extinction of the Pliocene species in the first half of the Pleistocene in Europe can then be regarded as an effect of competition with immigrant tundra species as well as of the climatic deterioration.

A second point of importance is the virtual absence of primary tundra forms in North America prior to the last glaciation. Whereas the Würm period in Europe is now recognized as including more than one glacial phase, and evidence is accumulating to support this interpretation for North America (Lemke et al., 1965), Deevey (1961) cautions against premature redefinition of the Wisconsin at this time. Typical lowland tundra ungulates and the mammoth are abundant in Wisconsin deposits in much of North America (see map in Charlesworth, 1957), but lemmings, quite common in Europe, were unknown in North America south of Alaska prior to the report of *Dicrostonyx hudsonius* from a late-Wisconsin sinkhole deposit in Pennsylvania (Guilday and Doutt, 1961; Guilday, 1963). The find was associated with such boreal microtines as *Synaptomys borealis*, *Phenacomys* cf. *ungava*, and *Microtus xanthognathus*. The Alaska lemmings first reported by Péwé (1957) in Wisconsin-age deposits have recently been identified as *D. torquatus* and *L. sibericus* (Repenning et al., 1964). Another report of significance is that of a single specimen of *Rangifer* in the loess deposits of the Fairbanks, Alaska, area of possible Illinoian age (Banfield, 1961, p. 35). However, only in the younger Wisconsin loess of this unglaciated area are *Rangifer* remains abundant. The conclusion to be drawn from these data is that the typical lowland tundra fauna that established itself in Europe in the last half of the Pleistocene did not reach North America that early and did not appear here until the final stage of the Ice Age (see Flerov, 1952, for a contrary opinion concerning *Rangifer*). Moreover, some forms, such as *Lepus timidus* (= *othus*), *Lemmus*, etc., may not have arrived on the North American tundra until the end of the Pleistocene, and they may never have occupied the periglacial tundra south of the ice sheet during the Wisconsin period (Rausch, 1963).

This conclusion focuses attention on the Palearctic as the area of the origin of tundra faunas. The present arctic tundra fauna of the Palearctic does not differ much in species from the Nearctic; this similarity is not surprising, because the Bering Sea barrier is quite easily bridged, the tundra habitats are circumpolar, and the radius of the Arctic Ocean is short. All these factors greatly facilitate faunal interchange (Udvardy, 1958, p. 55). The arctic tundra fauna that appeared in Europe in mid-Pleistocene and finally in North America at the end of that period may have evolved in northern or central Asia during the first half of the Pleistocene and occupied the arctic lowlands (cf. Kahlke, 1965). Evidence for this hypothesis is at present scanty (Sachs and Strelkov, 1960; Bazhanov and Kostenko, 1962), and, although Tugarinov (1934) made such a case, he appears to show the arctic tundra fauna evolving too early (Pliocene-early Pleistocene) and too far east (in Beringia). If he is correct, it is difficult to understand why this new tundra fauna did not cross the Bering Land Bridge into North America prior to late Pleistocene. Paleobotanical evidence indicates that, although Beringia may have had taiga vegetation in the early Pleistocene (Giterman and Golubeva, 1965; Wolfe and Leopold, 1967), it has supported tundra vegetation since mid-Pleistocene (Colinvaux, 1964), and a tundra fauna evolving in Beringia or in eastern Asia should have had ready access to North America.

Several explanations are possible. One is that the arctic tundra fauna evolved not in the eastern half of Eurasia, but farther west, in western and central Siberia, and that its belated appearance in North America simply represents its final terminus at the end of a long migration route and after penetrating the barrier of the east-Siberian mountain system. Westward spread into Europe would have been unhindered by such a barrier. Another possibility is that the incompleteness of the fossil record accounts for the conclusion that tundra species

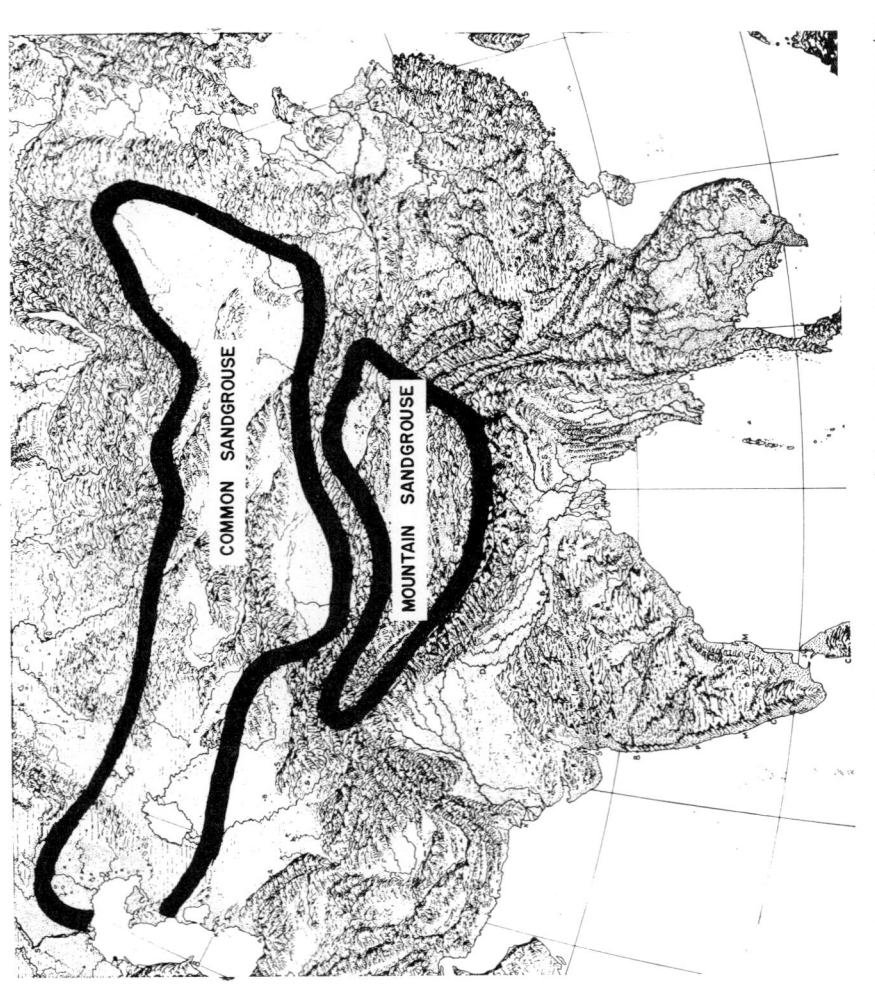

Fig. 6. Alpine species (Mountain sandgrouse) derived from Mongolian steppe ancestor.

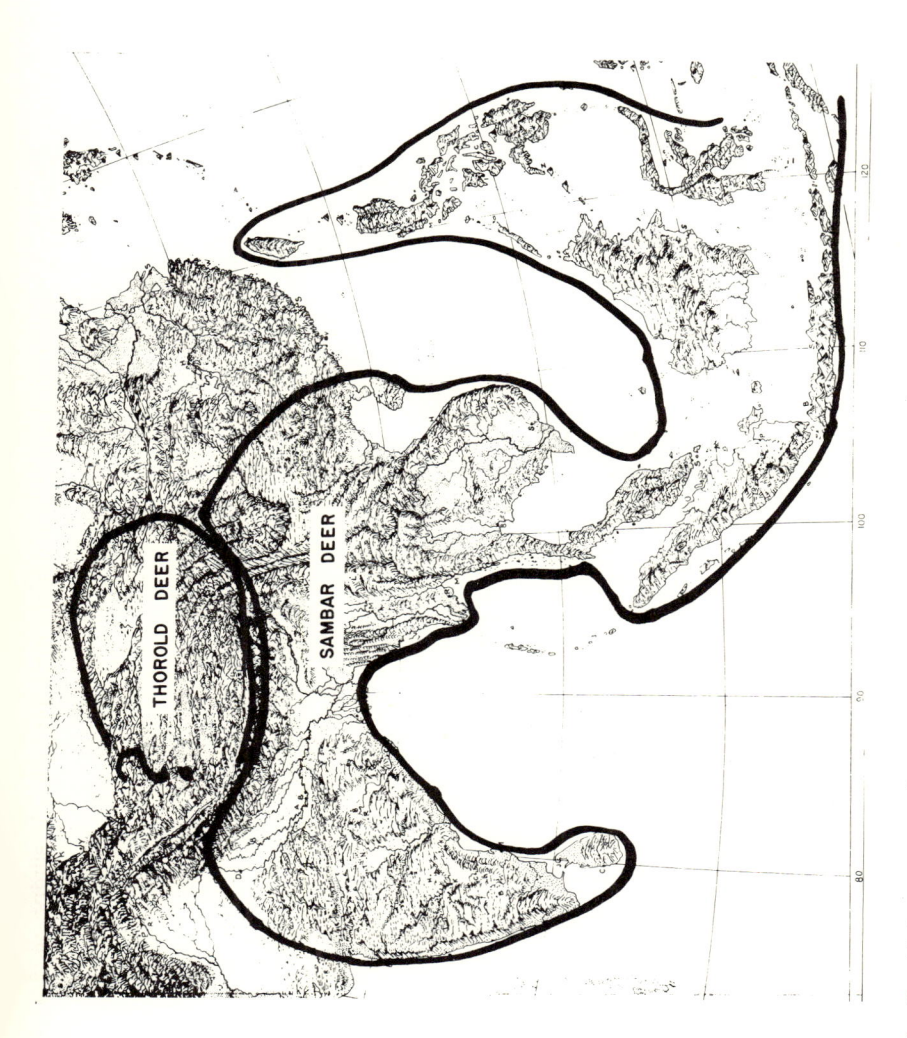

Fig. 7. Alpine species (Thorold deer) derived from Oriental forest ancestor (Flerov, 1952).

arrived late in North America, and that new finds will radically alter the picture presented here.

Alpine Tundra

The origin of the primary and montane elements of the alpine faunas is less uncertain. In Europe, fossil remains of the primary and montane alpine genera *(Marmota, Capra, Rupicapra)* are from about the same period as the lowland tundra fauna.

In North America, *Marmota* has been known throughout the Pleistocene, but these marmots were lowland, not alpine, forms. There are no published reports of fossil *M. caligata* or *M. broweri*, and only one record known to us, of Wisconsin age (see below). The rupicaprine *(Oreamnos)* and the sheep *(Ovis)* are the other principal alpine species, and they too first appear in the Wisconsin, as does the lowland tundra fauna.

However, in contrast to lowland tundra faunas, present alpine faunas show much geographic diversity. In particular, the Central Asian highland region (Mongolian-Tibetan region of Larson, 1957) possesses many more such birds and mammals than the corresponding Rocky Mountain highland region of the Nearctic or than the Alps and other ranges in Europe (Fig. 2). This fact has been pointed out in the past by many Old World students (Shtegman, 1938; Sushkin, 1925; Meinertzhagen, 1928). Meinertzhagen (1928, p. 494), referring specifically to the Tibetan Plateau, states that "Blanford was the first to recognize the importance of this [zoogeographical] subregion, claiming that among mammals it had 5 genera and 24 species peculiar to it. On looking into the avian population, we find there are 15 species and 12 subspecies peculiar to the Tibetan Plateau. In plant- and insect-life we also find that many forms are peculiar. Such a profusion of generic and specific types is unparalleled in any other continental area of similar size throughout the world... Tibet is, in short, a huge alpine island...." It seems likely, therefore, that the alpine tundra originally evolved in the Central Asian highlands as these were elevated during the Pliocene, and that the parent stocks for most of the evolving alpine species were part of a Mongolian steppe fauna. Shtegman (1938) has discussed avifaunal evolution in this light. A typical example is that of the sand grouse (Fig. 6).

The mammal fauna contains the following species pairs which are examples of such relationship:

Mongolian steppe	Tibetan alpine
Vulpes corsac	*V. ferrilata*
Bos taurus	*B. grunniens*
Procapra gutturosa	*P. picticauda*
Saiga tatarica	*Pantholops hodgsoni*
Lepus tolai	*L. oiostolus*

Marmota bobac, siberica	*M. himalayana, baibacina*
Equus hemionus	*Equus h. kiang*
Ochotona daurica	*O. tibetana*
Ochotona pallasii	*O. ladacensis*
Cricetulus spp.	*C. lama, alticola*

In addition, some elements from the forests of the Chinese region to the east were apparently isolated on the rising Tibetan plateau and contributed to the alpine fauna. Species pairs such as the following indicate this sort of relationship:

Oriental forest	Tibetan alpine
Felis pardus	*Felis uncia*
Moschus moschiferus	*M. m. berezovskii*
Cervus unicolor	*C. albirostris* (Fig. 7)
Petaurista sp.	*Eupetaurus cinereus*

Additionally, a number of montane (not primary alpine) species of the Central Asian highlands exhibit this affinity to eastern Asia, such as *Pseudois, Cuon,* and the rupicaprines *Budorcas, Nemorhaedus,* and *Capricornis,* and are evidently sprung from an older, montane fauna centered in the mountains of western China.

Elements of an alpine fauna derived from these two sources could then spread westward across the Middle East to the Alps via more or less continuous mountain systems, and to the northeast across Beringia into the North American Cordillera (Fig. 1). The direction and distance of such spread would have been controlled partly by the availability of montane habitat of a type suitable to the niche requirements of any given alpine species, by the plasticity and amplitude of the niche requirements of the species, and by the presence or absence of other species competing for these niche requirements in the invaded area. Finally, chance must have played an important part in dispersal over great distances. Of the primary Central Asian alpine mammals, *Marmota* (of the alpine type), *Capra,* and a rupicaprine *(Rupicapra)* reach the Alps, and alpine *Marmota* and a rupicaprine *(Oreamnos)* reach North America. *Marmota* first evolved in North America, but specialized alpine species subsequently developed in Eurasia and then returned to North America (R. S. Hoffmann, unpublished manuscript). *Capra* has been reported from an undated Pleistocene deposit in Iowa, but whether this represents an extinct native North American population remains uncertain (Reed and Palmer, 1964). *Cuon* also occurred in Europe and North America in the Pleistocene (Zeuner, 1959; Repenning, personal communication), but it did not persist outside Central Asia. Among the birds, *Leucosticte arctoa* (= *tephrocotis,* etc.), *Anthus spinoletta, Eremophila alpestris,* and *Cinclus* reach North America. The last three, plus *Gypaetus barbatus, Aegypius monachus, Tichodroma muraria, Prunella collaris,*

TABLE 2
Numbers of Primary and Montane Alpine Species, by Family

Region	Mammals												Total
	Soricidae	Ochotonidae	Leporidae	Sciuridae	Cricetidae	Zapodidae	Canidae	Ursidae	Mustelidae	Felidae	Equidae	Cervidae	Bovidae
Europe[a]	1	0	1	1	3	0	0	0	0	0	0	0	5	11
Central Asia	3	6	2	5	12	1	2	1	1	2	1	4	11	51
Eastern Siberia[a]	0	2	0	3	6	1	1	0	1	2	0	1	3	20
W. North America[a]	2	2	0	7	6	1	0	0	0	0	0	1	3	22
All areas	6	9	3	12	26	3	2	1	1	2	1	5	19	90

Region	Birds, nonpasseriform	Birds, passeriform	Total
	Anatidae Aegypidae Cathartidae Accipitridae Falconidae Phasianidae Gruidae Charadriidae Scolopacidae Recurvirostridae Laridae Pteroclidae Columbidae Apodidae Trochilidae Subtotal	Alaudidae Hirundinidae Corvidae Paridae Sittidae Certhiidae Troglodytidae Cinclidae Turdidae Sylviidae Timaliidae Nectariniidae Prunellidae Motacillidae Laniidae Fringillidae Subtotal	
Europe[a]	0 3 0 1 1 5 0 1 0 0 0 0 0 1 0 12	0 1 2 0 0 1 0 1 1 0 0 0 1 1 0 3 11	2
Central Asia	1 4 0 5 2 12 1 2 1 1 1 1 2 1 0 34	2 1 3 2 1 1 0 2 17 6 7 1 5 2 1 35 86	12
Eastern Siberia[a]	2 3 0 4 2 3 0 2 3 0 0 0 1 1 0 21	0 1 2 0 0 0 0 1 1 0 0 0 4 1 0 10 20	4
W. North America[a]	2 0 1 1 1 2 0 1 2 0 0 0 0 1 2 13	0 1 1 0 0 0 1 1 2 0 0 0 0 1 0 2 9	2
All areas	3 4 1 5 3 17 1 3 5 1 1 1 2 3 2 47	2 2 4 2 1 1 1 3 20 6 7 1 7 2 1 38 98	1

[a] Excluding arctic-alpine species occurring only in northern montane tundra.

Montifringilla nivalis, Emberiza cia, and two species of *Pyrrhocorax,* also reached the European mountains, and even more are found in the Caucasus (Vaurie, 1959, 1965; Ivanov and Shtegman, 1964).

That the Central Asian alpine tundra has the richest indigenous fauna of warm-blooded vertebrates, followed by Europe and finally North America, is clear from a family-by-family comparison (Table 2). It is especially rich in members of the families Fringillidae, Cricetidae (but not Muridae), and Bovidae; that these all diversified during the Pleistocene and Pliocene in the Palearctic is consistent with the interpretation of an alpine fauna as a recently evolved one.

Moreover, the richness of the Central Asian alpine tundra includes a cold-blooded vertebrate fauna. This is the only region of the globe that has developed a unique alpine fish fauna, evolving from central-eastern Asian lowland ancestors with isolation and uplift of the highlands (Hora, 1937; Nikol'skii, 1954). Similarly, this is the only place where specialized alpine amphibians and reptiles may be found (Terent'ev and Chernov, 1949; Swan and Leviton, 1962). However, a detailed consideration of these vertebrate groups is beyond the scope of this paper.

In sharp contrast to the Central Asian highlands, alpine faunas of the peripheral mountain systems (Alps, Rockies, etc.) are depauperate ones, formed of a few wide-ranging immigrant stocks from Central Asia, plus those lowland and montane species that are able to tolerate alpine conditions.

These differences in faunal diversity suggest that community organization in the alpine ecosystems of Central Asia (Zimina, 1964) must be more complex than has been found in the Rocky Mountains or in the Alps and that comparative studies (cf. Major and Bamberg, 1967) are necessary before an adequate understanding of alpine ecology is achieved. Such comparisons are of considerable theoretical interest in view of the recent work on niche ecology of birds and mammals (Klopfer and MacArthur, 1960).

PLEISTOCENE REFUGIA

Glacial and Interglacial Tundras

During successive glacial advances, much of northern North America and Eurasia was ice-covered. At glacial maxima, periglacial lowland tundra occurred in extensive areas in three or four isolated places: in eastern and central United States, from western Europe to central Siberia, near the Bering platform (Dillon, 1956; Larson, 1957), and in northern Greenland and adjacent Arctic islands (Rand, 1948; MacPherson, 1965). With deglaciation, such glacial tundra refugia expanded and coalesced, forming a more northerly circumpolar belt of arctic tundra. Alpine tundra formed in mountains as ice caps retreated might be continuous with the arctic lowland tundra, as in Scandinavia, the northern Urals, the east Siberian mountains, and the northern and central Rocky Mountains, or it might form an isolated tundra area, as in the Alps, Central Asian mountains, and southern Rocky Mountains. The extent of tundra in early- and late-glacial periods would thus be more comparable to what is found at present than to the isolated refugia of full-glacial periods (Dillon, 1956).

However, continued warming during at least some interglacial periods caused climatic and vegetational belts to shift even farther northward (Moreau, 1955). During some interglacial periods, then, lowland arctic tundra was isolated in relatively few areas and no longer formed a circumpolar belt (Larson, 1957). Probable areas of such interglacial tundra refugia are northern Greenland and the adjacent Canadian Archipelago, northern Alaska, eastern Siberia, and central Siberia between the Ob and Khatanga Rivers. This periodic isolation of circumpolar tundra populations caused genetic divergence that in some cases led to race or species formation. Distributional schemes of such tundra species can be related to these presumptive tundra refugia (Larson, 1957; Rand, 1948; MacPherson, 1965).

The alpine tundra and its faunas were also affected by periodic glaciation and interglacial warming, but more severely. During glacial maxima, alpine refugia existed in the central and southern Rocky Mountains, south of the main Cordilleran ice sheet, and westward on sufficiently high ranges to the coast. East Siberian and Central Asian glaciation, at least during the Würm, was not extensive, so alpine tundra persisted there (Moreau, 1955); this may also have been true of some European ranges, such as the Pyrenees (Taillefer, 1967). However, the Alps and Caucasus bore major ice sheets that nearly obliterated alpine tundra and forced many alpine forms *(Marmota, Capra, Rupicapra)* into the periglacial tundra (Zeuner, 1959). However, the persistence of a varied alpine fauna, particularly in the Caucasus (Vereshchagin, 1959), suggests that populations were able to survive under essentially alpine conditions on unglaciated ridges and nunataks. Conversely, interglacial warming must have restricted alpine tundra to the uppermost reaches of the highlands. The second ("Great", Mindel-Riss, Hoxnian) interglacial in particular may have driven alpine tundra completely out of the Alps and other European ranges, although tundra probably survived in the higher Caucasus and in the Central Asian ranges, including the Tibetan Plateau. Alpine tundra was probably also eliminated from the central and southern Rocky Mountains in interglacial periods, but remained, though restricted, in the northern Rockies, in Alaska's Brooks Range, and in the mountains of northeastern Siberia. Thus alpine tundra faunas were most adversely affected by both glacial and interglacial periods at both ends of the Holarctic system of mountains, in Europe, and in the central to southern Rockies. Central and eastern Asian alpine tundra areas were least disturbed, as their rich alpine faunas would seem to indicate. These faunas must have been the source of repeated movements of alpine animals westward into Europe and eastward into North America throughout the Pleistocene at times when warmth was not too great or glacial barriers too extensive.

The Hypsithermal Period

Although the origin and original spread of the alpine fauna may have proceeded according to the scheme outlined above, one final event was also important in shaping the present constitution of alpine ecosystems. The Hypsithermal, a period of markedly warmer climate than either the present or the early post-Wisconsin time preceding it (Deevey, 1961), is thought to have had marked effects on the distribution of many nontundra animals (Smith, 1957). In the Cascades and Rockies it apparently led to the disappearance of glaciers (Richmond, 1960), and most certainly it had a strong influence on the position of timberline and the alpine tundra above it. The best estimate of postglacial climatic and floristic changes in the Rockies is provided by Cottam et al. (1959). From these studies of the Wasatch Mountains of Utah they conclude that during early postglacial times the mean annual temperature was more than 11°F lower and that vegetational belts in the mountains were more than 3500 ft lower than at present. If the timberline was this much lower, very extensive areas of alpine tundra would have been present, even allowing for the areas covered by glaciers. During the subsequent Hypsithermal period there was a gradual upward shift of the vegetation zones. Temperatures during this period of maximum warmth may have approached an annual mean 4°F above that of the present climate, although recent work on hybrid oaks *(Quercus gambelii* x *Q. turbinella)* suggests that a change in the seasonal distribution of warmth may have been more significant than a difference in annual means (Cottam et al., 1959). A distance of 260 miles separates relict clones of this hybrid oak from hybrids in the present area of sympatry in Utah. This distance (the elevations are comparable) is approximately the equivalent of 1500 ft in altitude; thus timberline may have moved upward by this amount during the Hypsithermal. Such an upward movement of trees would have greatly restricted and in many cases completely eliminated alpine tundra in the central and southern Rocky Mountains. Pennak (1963) dates the warm period from 6000 to 3000 B.P. in the Colorado Rockies.

The warm period ended with climatic deterioration. This cooler climate not only shoved south the range of the warmth-requiring *Q. turbinella*, but also allowed for the reexpansion of alpine tundra areas in the Rockies.

The near-absence of mammals and rarity of birds with arctic-alpine distributions in temperate mountain regions is thus accounted for. Throughout the Quaternary, periods of warmth great enough to eliminate most of the alpine tundra have recurred, the most recent a few thousand years ago. A relict montane tundra population of lemmings, for example, isolated in the southern Rocky Mountains at the end of a cold period, would be eliminated by the ensuing period of warmth. Birds, being more mobile, could colonize alpine tundra areas initially, survive in more isolated populations, and, with the recurrence of suitable conditions, recolonize reestablished tundra areas. Thus the distributions *Lagopus leucurus, Leucosticte arctoa atrata, L. a. australis, Anthus spinoletta alticola,* and the various mountain races of *Eremophila alpestris,* all primary alpine forms, show evidence of more or less continued isolation in the central and southern Rocky Mountains during the Pleistocene. Invertebrates and plants, whose space requirements are less and vagility great, have an even greater proportion of "arctic-alpine" species. None of the primary alpine mammals has this sort of distribution, and those that occurred in the central and southern Rockies during the Pleistocene, such as *Dicrostonyx,* are now extinct (Guilday, in press). Montane mammals—such as the pika *(Ochotona princeps),* yellow-bellied marmot *(Marmota flaviventris),* water vole *(Microtus richardsoni),* and bighorn sheep *(Ovis canadensis)*—were early-Pleistocene inhabitants of the Rockies, survived the Wisconsin south of the ice sheets, and with the melting of the ice spread northward in the Rockies. In contrast, the distribution of the collared pika *(Ochotona collaris),* snow sheep *(Ovis nivicola,* including *dalli),* and Brooks Range marmot *(Marmota broweri)* (Rausch and Rausch, 1965) indicates that they were isolated from southerly relatives in the late Pleistocene but survived the Wisconsin in unglaciated Beringia (for the history of *Ovis,* see Stokes and Condie, 1961, and Chernyavskii, 1962). This hypothesis explains the absence of the first group in the Alaska-Yukon alpine area, and the second in the central and southern Rockies.

A few alpine species have distributions that permit two alternative hypotheses. The mountain goat *(Oreamnos americanus)* and hoary marmot *(Marmota caligata)* occur in the northern and central Rocky Mountains and Coast-Cascade system from central Alaska-Yukon south to Montana, Idaho, and Washington. Their absence in the southern Rocky Mountains suggests that they may not have occurred during Pleistocene glacial periods in the alpine zone of those ranges. If the species had occurred in the southern Rockies during the Pleistocene, it is argued, their present ranges would include this area, because transplants of *Oreamnos* to ranges outside the natural range have been highly successful (Lentfer, 1955). Survival in the Beringian refugium and postglacial southward dispersal, though limited by the ability of the species to cross intermontane valleys as the climate warmed, might explain their present distribution (P. L. Wright and C. H. Conaway, unpublished data).

Opposed to this hypothesis is fossil evidence that *Oreamnos* occurred in the central Rockies, as well as the northern Sierra Nevada, during the Wisconsin (Cowan, 1941; Hibbard, 1958). In addition, a marmot skull found in undated Pleistocene till near Superior, Montana, and provisionally referred to *M. caligata,* is in the University of Montana Zoological Museum collections. It appears, therefore, that both *Oreamnos americanus* and *Marmota caligata* occurred in montane areas south of the Wisconsin glaciers, but that they died out there during either the Wisconsin or, more probably, the Hypsithermal. Their present ranges are thus the result of post-Pleistocene spread northward from southern refugia, and survival during the Hypsithermal period only in the northern and central Rocky Mountain alpine. Why these forms survived, whereas *Dicrostonyx* succumbed, is probably explained by their different ecological niche requirements: The lemming is not primarily adapted to a montane alpine niche, whereas the rupicaprine and marmot are.

This second hypothesis also agrees with the modern absence of both *Oreamnos* and *M. caligata* in the Brooks Range of northern Alaska, an area they would be expected to occupy if they had lived in Beringia during the Wisconsin. It also agrees with the absence of conspecific or vicariant species populations in northeastern Siberia on the west end of the Beringian refugium, and with the absence of fossils of these species from Pleistocene deposits in Alaska (Péwé, 1957).

The Hypsithermal period thus had an effect on alpine ecosystems similar to, though of lesser magnitude than, the warmer interglacial periods. Its influence in Europe appears to have been somewhat less than in the Rockies, because a few more "arctic-alpine" species have persisted, and considerably less in eastern Siberia. The scarcity of "arctic-alpine" species in the Central Asian highlands is clearly not an effect of the elimination of alpine tundra during warm interglacial periods (see above). It is more likely an effect of the southerly position of this massif, with its east-west-trending ranges not directly connected to the more northerly ranges and separated during both glacial and interglacial periods by ecological barriers.

During glacial advances, extensive pluvial conditions developed in all midlatitude arid regions (Schwarzbach, 1963), including central and east Asia (Brooks, 1922; Kobayashi and Shikama, 1961). Between the Altai and more northerly Siberian ranges on the north and the systems of the Tien-Shan, Pamir, Tibetan Plateau, etc., on the south lies a series of lakes and drainage basins (especially the Balkhash-Alakol'-Ebi Nur basin) that are probably the remnant of an extensive pluvial lake system (Carruthers, 1914; Suslov, 1956), and that would have hindered dispersal by tundra species through the intervening mountain ranges (Dzhungarskii Alatau, Barlik, Tarbagatai, Saur, etc.) During interglacials, an arid belt occupied this same region, as at present. North, east, and west of the Altai-Sayan region, a forest barrier stretched from the enlarged Aral-Caspian-Black Sea to the Pacific Coast (Moreau, 1955) in glacial times and would have been even broader during interglacials. Thus it is probable that these barriers between the Central Asian highlands and the arctic tundra were never crossed during the Pleistocene by more than a few tundra species of mammals and birds.

Johansen (1956, 1958) considers that the following birds evolved first as montane forms in Central Asia and migrated through a steppe corridor into the lowland tundra during interglacial time: *Falco rusticola* (including *F. cherrug*), *Lagopus mutus, Charadrius morinellus, Eremophila alpestris,* and *Anthus spinoletta.* The narrow-skulled vole *(Microtus gregalis)* and long-tailed suslik *(Citellus undulatus)* may also have such a history. However, the opposite explanation, that these arctic-alpine species evolved first in lowland tundra and later invaded alpine habitats, seems more plausible in view of the ecology and distribution of all the above except *Charadrius, Eremophila,* and *Anthus.*

SUMMARY AND CONCLUSIONS

Geological and paleobotanical as well as biogeographical evidence supports the conclusion that tundra is the most recently evolved of all major ecosystems. It probably appeared first as alpine tundra in the late Tertiary (late Miocene-early Pliocene?) but did not achieve significant extent, particularly in the high-latitude lowlands, until the late Pliocene. Circumpolar arctic tundra and extensive alpine tundra are a product of the Pleistocene. Tundra floras probably evolved first in the Holarctic highland, particularly in Central Asia and the Rocky Mountains, and with continued late-Tertiary and Quaternary cooling they spread to the lowlands (Weber, 1965; Gerasimov, 1967).

Present tundra-inhabiting vertebrates fall into two distinct groups, those living on arctic and those on alpine tundra. Birds and mammals living in both arctic and alpine regions are not numerous, except in areas of intergradation, where northern mountain ranges extend into the circumpolar tundra. Alpine species can be classified as primary, montane, and secondary forms, according to their ecological requirements, and arctic species can be grouped as primary and secondary tundra inhabitants. Primary alpine or arctic tundra vertebrates (or, in some cases, montane) are of greatest value in interpreting the history of tundra ecosystems.

Pleistocene lowland tundra faunas probably originated in central Eurasia, when extensive tundra replaced cold-temperate steppe and taiga several times during the early Pleistocene. Birds and mammals already adapted to the very cold winters of the continental climate in these latitudes would be better preadapted to survive in the new lowland tundra climates of Europe or eastern Asia.

Lowland tundra vertebrates, migrating from Central Asia, first appeared in Europe in mid-Pleistocene, but not in North America until the Wisconsin or post-Wisconsin. This time difference may be only apparent because of an incomplete fossil record, but it is more likely a result of differential rate of spread west- and eastward. To the west, a broad, unbroken periglacial belt of tundra led into Europe. To the east the tundra fauna had to pass through both the glaciated mountains of northeast Siberia and the Bering Straits area, which was only intermittently bridged. Beyond Beringia, ice was often a continuous barrier to migration farther south. These barriers must have hampered considerably the rate of migration into North America.

The alpine tundra vertebrate fauna probably evolved earlier than the lowland tundra vertebrates, in the Mongolo-Tibetan Plateau region. Both steppe and forest stocks contributed to the developing alpine fauna during the Pliocene-Pleistocene period. (Many early authors, however, consider the fauna to be much older; cf. Sushkin, 1925.) Most alpine forms did not contribute to the Pleistocene lowland tundra fauna, however, because they were already too specialized and isolated from the lowland tundra by ecological barriers (forest, pluvial lakes). A few species may be exceptions: the dotterel *(Charadrius morinellus)*, horned lark *(Eremophila alpestris)*, and water pipit *(Anthus spinoletta)* may be originally alpine species that colonized lowland tundra during the Pleistocene. Similarly, *Alopex* may be derived from an alpine fox (the *Vulpes ferrilata — corsac* group).

Following its evolution in the Central Asian highlands, the alpine fauna (and flora) migrated both east and west along fairly continuous mountain chains to Europe and North America. The greatest ecological barrier in this Holarctic mountain system, the Bering Straits area, may explain why (as in the case of Pleistocene lowland tundra species) immigrant primary alpine species appeared later in North America than in Europe.

Throughout the Pleistocene, tundra has been repeatedly split into isolated refugia during the full-glacial and interglacial periods, as can be shown through the present distribution of certain groups of species.

However, frequent reconstitution of the circumpolar arctic tundra, the short distance around the Arctic Ocean, and the presence of an ice-free Bering land bridge combined to produce a very high degree of homogeneity of the arctic tundra fauna, thus obliterating to a great extent incipient divergence and speciation in the various refugia.

The only major alpine tundra refugia, in both glacial and interglacial periods, have been the Central Asian highlands, Siberian and Alaskan mountains, and perhaps the Caucasus. Interglacial warm periods in particular, and most recently the Hypsithermal, repeatedly eliminated alpine tundra in most montane areas. Moreover, these warm periods prevented the establishment of "arctic-alpine" distributions for most mammals and birds, although a few birds, and many plants and invertebrates, being more mobile and requiring less space, have established such distributions.

Following the extirpation of the vertebrate component of the alpine ecosystems, there was reimmigration of primary alpine species from the major alpine tundra refugia, the Central Asian highland being the main hearth. Mountain ranges peripheral to these refugia, such as the Alps and the central and southern Rocky Mountains, are therefore depauperate, with only a few immigrant primary alpine species of Central Asian origin. In the absence of a rich fauna of primary and montane alpine species, most alpine faunas in these peripheral mountain ranges consist of secondary species—widespread, adaptable forms able to tolerate alpine conditions and ranging up from below timberline, but not especially adapted to the alpine environment.

This geographic diversity in alpine faunas suggests that comparative studies in different alpine ecosystems will be valuable for a fuller understanding of niche ecology and community organization, the general theoretical importance of which has been recently emphasized.

Acknowledgments

Much of the field work that provided the stimulus for this paper was supported by National Science Foundation Grants 5174, G11568, B9486, and B14090. A National Academy of Sciences Exchange Fellowship enabled Hoffmann to work in the Zoological Institute of the Academy of Sciences of the USSR and other Soviet research institutions, where he benefited from conversations with colleagues too numerous to mention by name. Dr. Charles A. Repenning, U.S. Geological Survey, suggested several valuable additions to the manuscript.

REFERENCES

Arnold, C. A., 1959, Some paleobotanical aspects of tundra development: Ecology, v. 40, pp. 146-148.

Banfield, A. W. F., 1961, A revision of the reindeer and caribou, genus *Rangifer:* National Museum Can. Bull., 177, 137 pp.

Bazhanov, V. S., and N. N. Kostenko, 1962, Atlas rukovodyashchikh form mlekopitayushchikh Antropogena Kazakhstana: Alma-Ata, Akad. Nauk Kazakh. SSR, 110 pp.

Bliss, L. C., 1956, A comparison of plant development in microenvironments of arctic and alpine tundras: Ecol. Monograph, v. 26, pp. 303-337.

Brooks, C. E. P., 1922, The evolution of climate: New York, R. V. Coleman, 173 pp.

Brown, F. M., 1942, Animals above timberline: Colorado Coll. Publ., Studies Ser., 33, 29 pp.

Carruthers, D., 1914, Unknown Mongolia, 2 vols. (2nd ed.): London, Hutchinson and Co., 659 pp.

Charlesworth, J. K., 1957, The Quaternary era, 2 vols.: London, Edward Arnold, 1700 pp.

Chernyavskii, F. B., 1962, O sistematicheskikhvzaimootnosheneyakh i istorii snezhnikh baranov starovo i novovo sveta: Byul. Mos. Obshchestva Ispytatelie Prirody Otd. Biol., v. 67, pp. 17-26.

Colinvaux, P. A., 1964, The environment of the Bering Land Bridge: Ecol. Monograph, v. 34, pp. 297-329.

Cottam, W. P., J. M. Tucker, and R. Drobnik, 1959, Some clues to Great Basin postpluvial climates provided by oak distributions: Ecology, v. 40, pp. 361-377.

Cowan, I. McT., 1941, Fossil and subfossil mammals from the Quaternary of British Columbia: Trans. Roy. Soc. Can., Sect. II, v. 35, pp. 39-49.

Deevey, E. S., 1961, Recent advances in Pleistocene stratigraphy and biogeography, *in* Vertebrate Speciation, W. F. Blair (ed.): Austin, Univ. Texas Press, pp. 594-623.

Dillon, L. S., 1956, Wisconsin climate and life zones in North America: Science, v. 123(3188), pp. 167-176.

Dorf, E., 1960, Climatic changes of the past and present: Am. Scientist, v. 48, pp. 341-364.

Fejfar, O., 1961, Review of Quaternary vertebrata in Czechoslovakia: Inst. Geol. Warsaw, v. 34, p. 113.

Flerov, K. K., 1952, Kabargi i oleni, *in* Fauna SSSR, Mlekopitayushchie, v. 1, No. 2: Moscow-Leningrad, Akad. Nauk, 255 pp.

Gerasimov, I. P., 1967, Natural landscapes of high mountain regions of the USSR: Boulder Colo., Intern. Assoc. Quaternary Research, VII Congr., p. 161 (abstracts).

Giterman, R. E., and L. V. Golubeva, 1967, Developmental history of the vegetation of eastern Siberia during the Anthropogene period: Boulder, Colo., Intern Assoc. Quaternary Research, VII Congr., p. 170 (abstracts).

Guilday, J. E., 1963, Pleistocene zoogeography of the lemming *(Dicrostonyx)*: Evolution, v. 17, pp. 194-197.

_____, in press, Pleistocene zoogeography of the lemming *Dicrostonyx* (Cricetidae: Rodentia): A reevaluation: Univ. Colorado Earth Sci. Ser.

_____, and J. K. Doutt, 1961, The collared lemming *(Dicrostonyx)* from the Pennsylvania Pleistocene: Proc. Biol. Soc. Wash., v. 74, pp. 249-250.

Hibbard, C. W., 1958, Summary of the North American Pleistocene Mammalian local faunas: Mich. Acad. Sci., Arts Lett., Papers, v. 43, pp. 3-32.

_____, D. E. Ray, D. E. Savage, D. W. Taylor, and J. E. Guilday, 1965, Quaternary mammals of North America, *in* The Quaternary in the United States, H. E. Wright, Jr., and D. G. Frey (eds.): Princeton, N.J., Princeton Univ. Press, pp. 509-525.

Holm, T., 1923, The vegetation of the alpine region of the Rocky Mountains in Colorado: U.S. Natl. Acad. Sci. Mem., v. 19, pp. 1-45.

Hora, S. L., 1937, Comparison of the fish-faunas of the northern and the southern faces of the Great Himalayan Range: Rec. Indian Museum, v. 39, pp. 241-250.

Ivanov, A. I., and B. K. Shtegman, 1964, Kratkii opredelitel' ptits SSSR: Moscow-Leningrad, Nauka, 528 pp.

Johansen, H., 1956, 1958, Revision und Entstehung der Arktischen Vogel-fauna, I, II: Acta Arctica, Fasc. VIII, IX, Copenhagen, E. Munksgaard, v. 98, 131 pp.

Johnson, P. L., and W. D. Billings, 1962, The alpine vegetation of the Beartooth Plateau in relation to cryopedogenic processes and patterns: Ecol. Monographs, v. 32, pp. 105-135.

Kahlke, H. D., 1965, On the earliest representatives of the genera *Rangifer* and *Ovibos* in the Old World: Boulder, Colo., Intern. Assoc. Quaternary Research, VII Congr., p. 253 (abstracts).

Kendeigh, S. C., 1961, Animal ecology: Englewood Cliffs, N.J., Prentice-Hall, 468 pp.

King, P. B., 1958, Evolution of modern surface features of western North America, *in* Zoogeography, C. L. Hubbs (ed): Washington, D.C., Am. Assoc. Advan. Sci. Publ., v. 51, pp. 3-60.

Klopfer, P. H., and R. A. MacArthur, 1960, Niche size and faunal diversity: Am. Natl. Hist. Museum, v. 94, pp. 293-300.

Kobayashi, T., and T. Shikama, 1961, The climatic history of the Far East, *in* Descriptive palaeoclimatology, A. E. M. Nairn (ed.): New York, Wiley (Interscience), pp. 292-306.

Kowalski, K., 1959, Katalog ssaków Plejstocenu Polski: Warszawa, Polska Akad. Nauk, 267 pp. (English summary, pp. 225-245).

Kurtén, B., 1963, Notes on some Pleistocene mammal migrations from the Palearctic to the Nearctic: Eiszeitalter und Gegenwart, v. 14, pp. 96-103.

Larson, S., 1957, The suborder Charadrii in arctic and boreal areas during the Tertiary and Pleistocene: Acta Vertebrat., No. 1, 84 pp.

Lemke, R. W., W. M. Laird, M. J. Tipton, and R. M. Lindvall, 1965, Quaternary geology of northern Great Plains, *in* The Quaternary of the United States, H. E. Wright, Jr., and D. G. Frey (eds.): Princeton, N.J., Princeton Univ. Press, pp. 15-27.

Lentfer, J. W., 1955, A two-year study of the Rocky Mountain goat in the Crazy Mountains, Montana: J. Wildlife Management, v. 19, pp. 417-429.

MacGinitie, H. D., 1958, Climate since the late Cretaceous, *in* Zoogeography, C. L. Hubbs (ed.): Washington, D.C., Am. Assoc. Advan. Sci. Publ., v. 51, pp. 61-79.

MacPherson, A. H., 1965, The origin of diversity in mammals of the Canadian arctic tundra: Syst. Zool., v. 14, pp. 153-173.

Major, J., and S. A. Bamberg, 1967, A comparison of some North American and Eurasian alpine ecosystems: This volume, Chap. 5.

Meinertzhagen, R., 1928, Some biological problems connected with the Himalaya: Ibis, 12th ser., v. 4, pp. 480-533.

Menzbier, M., 1923, Ueber die Entstehung der Fauna der Tundren: Bull. Soc. Nat. Moscow, v. 32, pp. 76-98.

Moreau, R. E., 1955, Ecological changes in the Palearctic region since the Pliocene: Proc. Zool. Soc. London, v. 125, pp. 253-295.

Nikol'skii, G. V., 1954, Special ichthyology (2nd ed.): Jerusalem, Natl. Sci. Found. and Israel Program for Sci. Transl. (English transl., 1961), 530 pp.

Nimlos, T. J., and R. C. McConnell, 1965, Alpine soils in Montana: Soil Sci., v. 99, pp. 310-321.

Pennak, R. W., 1963, Ecological and radiocarbon correlations in some Colorado mountain lake and bog deposits: Ecology, v. 44, pp. 1-15.

Péwé, T. L., 1957, Permafrost and its effects on life in the north, *in* Arctic Biology, H. P. Hansen (ed.): Biol. Colloq. Oregon State Chapter Phi Kappa Phi, v. 18, pp. 12-25.

Rand, A. L., 1948, Glaciation, an isolating factor in speciation: Evolution, v. 2, pp. 314-321.

Rausch, R. L., 1963, A review of the distribution of Holarctic Recent mammals: Honolulu, Tenth Pacific Sci. Congr., Pacific Basin Biogeograph. Symp., pp. 29-43.

_____, and V. R. Rausch, 1965, Cytogenetic evidence for the specific distinction of an Alaskan marmot, *Marmota broweri* Hall and Gilmore *(Mammalia: Sciuridae):* Chromosoma, v. 16, pp. 618-623.

Reed, C. A., and H. A. Palmer, 1964, A late Quaternary goat *(Capra)* in North America?: Z. Saugetierk., v. 29, pp. 372-378.

Repenning, C. A., D. M. Hopkins, and M. Rubin, 1964, Tundra rodents in a late Pleistocene fauna from the Tofty placer district, central Alaska: Arctic, v. 17, pp. 177-197.

Richmond, G., 1960, Glaciation of the east slope of Rocky Mountain National Park, Colorado: Bull. Geol. Soc. Am., v. 71, pp. 1371-1382.

Sachs, V. N., and S. A. Strelkov, 1960, Mesozoic and Cenozoic of the Soviet arctic, *in* Geology of the Arctic, v. 1, G. O. Raasch (ed.): Toronto, Univ. Toronto Press, pp. 48-67.

Schwarzbach, M., 1963, Climates of the past. An introduction to paleoclimatology: Princeton, N.J., Van Nostrand, 328 pp.

Shtegman, B. K., 1938, Osnovi ornitogeograficheskovo deleniya Palearktiki: Fauna SSSR, Nov. Ser. No. 19, Ptitsi, v. 1, No. 2, Moscow-Leningrad, Akad. Nauk, pp. 1-76 (Russian), 77-156 (German).

Smith, P. W., 1957, An analysis of post-Wisconsin biogeography of the Prairie Peninsula region based on distributional phenomena among terrestrial vertebrate populations: Ecology, v. 38, pp. 205-218.

Stokes, W. L., and K. C. Condie, 1961, Pleistocene bighorn sheep from the Great Basin: J. Paleontal., v. 35, pp. 598-609.

Sushkin, P., 1925, Outlines of the history of the Recent fauna of Palearctic Asia: Proc. Natl. Acad. Sci. U.S., v. 11, pp. 299-302.

Suslov, S. P., 1956, Physical geography of Asiatic Russia: San Francisco, W. H. Freeman (English Transl. 1961), 594 pp.

Swan, L. W., and A. E. Leviton, 1962, The herpetology of Nepal: A history, checklist, and zoogeographical analysis of the herpetofauna: Proc. Calif. Acad. Sci., v. 32, pp. 103-147.

Taillefer, F., 1967, The extent of Pleistocene glaciation in the Pyrenees: This volume, Chap. 17.

Terent'ev, P. V., and S. A. Chernov, 1949, Opredelitel' presmikayushchikhsya i zemnovodnikh: Moscow, Sovetskaya Nauka, 339 pp.

Tugarinov, A. Ya., 1934 (1935), Essay on the history of the Arctic fauna of Eurasia: Second Intern. Congr. INQUA, Fasc. 5, pp. 47-58.

Udvardy, M. D. F., 1958, Ecological and distributional analysis of North American birds: Condor, v. 60, pp. 50-66.

Vaurie, C., 1959, 1965, The birds of the Palearctic fauna, 2 vols.: London, H. F. & G. Witherby, 762, 761 pp.

Vereshchagin, N. K., 1959, Mlekopitayushchie Kavkaza: Moscow-Leningrad, Akad. Nauk, 703 pp.

Weber, W. A., 1965, Plant geography in the southern Rocky Mountains, *in* The Quaternary of the United States, H. E. Wright, Jr., and D. G. Frey (eds.): Princeton, N.J., Princeton Univ. Press, pp. 453-468.

Wolfe, J. A., and E. B. Leopold, 1967, Tertiary and early Quaternary vegetation of Northeast Asia and Northwest North America, *in* The Bering Land Bridge, D. M. Hopkins (ed.): Stanford, Calif., Stanford Univ. Press.

Zeuner, F. E., 1959, The Pleistocene period: London, Hutchinson and Co., 447 pp.

Zimina, R. P., 1964, Zakonomernosti vertikal'novo rasprostraneniya mlekopitayushchikh: Moscow, Nauka, 157 pp.

9

Some Cordilleran Plants Disjunct in the Sierra Nevada of California, and Their Bearing on Pleistocene Ecological Conditions

JACK MAJOR AND SAMUEL A. BAMBERG
Department of Botany
University of California
Davis, California

Abstract

Several subalpine to alpine plants are disjunct from the Cordillera of eastern Nevada or even Colorado on the east or from the Klamath Lake region or even the Wallowa Mountains on the north to an area of marble bedrock in the Sierra Nevada of California. Their migration to the Sierra Nevada is believed to have been by nearly continuous distribution and not by long-distance dispersal. Such continuous migration required habitats across the present Great Basin different from today's. Modern habitats suitable for migration of microthermal, hygricole plants have been described from the high, continental mountains of Central Asia. These habitats are riverine bogs over permafrost in a cold, continental steppe or desert landscape. Evidence for the presence of such ecological conditions in the Great Basin during glacial periods includes patterned ground, now associated with continental, dry, cold climates if not permafrost, and the expanded Pleistocene lakes of the Great Basin. The latter indicate colder, not wetter and snowier conditions. Some other plant distributions across the Great Basin support the hypothesis suggested.

In or associated with an extensive area of marble bedrock on the eastern side of the Sierra Nevada are six plant taxa widely disjunct from the Cordillera (Major and Bamberg, 1963). How did these great disjunctions in range arise? On the basis of present geographical distributions of these plants, closely related taxa, associated plants, and contemporary ecological conditions in the subalpine Convict Creek basin of the Sierra Nevada, we suggest Pleistocene habitat changes across the Great Basin. These changes not only fit the increasing amount of evidence on the nature of the glacial-age conditions, but they also allow a continuous migration path for arctic and boreal plants across that presently cold steppe zone.

THE DISJUNCT TAXA

The disjunct plant taxa and their geographical areas of distribution are as follows: *Pedicularis crenulata* Benth. in D.C. is known from the Schell Creek Range in eastern Nevada near Ely, but it is evidently absent from adjacent Utah. It is common in mountain meadows of the Colorado Rockies from northern New Mexico north to the western side of the Wind River Range in Wyoming. At Convict Creek on the eastern front of the Sierra Nevada, this plant occurs widely disjunct in mountain meadows below the terminal moraine, where it borders the sagebrush (*Artemisia tridentata* Nutt.) cold steppe. *Draba nivalis* Liljebl. ssp. *elongata* (Wats.) occurs in the alpine zone of the Ruby Mountains of northeastern Nevada and in the Wallowa Mountains of northeastern Oregon. It is widespread in the central and southern Rocky Mountains. In the arctic it evidently grades into the circumpolar *Draba nivalis*. The subspecies is probably a product of evolution south of the main areas of Pleistocene glaciation. It occurs in the Convict Creek basin at high altitudes, well above the timberline (here at about 3250 m) in areas of very late persisting snow, on raw, open, gravelly soil derived from disintegrated marble. A characteristic associate is *Oxyria digyna* (L.) Hill.

The other four Cordilleran disjunct species in the Convict Creek basin are associated in calcareous seepage areas or in subirrigated, marly mountain meadows. The boreal- to arctic-circumpolar *Arctostaphylos uva-ursi* Spreng. is disjunct from the mountains near Klamath Lake in southern Oregon and from the Ruby Mountains to Convict Creek. *Salix brachycarpa* Nutt. is disjunct from occurrences in the north in the Wallowa Mountains of northeastern Oregon and the Wenatchee Mountains of central Washington (on serpentine), and in the east in the Alta area of the Wasatch Range of northern Utah and on the Markagunt Plateau in southern Utah. It is scattered in the Rocky Mountains from subarctic Canada to Colorado. In the arctic it grades into the *Salix glauca* L. complex and extends across the boreal forest zone to Gaspé in Quebec. It can also be considered a product of evolution south of the main area of Pleistocene glaciation. *Kobresia myosuroides* (Vill.) Fiori et Paol. is disjunct from the Wallowa Mountains in Oregon and the central Uinta Mountains of northeastern Utah. Numerous botanists consider this plant to be a climax dominant of the alpine vegetation in Colorado, where it occurs on wind-exposed sites with well-developed soil and vegetation, and snow cover is shallow or nonexistent much of the year. At Convict Creek, on the other hand, this plant occurs in subalpine situations and is buried under snow all winter, probably from November to June. *Scirpus pumilus* Vahl is disjunct from Convict Creek to one station in the central Colorado Rockies, to Montana, to Saskatchewan in an alkaline bog on the plains, and to a few scattered stations in the northern Rockies and the Canadian taiga (in marly springs). It is disjunct from northernmost Norway to the Alps and Caucasus, and it is scattered eastward to Central Asia, Mongolia, Lake Baikal, and western China. Its stations are frequent only in the Pamir.

ECOLOGY OF THE DISJUNCTS

The disjunct plants at Convict Creek occur in a variety of habitats. At lower elevations their sites include meadows with cold-air drainage and cold ground water along the mountain streams that extend down into the sagebrush (*Artemisia tridentata* Nutt.) cold steppe of the Great Basin. At higher elevations are marly, subalpine meadows with a high water table, calcareous subalpine springs, and calcareous seepage areas. Finally, they occur above timberline on wet, gravelly, calcareous sites with long-lasting snow cover.

Such habitats are uncommon in the Sierra Nevada. Calcareous rock is rare. Most of the range consists of granite with scattered pendants of acidic metamorphic rocks.

Climatically, the Sierra Nevada has summer drought and winter precipitation. Summer thunderstorms occur in the mountains only sporadically. The climate is an extension of the mediterranean coastal one.

Thus the Sierra Nevadan habitats described for the disjunct plants are nonzonal, because they are both calcareous and permanently wet. Such sites are favorable for rare plants (Gankin and Major, 1965). However, the demonstration of ecological fitness of a plant taxon for its habitat is only part of the reason why a particular plant taxon occurs where it does. The other is how the disseminules of the plant ever reached the habitat in question. This paper is concerned more with the second part of this problem of plant geography.

HYPOTHESES ON PLANT MIGRATION

Several hypotheses could be used to explain the disjunction of the six Sierra Nevadan plants. One is long-distance dispersal by birds that may frequent the wet habitats of these plants and pick up the seeds in mud or as food. An objection to this idea is that other calcareous areas of the Sierra Nevada evidently lack these plants (Munz and Keck, 1959) — not only in the floristically well-explored Mineral King area on the west side of the crest of the range, but also in the many other scattered areas with marble outcrops. The plants are also absent from the calcareous, and probably saline, areas that are quite common north of Convict Creek. Such areas with the halophytic *Triglochin maritimum* L. var. *debile* Jones are known at Tuolumne Meadows, in the Dana Fork, and along Slate Creek near Tioga Pass at latitude 37°55'N in the subalpine belt above 2600 m elevation. The *Triglochin* is described by Löve and Löve (1958, p. 160) as a 16-ploid species limited to continental western North America. None of our disjunct species has been reported from these other calcareous areas, all of which have the wet sites presumed favorable for long-distance seed transport by birds.

The probability of long-distance dispersal is further reduced by the presence of our six disjuncts in at least three quite different kinds of habitats, all well separated geographically. At least *Salix brachycarpa* is an unlikely candidate for avian dispersal because its short-lived seeds are few, hairy, and unpalatable. Too, we know of no species of birds that frequent or feed in these habitats and then migrate between the areas of disjunction. Seagulls occur, but they limit themselves to water bodies except in agricultural areas. The birds characteristic of high altitudes in the Sierra Nevada (Miller, 1951) migrate only to adjacent lower altitudes in winter or in a north-south direction, not east-west across the Great Basin. Kotilainen (1958, p. 146) points out that the arctic-alpine floristic element is distributed southward in the high mountains over the entire northern hemisphere, and that this circumstance alone makes it most improbable that birds are responsible for the distribution of these species. The burden of proof is on those who would have birds distribute the seeds of six plants of such varied habitat requirements across the Great Basin. The literature on American plant geography and ecology contains no examples of such distribution or even good evidence that it has occurred. In general the Great Basin is a barrier between floristic regions.

A possibility is that the distribution of our plants dates from Tertiary time, and it has been disrupted since. Usually Tertiary relics are isolated phylogenetically as well as spatially, but our plants are nominally only spatial disjuncts.

Are our plants very recent migrants? Wright et al. (1965, p. 43) have suggested that an outlier of *Larix laricina* (DuRoi) K. Koch southwest of the general limit of *Larix* in Minnesota is not a relic disjunct but a recent invader, because pollen diagrams "imply that the *Larix* has returned to the region only in the last few thousand years, after the mid-postglacial dry period." This area is not shown as disjunct for *Larix* on Little's map (Fowells, 1965, p. 227), but the scale of 1/39,500,000 may not adequately represent the facts. At any rate, the suggestion is a most interesting one and deserves evaluation by dot-mapping the species and by pollen analyses in the vicinity of more widely disjunct stations of *Larix*. Since seed dissemination decreases geometrically with distance, the *Larix* disjunction of a few tens of kilometers is of a different order of magnitude than those at Convict Creek. If the Sierra Nevadan plants are recent migrants we can draw up a very long list of plants that should be in the Sierra Nevada but in fact are not, and another list of plants that are rare but should be widespread.

If our plants' migration is somehow taken for granted or pushed back into a remote and inexplicable past, it might be expected that these plants would persist just where they are found today on non-zonal, calcareous, wet sites. The abundant evidence on the ecology of these circumpolar plants indicates they are not physiologically limited to such sites but rather occur in nonzonal habitats where competition from zonal plants is lacking (Gankin and Major, 1965).

Are the present disjunctions the remnant of a once continuous northward distribution from Convict Creek to the Klamath Lake Area *(Arctostaphylos uva-ursi)* or the Wallowa Mountains? *Pedicularis crenulata* does not fit this pattern at all, and we believe it does not fit the other species either, because edaphically suitable sites to the north do not have relic populations of these plants. If the plants ever occurred in this area, they should have left relic populations as evidence. Probably our plants are adapted to a drier, more continental climate than that in the Cascade region of northern California, at least. This area is much the wettest and most maritime part of the Cascade-Sierra Nevada axis in California.

Another hypothesis on migration is that past climates were sufficiently different from those of the present to make possible a continuous distribution of these presently disjunct plants and others of similar ecology east-west across the present area of disjunction. The disjunctions between arctic and alpine areas in Eurasia for flowering plants and mosses having very similar areas of distribution have generally been explained as a product of southward movement of tundra conditions in glacial times to the southern, temperate-zone mountains. However, Kotilainen (1958) points out that many of these plants are stenotopic and uncommon, being limited in the north to rock faces, ravines, springs, and eutrophic bogs. It is difficult to understand where in a loessial or outwash landscape, even if of tundra or cold-steppe ecology, such plants could find suitable habitats. Kotilainen appeals to observations along the Yenesei River of Siberia, where these plants grow on steep, eroding banks. He suggests that the great Urstromtäler of glacial times would provide similar competition-free, raw soils. Raw soil in the tundra itself, a result of frost action, would offer stepping stones on the migration route. Kotilainen's suggestions do not exactly fit our present needs for a migration route, because most of the western American mountain ranges run north-south and therefore are themselves continuous migration paths. The

Cascade-Sierra Nevada axis, however, does not seem to be a migration route for our particular plants, as noted above. But north-south ranges may help bridge some distribution gaps. Of course the exchange of plants went not only from north to south but also from south to north; alpine plants became arctic.

Our Great Basin area of disjunction is now occupied by a cold steppe, with associated halophytes in the intermontane basins or playas, and by xerophytic montane vegetation on the upper slopes of the mountain ranges. If life zones here were simply lowered by glacial climates 1200 to 1500 m, the timberline (now about 3400 m) would still have stood above the valley floors at 1500 m. There would still be no continuous tundra or even forest tundra across the Great Basin. In the drier and more continental climate associated with at least the waning of glaciation, lowering of timberline would be less.

PERMAFROST BOGS IN A COLD-STEPPE LANDSCAPE

It is not necessary to postulate a tundra zone to have a route of free migration for many tundra plants across the Great Basin. Lavrenko (1956) has summarized descriptions from the extremely continental mountains of central Asia for a kind of cold, *Carex* bog containing, in addition to the grasslike plants, many arctic-alpine to subalpine and boreal taxa. These bogs traverse cold deserts whose landscapes are characterized by such xerophytes as *Eurotia ceratoides* (L.) C.A.M., *Artemisia skorniakowii* C. Winkl., *A. lehmanniana* Bge., or, in more mesic, cold-steppe conditions, *Stipa glareosa* P. Smirn. and *S. orientalis* Trin. The bogs are formed over permafrost and lie along the rivers.

Arctic-alpine herbs found in these bogs include *Thalictrum alpinum* L., *Gentiana amarella* L., and *Parnassia palustris* L., which are also found in the Convict Creek basin at high altitudes. The last again illustrates speciation south of the area of continental glaciation. In these Asiatic bogs and also in the Sierra Nevada are *Utricularia vulgaris* L., *Potamogeton gramineus* L. (as *P. heterophyllus* Schreb., see Hultén, 1962, p. 110), *Triglochin maritimum* L. (see above and Hultén, 1962, p. 121), and *Potentilla anserina* L. Other familiar arctic-alpine plants mentioned by Lavrenko include *Polygonum viviparum* L., *Saxifraga hirculus* L., *Pedicularis verticillata* L., *Allium schoenoprasum* L. (Hultén, 1962, p. 99), *Sanguisorba officinalis* L., *Equisetum palustre* L. (Hultén, 1962, p. 99), *Triglochin palustre* L. (Hultén, 1962, p. 112), *Lomatogonium carinthiacum* (Wulfen). A. Br., *Swertia marginata* Schrenk. (Grossgeim *et al.*, 1952, p. 636), etc. Shrubs include *Salix* spp., *Betula humilis* Schrank., *B. rotundifolia* Spach., and *Dasiphora (= Potentilla) fruticosa* (L.) Rydb. The last is very common in the subalpine to alpine Sierra Nevada, including Convict Creek. In the Sierra Nevada it is a preferential species for calcareous substrates.

Mesic northern mosses in the central Asian bogs include *Aulocomnium palustre* (Hedw.) Schwaegr., *Drepanocladus fluitans* (Hedw.) Warnst., *D. exannulatus* (Gümb.) Warnst., *D. sendtneri* (Schimp.) Warnst., *D. intermedius* (Lindb.) Warnst., *D. uncinatus* (Hedw.) Warnst., *Bryum pseudotriquetrum* (Hedw.) Schwaegr. (= *B. ventricosum* Dicks.), *Campylium stellatum* (Hedw.) J. Lange et C. Jens., *Rhytidium rugosum* (Hedw.) Lindb., *Polytrichum juniperinum* Hedw., *Oncophorus virens* (Hedw.) Brid., *Philonotis tomentella* Mol. (= *Ph. alpicola* Jur.), *Calliergon turgescens* (Th. Jens.) Lindb., etc.

The dominant grasslike plants are also northern or arctic-alpine species. Those also occurring in the Convict Creek flora include *Kobresia myosuroides* (Vill.) Fiori et Paol. (Hultén, 1962, p. 47), *Deschampsia caespitosa* (L.) P.B. (Hultén, 1962, p. 66), and *Carex inflata* Huds. (= *C. rostrata* Stokes according to Hultén, 1962, p. 104). One species that is closely related to the boreal, western North American *Carex kelloggii* W. Boott occurring at Convict Creek, to the amphiatlantic *C. nigra* (L.) Reich., and to *C. hindsii* Clarke is the Asiatic *C. wiluica* Meinsh., according to Hultén (1958, p. 126). In the Asiatic bogs is *C. pseudofoetida* Kük., which is considered by Hultén (1962, p. 48) to be part of the variable *C. maritima* Gunn., a taxon often concealed as *C. incurva* Lightf., although in the alpine Sierra Nevada of California it is disguised as *C. incurviformis* Mack. var. *danaensis* (Stacey) F. J. Hermann (Munz and Keck, 1959, p. 1437), which occurs at Convict Creek and is disjunct from Colorado. The Sierra Nevadan *C. vesicaria* is in the Asiatic vegetation along with several close relatives (Hultén, 1962, p. 68ff.). Other familiar northern taxa mentioned by Lavrenko include *Carex microglochin* Wahlenb. (Hultén, 1958, p. 233), *C. pauciflora* Lightf. (Hultén, 1962, p. 87) with its close relatives, and *C. rhynchophysa* C.A.M. (= *C. levirostris* Blytt according to Hermann, 1956, p. 177, 192). Another is *C. karoi* Freyn, a part of the *C. capillaris* L. group along with *C. ledebouriana* C.A.M. (mapped by Hultén, 1962, p. 55) from the data of Löve et al., 1957. Others are *C. coriophora* Fisch. et Mey. and *C. stilbophaea* Krecz., which are both considered to be parts of *C. atrofusca* Schkuhr by Hultén (1962, p. 46), along with the American cordilleran *C. podocarpa* R. Br. and the Tien-Shan-Pamir-western Himalayan *C. oxyleuca* V. Krecz., mentioned by Stanyukovich (1949, p. 82, 126). *C. melanantha* C.A.M. of the section *Atratae* and *C. orbicularis* Boott of the section *Acutae* are both central Asiatic endemics of the high mountains from the Altai to Afghanistan and Tibet (Ovchinnikov, 1963, pp. 104-107, 110-112, 115). *Eriophorum angustifolium* Roth and *E. polystachyum* L. (both treated as *E. angustifolium* by Hultén, 1962, p. 58), *E. latifolium* Hoppe (loc. cit.), *E. humile* Turcz. (part of *E. vaginatum* L. according to Hultén, 1962, p. 172), *Eleocharis euuniglumis* Zinserl. (a part of the *E. uniglumis* s.l. complex mapped by Hultén, 1962, p. 121), *Juncus castaneus* Sm. (Hultén, 1962, p. 28), *J. triglumis* L. (Hultén, 1962, p. 48) are other northern plants in these Asian bogs.

TABLE 1

Climatic Data from the Desert of the High Pamir; in California About 300 m Below Timberline in the Sierra Nevada 55 km Northwest of the Convict Creek Basin; and in Nevada in the Nearby White Mts. 450 m Above Timberline, in Smoky Valley, and on the Humboldt River of the Great Basin

Station	Lat., °N	Long., °W	Elev., m	J	F	M	A	M	J	J	A	S	O	N	D	Yr.	Ppt., mm	Run-off, mm	Max. soil-water storage[a], mm
Murgab, Pamir[b]	33°34'	74°07'E	3640	-17.7	-14.0	-7.0	0.2	6.1	10.0	13.6	13.0	7.5	-0.4	-8.2	-15.4	-1.0	72	0	23
Kara-Kul, Pamir[c]	39°00'	73°28'E	3994	-19.4	-16.1	-10.4	-4.2	1.0	5.0	8.3	7.7	3.0	-3.4	-9.2	-16.3	-4.5	62	0	31
Ellery Lake, Sierra Nevada[d]	37°56'	119°14'	2930	-4.9	-5.1	-2.9	-0.3	+3.7	7.9	12.7	12.2	8.7	+3.9	-0.3	-3.7	2.6	694	467	100
Barcroft Lab., White Mts., Nevada[e]	37°35'	118°15'	3800	-9.4	-9.9	-9.2	-5.6	-3.1	+3.6	7.2	6.7	4.0	-1.0	-4.7	-7.2	-2.4	368	188	100
Fish Creek Ranch, Nevada[f]	39°16'	116°00'	1850	-6.6	-3.8	0.2	4.2	9.4	13.6	17.8	16.5	12.6	7.3	-0.6	-4.0	5.6	149	0	63
Elko, Nevada[g]	40°50'	115°47'	1549	-4.9	-1.3	3.1	7.4	11.5	16.3	20.7	19.3	13.8	8.8	2.3	-3.3	7.8	246	16	100

[a] Runoff or Thornthwaite's "water surplus" (1948) and maximum soil storage of available water are calculated (Thornthwaite et al., 1957) assuming 100 mm of soil stored water, unequally available as used.
[b] Chelpanova, 1963, p. 376.
[c] Ladygina, 1960, p. 256.
[d] USWB summaries, 1925-1947.
[e] Pace, 1963.
[f] USWB summaries, 1943-1964.

The above-named plants indicate that the central Asian riverine bogs over permafrost offer suitable habitats for arctic-alpine plants. Stanyukovich (1949, p. 126, 128, etc.) provides some concrete stand descriptions of this kind of vegetation from the Pamir. Only one of our disjunct species is included above, namely, *Kobresia myosuroides;* but, because Lavrenko (1956) gives only one stand survey, some very interesting species from our standpoint may have been omitted from the discussion. Much of the cited literature is not available to us.

These Central Asian *Carex* bogs have the hummocky surface often associated with permafrost, and in fact Lavrenko assigns permafrost a dominant role in their occurrence. The permafrost gives a persistently cold habitat, one saturated with water much of the time (even in a very arid climate), gley processes in the soil, peat accumulation, and inhibition of soil acidification by lack of leaching of water through the solum. Stanyukovich (1949, p. 20) further discusses these soils. In short, these bogs provide conditions suited to alpine plants and in particular to calcicole alpine plants.

Lavrenko's *Carex* bogs accompany the rivers of the Khangai Mountains of Mongolia, through the southeastern Soviet Altai, the Mongolian Altai, central and northern Tien-Shan, and eastern Pamir. The dimensions of these bogs may be measured in meters or kilometers.

The temperature climate of these bogs is indicated in Table 1, along with data for the Sierra Nevada and Great Basin. The data are discussed below.

Our suggestion is that such permafrost bog habitats in the Great Basin during glacial periods offered migration paths for the disjunct calcicoles now found in the Convict Creek basin.

DISCUSSION

The ecological conditions under which our disjunct plants now persist in the Sierra Nevada are similar to those of the bogs of the cold and continental steppe of Central Asia. Both kinds of sites are very cold, both in the soil and in the air immediately above the soil; they are permanently water-saturated, calcareous, gleyed, and highly organic. Their water saturation is dependent in central Asia on permafrost, as in the arctic and in the Sierra Nevada on subirrigation and seepage.

The bogs in the central Asian mountains are surrounded now by a cold, continental steppe. *Eurotia, Artemisia, Astragalus, Oxytropis, Stipa, Poa,* and *Elymus* are common genera there as in the Great Basin. Zabirov's (1955, pp. 21-22) and Lavrenko's (1956, pp. 347-348) illustrations show vividly the contrast between the two associated habitats and vegetation— the zonal cold steppe and local permafrost bog.

Although the Great Basin has few rivers, the Humboldt almost entirely crosses the northern part of the Basin from east to west, the western Walker, Truckee, and other rivers drain the east slope of the Sierra Nevada, the Owyhee, Malheur, John Day, and other tributaries of the Snake River are in the north, and the Sevier River penetrates the area on the east. In a glacial period these streams and others that are now inconsequential would have been better integrated into more continuous, permanent systems, more closely spaced, and larger. Their floodplains could have offered opportunities for bogs of the kind described by Lavrenko if regional climates were sufficiently cold.

At present the Pamir is a more arid region than the Great Basin (Table 1), but it is not too dry to form riverine bogs over permafrost.

Was permafrost a widespread phenomenon in the Great Basin when glaciers occupied the mountains? Evidence comes from periglacial soil phenomena (Flint, 1957, pp. 195-206; Frenzel, 1960). For ice wedges to form it seems that the climate must have been cold enough to form and maintain permafrost. Permafrost is not a necessary condition for frost structuring of soils, but it obviously promotes their formation when it is present.

Schafer (1949) described traces of ice wedges from central Montana. Very large fossil stone rings are known from Shasta County in northeastern California within the Great Basin (Masson, 1949), from central Washington (Kaatz, 1959), from eastern Oregon (Brunnschweiler, 1962), and from southern Idaho (Malde, 1964). Their formation is ascribed to frost-associated soil patterning in a periglacial climate. Stone stripes in northern Utah (Williams, 1958) extend such a cold climate somewhat farther south. Perhaps even some of Carter's (1964) small stone circles from the Colorado and Mojave deserts may have had a frost-climate origin. Carter suggested they were primitive men's food-storage depots associated with the full-glacial. Williams proposed that the Little Ice Age provided the necessary cooling, but others suggested late-Pleistocene time. Brunnschweiler (1962, p. 24) maps loess and frost-debris tundra across the northern Great Basin during the Wisconsin maximum.

Certainly glacial climates in the Great Basin were much colder than today. Widespread frost structuring of soils extended southward at least into the northern Great Basin. We suggest that the climate was then as cold as it is now in the high mountain valleys of central Asia. If the zonal depression associated with glaciation in the Sierra Nevada was 1200 to 1500 m, the corresponding lowering of temperature would be 7 to 9°C at the rate of -0.6°C/100 m. Thus the Fish Creek Ranch and Elko mean annual temperatures (Table 1) could have been 0 to -4°C in glacial times, and these figures correspond to those in the present Pamir. The more continental climate of late-glacial time would have caused a marked lowering of winter minima without a proportional drop in summer maxima. The present temperatures in the alpine region of the Sierra Nevada may be indicated by that for Ellery Lake, or for timberline 300 m above Ellery Lake. The mean annual temperature would be 2.6 - 1.8 = 0.8°C and in the alpine region above would be lower. This corresponds to alpine temperatures in the adjacent White Mountains.

If we argue by analogy from conditions in Eurasia, permafrost steppe might have extended very far south into the Great Basin during the glacial intervals. Moskvitin (1960, p. 45) described permafrost desert extending 1200 km southeast of the Riss ice border into the lowest Volga region (45°N). Such a distance south from the Montana border of continental ice would place permafrost south to 37°N, almost to the latitude of Mt. Whitney in the southern Sierra Nevada, south of Convict Creek, and through the *Coleogyne ramosissima* Torr. zone to the present northern border of the creosote bush (*Larrea divaricata* Cav.) hot desert. The climate would have been dry enough (little snow cover) so that cold air temperatures were effective in freezing the soil. The entire cold steppe of the Great Basin as presently constituted would have been included within this permafrost area. The Russian Würm boundaries in Moskvitin's area were about 200 km north of the Riss. Frenzel's (1960, p. 69) map shows Würm permafrost extending even greater distances from the ice front — 1000 km south to the north shore of the Black Sea and 1500 km southeast to the Caspian lowland.

The coincidence of glacial and pluvial periods in the Great Basin (Flint, 1957, pp. 222-224) might be thought to conflict with our hypothesized late-Pleistocene landscape. That is, a pluvial period is often believed to have resulted from increased precipitation (Antevs, 1928, pp. 32-33; Hare, 1953; Drury, 1956, p. 87; Flint, 1957, p. 225).

Increased precipitation would eliminate a cold steppe by extending the montane forests down to the valley floors. It would also give a deep snow cover that would prevent deep soil freezing.

Increased runoff in a given region, resulting in widespread lakes, is caused by an increase in excess of precipitation over evapotranspiration — except in a nival climate. This increase can quite as well be caused by less evapotranspiration related to lower temperatures (Thornthwaite, 1948) as by increased precipitation. Lake-rich regions such as the Tibetan plateau and the arctic coast of Alaska are, in fact, regions of very slight precipitation. They are cold. Snyder and Langbein (1962) concluded that the climate of the Pluvial Great Basin lakes was still arid, with less precipitation than evapotranspiration. Galloway (1965) even deduced that increased runoff resulting from decreased evapotranspiration during "pluvial" time in southeastern Australia was more than sufficient to account for formerly high lake levels. In fact, he concluded that precipitation then was less than today. He reviews similar situations from other areas in or just north of the deserts in the horse latitudes, and Frenzel and Troll (1952, p. 165), Flint (1957, p. 489), Wissmann (1956, p. 219), and Frenzel

(1960, pp. 64-66) all adduce much evidence that in glacial periods continental regions became even more continental, and precipitation actually decreased. Increased continentality means lower winter temperatures and therefore permafrost formation in the extreme case.

We have listed a number of studies describing widespread occurrence of fossil stone rings just north of the Great Basin. Williams (1959, p. 483) says these soil structures are formed only in wind-exposed areas and, by implication, lack snow cover. Increased fluctuations of soil temperature would therefore occur, particularly across the frost line. In fact, under a deep snow cover the soil surface remains just above 0°C, with no freeze and thaw. Snow cover, however, can be shallow not only because of wind exposure but also because of insignificant precipitation.

The great Pleistocene lakes, Bonneville, Lahontan, Russell (enlarged Mono Lake), etc. (Flint, 1957, pp. 227-229), would not necessarily indicate greatly increased precipitation in the Great Basin. Nor would their presence so ameliorate the continental climates associated with glaciation that permafrost could not form, the regional temperatures otherwise being low enough. The numerous large lakes of the high eastern Pamir, including the giant Kara Kul (Table 1), where permafrost is 236 m deep, do not conspicuously mellow the very rigorous climate of that region (Zabirov, 1955, p. 19). Given sufficient cold, the freshwater Pleistocene lakes would have been frozen much of the year, and they would no more ameliorate low temperatures than does the frozen Arctic Ocean north of Alaska.

On the other hand, the great Pluvial lakes of glacial times in the Great Basin would certainly act as partial barriers to plant migration. According to the map by Snyder et al. (1964), however, this barrier would be mostly just west of the Wasatch Mountains, where a water surface at the highest level of Lake Bonneville extended from about 38 1/2 to 42°N (350 km) and was about 200 km wide. The very irregularly and discontinuously shaped Lake Lahontan on the western side of the Great Basin would have acted as only a partial barrier, and then for only the low northern Sierra Nevada and Cascade ranges within California. The more or less continuous or progressively equiformal nature of alpine plant distributions southward into these mountains indicates that plants migrated freely to them from the north. Westward from the central High Plateaus of Utah, there were almost no real water barriers to plant migration — i.e., lakes were widely scattered and narrower than the normal dispersal capacity of the plants' disseminules.

A very dry, very cold steppe landscape across the Great Basin can be considered possible in glacial times, until pollen analyses show that it did not occur. Such a landscape would indicate an intensification of present conditions, with lower temperatures, less precipitation, and increased continentality — all associated with glaciation in the bordering and included mountain ranges and to the north.

The present cold-steppe plants, many of which can also be alpine plants (see below), would thus not have been displaced during the glacial intervals. Their relic absence from the more mesic habitats in the present hot deserts to the south substantiates their glacial persistence in situ and lack of glacial-age migration southward.

With intensification of its more disagreeable characteristics, the Great Basin could become very like the eastern Pamir. Then the type of bog that formed over permafrost along the rivers, as described by Lavrenko (1956) from the high, mountainous landscapes of Central Asia, would be probable in the glacial Great Basin. The bogs would be possible routes of migration for calcicole arctic-alpine plants across the Great Basin and therefore between the Rocky Mountains proper and the Sierra Nevada.

CORROBORATION FROM DISTRIBUTIONS OF OTHER PLANTS

Although disjunctions in the geographical distributions of arctic-alpine taxa are known across the Great Basin, similar disjunctions in the ranges of forest species are not. In fact, the dominant trees of the Rocky Mountain subalpine forest, namely, *Abies lasiocarpa* (Hook.) Nutt. and *Picea engelmanii* Parry ex Engelm., do not reach California or evidently have come around through the more continuous mountain ranges north of the Great Basin. *Pinus contorta* Dougl. ex Loud. even shows subspecific differences on the two sides of the Great Basin. Most of the trees in the Rocky Mountain and Sierran forests are different. This evidence, then, supports our conclusion that in glacial periods there was no continuous forest zone across the northern Great Basin.

Conditions must have been quite different across the area immediately south of the Great Basin — across the present Sonoran and Mohave deserts and their included mountain ranges. In this region are several more or less mesic species, all with southern affinities, which extend right across the area to the Sierra Nevada. The species include *Pinus aristata* Englm., *P. flexilis* James, *P. ponderosa* Dougl., *Abies concolor* (Gord. et Glend.) Lindl., *Quercus chrysolepis* Liebm., *Q. turbinella* Greene, *Jamesia americana* T. et G., *Petrophytum caespitosum* (Nutt.) Rydb., *Chamaebatiaria millefolium* (Torr.) Maxim., *Holodiscus microphyllus* Rydb., *Arbutus menziesii* Pursh and its Arizona relatives, *Cercis occidentalis* Torrey ex Gray, *Ribes quercetorum* Greene, *Saxifraga jamesii* Torr., etc. All these are plants of low or montane altitudes, not alpine. *Pinus aristata* is subalpine in the Sierra Nevada and adjacent White Mountains but occupies lower, montane levels in Colorado and Utah. *Pinus flexilis* occupies a very wide range of altitudes and zones, from plains bordering the shortgrass in eastern Wyoming or sagebrush in Idaho to subalpine areas from Utah to California. *Pinus ponderosa* and *Abies concolor* are montane-zone indicators everywhere throughout their very wide range. Here in the southern Great Basin there may well have been in glacial times a more or less continuous forest vegetation.

It is of interest that McMillan (1948) concluded that the flora of the Deep Creek Mountains in westernmost Utah has most connections toward the south. These mountains are a typical Great Basin range situated just west of the salt flats of the Great Salt Lake desert, on the Nevada line south of Wendover. Their flora is mesic at higher altitudes and forms an island of forest vegetation within one of the driest parts of the northern Great Basin desert.

As noted above, other routes of migration are possible to the Sierra Nevada besides across the Great Basin. Obviously many of the alpine and boreal plants of the Sierra Nevada reached their present southern extensions by migrating along the mountain chains. Examples are such plants as *Asplenium viride* Huds (Hultén, 1962, p. 101), *Carex limosa* L. (Hultén, 1962, p. 93), *Draba fladnizensis* Wulf. (Hultén, 1958, p. 227), *Tsuga mertensiana* (Bong.) Carr., *Pinus albicaulis* Engelm., *Pinus monticola* Dougl., *Epilobium latifolium* L., *Stellaria umbellata* Turcz., *Luzula spicata* (L.) DC. (Hulten, 1958, p. 237), *Veronica alpina* L. (including *V. wormskjoldii* Roem. et Schult.) (Hultén, 1958, p. 55), *Crepis nana* Richards, *Arenaria rubella* (Wahl.) Sm., *Sibbaldia procumbens* L. (Hultén, 1958, p. 237), *Oxyria digyna* (L.) Hill, *Adiantum pedatum* L. var. *aleuticum* Rupr., and *Sagina saginoides* (L.) Karst. var. *hesperia* Fern. These taxa show a nice series of equiformal, progressive areas that leave little doubt as to their migration path. Many of Hultén's maps now need correction. The northern gap in the distribution area of our disjunct plants is too great to include the disjuncts with this group of northern migrants. Had they occurred during glacial periods in the area between Oregon and their present stations in the southern Sierra Nevada (37°30'N), they should have left relic stations on some of the high mountains of northern California and southern Oregon. No such stations are known. On the east-west route, the Great Basin ranges between the Ruby Mountains and the Sierra Nevada lack a mesic alpine belt; steppe or arid forest vegetation covers their summits.

The Pleistocene consisted of repeated couplets of climatic variation. Cooling, which made more favorable ecological conditions for microthermal alpine and arctic plants south of and at lower elevations than their original areas, was followed by warming, which had the opposite effect. The above plants show the effects of cooling. A genus that may show the effects of warming is the mainly Californian *Hulsea* T. et G. This genus has six lowland to montane species limited to southern California or adjacent northern (Sierran) California, Nevada, or Lower California. Two others are alpine and reach the northern Cascade and Wallowa Mountains (*H. nana* Gray) or even southwestern Montana (*H. algida* Gray). These alpine plants must have migrated northward as the glacials gave way to warmer climates.

Other cold-steppe plants now found at high altitudes in the Sierra Nevada may have come by the trans-Great Basin route, according to present distributions. An outstanding example, *Carex filifolia* Nutt., is known from only a very few stations in the southern Sierra Nevada (Sharsmith, 1940, p. 141; Howell in Munz and Keck, 1959, p. 1449; Howell, 1961). It is a dominant of the northern Great Plains grass steppe (mixed prairie of Weaver and Albertson, 1956, pp. 39-40) from Colorado northward. In Montana it also forms part of the alpine tundra and occurs above timberline on isolated mountain ranges. Its continuous range is from Texas and New Mexico northward through southern Saskatchewan and Manitoba to southern Alberta. Gjaerevoll (1958, p. 44) maps its distribution in Yukon and Alaska, where it is disjunct in relic prairie vegetation on nonzonal soils. It is also scattered to northern British Columbia, according to Porsild and Crum (1961, p. 156). It is in the northern cold steppe of Washington, Oregon, Idaho, and southern British Columbia. It has one station in Nevada (Holmgren, 1942, p. 42) and another in the San Rafael Swell of central Utah (Lewis, 1958, pp. 26-27), and it is rare in Arizona. It was reported from an isolated station in northeastern Labrador (Fernald, 1950, p. 330), but Dahl (1962) says the specimen is the common and widespread circumpolar, arctic-alpine *Carex rupestris* All. — a more likely conclusion.

Oryzopsis hymenoides (R. et S.) Ricker, *Stipa comata* Trin. et Rupr., *Artemisia arbuscula* Nutt., *Lygodesmia spinosa* Nutt., *Tetradymia canescens* DC., *Erigeron linearis* (Hook.) Piper (Major et al., 1966), and *Muhlenbergia richardsonis* (Trin.) Rydb. are other widespread cold-steppe plants that are alpine in the Sierra Nevada. These plants could well have been part of the glacial-period cold-steppe vegetation outside the riverine bogs where arctic-alpine plants grew, just as they are cold-steppe to alpine plants today.

A great danger in the use of plant-geographical data such as the above to demonstrate particular points of floristic history by citing the distributional areas of particular species is that the whole flora is not considered, and the plants omitted may well illustrate quite other events. The obvious solution is to consider whole floras and not merely selected excerpts. We therefore need to define floras theoretically and rationally and not simply as geographical or political accidents. The local flora discussed should be very well known as to species content, ecology of the species, and total distributional areas not only of all the species in the flora but also of their near relatives.

REFERENCES

Antevs, E., 1928, The last glaciation: Am. Geograph. Soc. Res. Ser., v. 17, 292 pp.

Brunnschweiler, D., 1962, The periglacial realm in North America during the Wisconsin glaciation: Biul. Peryglacjalny, v. 11, pp. 15-27.
Carter, G. F., 1964, Stone circles in the deserts: Anthropol. J. Can., v. 2, pp. 2-6.
Chelpanova, O. M., 1963, Central Asia, v. 3, *in* Climates of the USSR (in Russian): Leningrad, Gidrometerol. Izd., 447 pp.
Dahl, E., 1962, Three misidentified, so-called cordilleran species in eastern North America: Rhodora, v. 64, pp. 117-121.
Drury, W. H., Jr., 1956, Bog flats and physiographic processes in the upper Kuskokwim River region, Alaska: Cambridge, Mass., Harvard Univ., Gray Herbarium Contrib., v. 178, 130 pp.
Fernald, M. L., 1950, Gray's Manual of Botany, 8th ed.: New York, American Book Co., 1632 pp.
Flint, R. F., 1957, Glacial and Pleistocene geology: New York, Wiley, 553 pp.
Fowells, H. A. (ed.), 1965, Silvics of forest trees of the United States: U.S. Dept. Agr., Forest Serv., Agr. Handbook, 271, 762 pp.
Frenzel, B., 1960, Die Vegetations- und Landschaftszonen Nordeurasiens während der letzten Eiszeit und während der postglazialen Wärmezeit, I. Tiel, Allgemeine Grundlagen: Akad. Wiss. Lit. (Mainz), Abhandl. Math. Nat. Kl., v. 1959(13), pp. 1-165.
_____, and C. Troll, 1952, Die Vegetationszonen des nördlichen Eurasiens während der letzten Eiszeit: Eiszeitalter Gegenwart, v. 2, pp. 154-167.
Gankin, R., and J. Major, 1965, *Arctostaphylos myrtifolia*, its biology and relationship to the problem of endemism: Ecology, v. 45, pp. 792-808.
Galloway, R. W., 1965, Late Quaternary climates in Australia: J. Geol., v. 73, pp. 603-618.
Gjaerevoll, O., 1958, Botanical investigations in central Alaska, especially in the White Mountains, I. Pteridophytes and monocotyledons: Kgl. Norske Videnskab. Selskabs Skrifter, v. 1958(5), pp. 1-74.
Grossgeim, A. A., B. K. Shishkin, and E. G. Bobrov, 1952, *Gentianaceae, in* Flora USSR (in Russian): Leningrad, Akad. Nauk USSR, Izd., v. 18, pp. 525-645.
Hare, F. K., 1953, Two pictures of the recent past: Arctic, v. 6, pp. 58-60.
Hermann, F., 1956, Flora von Nord- und Mitteleuropa: Stuttgart, G. Fischer, 1154 pp.
Holmgren, A. H., 1942, Handbook of the vascular plants of northeastern Nevada: Logan, Utah, U.S. Dept. Interior and Utah State Agr. Coll. Grazing Service, 214 pp.
Howell, J. T., 1961, The Tompkins-Tehipite expedition of the California Academy of Sciences: Leaflet West. Botan., v. 9, pp. 181-187.
Hultén, E., 1958, The amphatlantic plants and their phytogeographical connections: Kgl. Svenska Vetenskapsakad. Handl., Fjärde Ser., v. 7(1), pp. 1-341.

_____ 1962, The circumpolar plants. I. Vascular cryptogams, conifers, monocotyledons: Kgl. Svenska Vetenskapsakad. Handl., Fjärde Ser., v. 8(5), pp. 1-275.

Kaatz, M. R., 1959, Patterned ground in central Washington, a preliminary report: Northwest Sci., v. 33, pp. 145-156.

Kotilainen, M. J., 1958, Ein Beitrag zur Erklärung der Vermischung des arkto-alpinen Florenelementes im Quartär, *in* Festschrift Werner Lüdi, M. Welten, and H. Zoller, (eds.): Zürich, Veröffentl. Geobot. Inst. Rübel, v. 33, pp. 145-153.

Ladygina, G. M., 1960, On the altitudinal distribution and some questions of the dynamics of the deserts of the mountainous Badakhshansk autonomous region (in Russian): Akad. Nauk SSSR Probl. Botan., v. 5, pp. 254-264.

Lavrenko, E. M., 1956, On central Asiatic mountain *Carex* bogs and on the Siberian-Mongolian element in the flora of the Caucasus, *in* Akademiku V. N. Sukachevu k 75-letiyu so Dnia Rozhdeniia, E. M. Lavrenko, S. Yu. Lipshits, V. B. Sochava, and B. K. Shishkin (eds.) (in Russian): Leningrad, Akad. Nauk SSSR, pp. 340-353.

Lewis, M. E., 1958, *Carex*, its distribution and importance in Utah: Brigham Young Univ. Sci. Bull., Biol. Ser., v. 1(2), pp. 1-43.

Löve, A., and D. Löve, 1958, Biosystematics of *Triglochin maritimum* agg.: Nat. Can., v. 85, pp. 156-165.

_____, D. Löve, and M. Raymond, 1957, Cytotaxonomy of *Carex* section *Capillares:* Can. J. Botan., v. 35, pp. 715-761.

McMillan, C., 1948, A taxonomic and ecological study of the flora of the Deep Creek Mountains of central western Utah: Salt Lake City, Univ. Utah M.S. thesis.

Major, J., and S. A. Bamberg, 1963, Some Cordilleran plant species new for the Sierra Nevada of California: Madrono, v. 17, pp. 93-109.

_____, E. Parchim, and C. K. Simis, 1966, The disjunct area of *Erigeron linearis* (Hook). Piper into the Sierra Nevada of California (manuscript).

Malde, H. E., 1964, Patterned ground in the western Snake River Plain, Idaho, and its possible cold-climate origin: Bull. Geol. Soc. Am., v. 75, pp. 191-208.

Masson, P. H., 1949, Circular soil structures in northeastern California: Calif. Dept. Nat. Resources Div. Mines Bull., v. 151, pp. 61-71.

Miller, A. H., 1951, An analysis of the distribution of the birds of California: Univ. Calif. Publ. Zool., v. 50, pp. 531-644.

Moskvitin, A. I., 1960, Paleogeography of southeastern Europe in the Pleistocene, *in* Chronology and Climates of the Quaternary Period, V. I. Gromov, I. I. Krasnov, K. V. Nikiforova, and E. V. Shantser, (eds.) (in Russian): Intern. Geol. Congr., 21st Session, Rept. Soviet Geol., Probl., 4, pp. 41-47.

Munz, P. A., and D. D. Keck, 1959, A California flora: Berkeley, Univ. Calif. Press, 1618 pp.

Ovchinnikov, P. N. (ed.), 1963, Flora of the Tadzhik SSR, v. 2, *Cyperaceae-Orchidaceae* (in Russian): Leningrad, Izd. Akad. Nauk SSSR, 456 pp.

Pace, Nello, 1963, Climatological data summary for the decade 1 January 1953 through 31 December 1962 from the Crooked Creek Laboratory (10,150 feet) and the Barcroft Laboratory (12,470 feet): Berkeley, Univ. Calif. White Mountain Res. Sta.

Porsild, A. E., and H. A. Crum, 1961, The vascular flora of Liard Hotsprings, B.C., with notes on some bryophytes, *in* Contrib. Botan., 1959: Natl. Museum Can. Bull., v. 171, pp. 131-197.

Schafer, J. P., 1949, Some periglacial features in central Montana: J. Geol., v. 57, pp. 154-174.

Sharsmith, C. W., 1940, A contribution to the history of the alpine flora of the Sierra Nevada: Berkeley, Univ. Calif., Ph.D. thesis, 274 pp.

Snyder, C. T., and W. B. Langbein, 1962, The Pleistocene lake in Spring Valley, Nevada, and its climatic implications: J. Geophys. Res., v. 67, pp. 2385-2394.

_____, G. Hardman, and F. F. Zdenek, 1964, Pleistocene lakes in the Great Basin: U.S. Geol. Surv. Misc. Geol. Inv. Map I-416.

Stanyukovich, K. V., 1949, Vegetation of the eastern Pamir (in Russian): Moscow, Gos. Izd. Geogr. Lit., Zap. Vses. Geogr. Obshchestva N.S., v. 10, pp. 1-159.

Thornthwaite, C. W., 1948, An approach toward a rational classification of climate: Geograph. Rev., v. 38, pp. 55-94.

_____, J. R. Mather, and D. B. Carter, 1957, Instructions and tables for computing potential evapotranspiration and the water balance: Drexel Inst. Tech., Publ. Climatol., v. 10, pp. 183-311.

USWB, 1930-1964, Climatic summary of the United States, Section 18, southern California: U.S. Weather Bureau, 1930, Supplements for 1931-1952, 1951-1960.

Weaver, J. E., and F. W. Albertson, 1956, Grasslands of the Great Plains: Lincoln, Neb., Johnson Publ. Co., 395 pp.

Williams, J. S., 1958, Stone stripes at low altitudes, northern Utah: Bull. Geol. Soc. Am., v. 69, p. 1749 (abstract).

Williams, P. J., 1959, An investigation into processes occurring in solifluction: Am. J. Sci., v. 257, pp. 481-490.

Wissmann, H., 1956, On the role of nature and man in changing the face of the dry belt of Asia, *in* Man's role in changing the face of the earth, W. L. Thomas, Jr. (ed.): Chicago, Univ. Chicago Press, pp. 278-303.

Wright, H. E., Jr., J. E. Stone, E. J. Cushing, and C. L. Matsch, 1965, Minnesota, *in* Guidebook for Field Conf. C, Upper Mississippi Valley, 7th INQUA Congress: Lincoln, Neb. Acad. Sci., pp. 30-56.

Zabirov, P. D., 1955, Glaciation of the Pamir (in Russian): Moscow, Gos. Izd. Geogr. Lit., 372 pp.

10
Botanical Dating
of Recent Glacial Activity
in Western North America

LESLIE A. VIERECK
Institute of Northern Forestry
U.S. Forest Service
Juneau, Alaska

Abstract

Tree-ring analysis and lichen growth rates provide useful tools for dating glacial events during the past five centuries. From botanical evidence the dates of historical maxima and main advances of 51 glaciers in western North America are given.

All areas show a glacial maximum in the past 300 years that was the greatest of the past 500 to 1000 years and probably the greatest since late-glacial time. In most areas there is evidence of advances sometime in the 17th, 18th, and 19th centuries. In British Columbia the glacier maximum was predominantly in the 1700's, with a readvance in the mid-1800's. In Alaska only the glaciers in the Alaska Range show evidence of a late-1500 and mid-1600 advance. In the vicinity of the Juneau Ice Field and in Glacier Bay the most commonly recorded maximum was the mid-1700's. On the Kenai Peninsula and in the Prince William Sound area a major advance in the late 19th to mid-20th century has destroyed most evidence of earlier advances.

Accurate dating of changes in glacier termini during the past several centuries utilizes methods developed by botanists. Carbon-14 methods can conveniently be used for determining dates of glacial activities during the late glacial,* early postglacial, and hypsithermal but are of little use for dating moraines of the past several hundred years. Several botanical techniques that give relatively accurate ages of moraines up to 500 years have been successfully used in Alaska, Canada, and the northwestern United States. This paper attempts to

---
*Terminology in this paper follows Heusser, 1960.

bring together published data on recent fluctuations in western North American glaciers obtained through the use of botanical methods, and it adds results of my own dating of glacial moraines in south-central Alaska.

METHODS

As a glacier advances in a valley it removes the vegetation and soil in its path. The retreating glacier leaves a trimline that sharply contrasts mature vegetation with the bare area in which the vegetation was destroyed. In forested valleys trees were pushed over by the ice or undermined and tipped by glacial erosion along this line. If these trees remain alive the actual year of tipping can be ascertained by examination of the tree rings (Fig. 1). This method, as described by Lawrence (1950), relies on the fact that growth rings in a tipped tree are not symmetrical. Sometimes, when a tree has been scarred by the ice or by a boulder rolling off the ice, the year of scarring can be determined by a study of the growth rings.

Trees adjacent to a glacier at its maximum may show reduced growth rates while the ice was near. Some trees seem more affected than others, so the method is not totally reliable. However, Bray and Struik (1963) have successfully used it for dating an 1843 maximum of the Yoho Glacier in British Columbia.

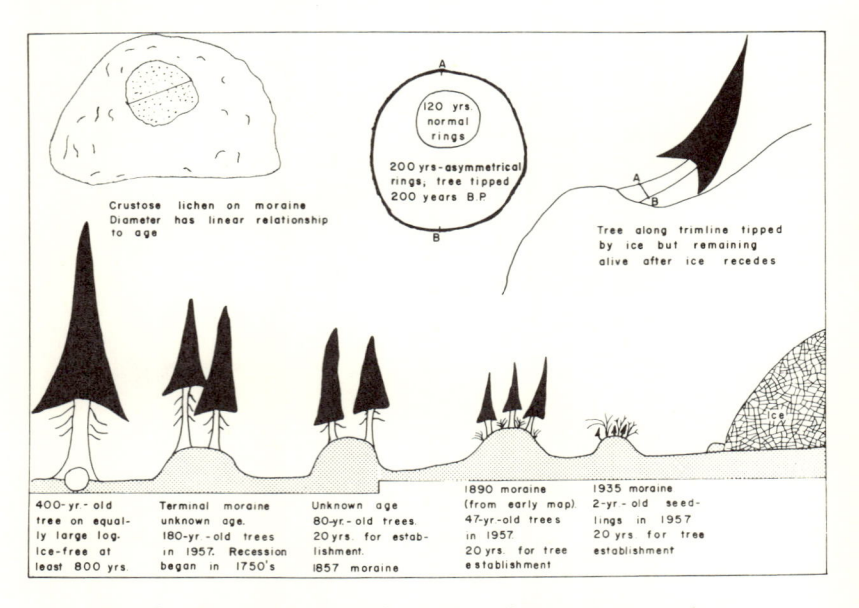

Fig. 1. Botanical methods used in dating glacier advances and recessions.

As a glacier recedes the deglaciated surfaces are soon colonized by vegetation. If the ages of the plants can be determined, the approximate time since glaciation can be determined. In timbered areas the most reliable method is to obtain the age of coniferous trees through counting annual rings. Two correction factors must be determined and applied.

The number of years from deglaciation until the establishment of seedlings varies greatly in different localities because of differences in climate and availability of seed source (see Table 1). In the Juneau Ice Field area Lawrence (1950) has estimated that only 3 to 5 years pass between the time of deglaciation and the establishment of Sitka spruce [*Picea sitchensis* (Bong.) Carr.]. In nearby Glacier Bay, on the other hand, deglaciation is faster than tree migration and, according to Lawrence (1958), 50 to 100 years are required for the establishment of tree seedlings in the upper end of the fiords. In British Columbia Bray and Struik (1963) used 20 to 40 years with a mean of 28 years for the Yoho Glacier; Heusser (1956) used 17 years for the same area. The seeding factor can best be determined by dating trees on young moraines that have been mapped and photographed in the past 50 years. Where these conditions cannot be met, the determined dates are less reliable.

It is difficult or impossible to obtain a core from a large tree at a height of less than 75 to 100 cm above the ground because of the enlargement of the trunk at the base of the tree. The length of time that it took the tree to grow to the height at which it is cored must be added to the age obtained from the tree-ring core. Under severe environmental conditions this may be as much as 25 to 30 years. At the Mendenhall Glacier, an area of relatively rapid tree growth, Lawrence (1958) determined that it took 10 years for a tree to reach a height of 30 inches (76 cm). If possible, tree-ring counts should be made at ground level. Otherwise, a correction factor for seedling growth should be determined and added to the total age of the tree.

Moraines above the treeline are more difficult to date. Small, slow-growing alpine willows can sometimes be used, but their age is usually less than 100 years. Beschel and Webb (unpublished manuscript) have found that, on Axel Heiburg Island, rings of *Salix arctica* did not give a reliable indication of age because many years pass without any rings being produced.

Lichens offer a dating method that has proved useful under some conditions. Crustose lichens, plastered to rocks, grow at a slow and constant rate, and their diameters indicate relative age. Beschell (1961, 1957) has used lichen measurements successfully in Greenland and Europe. Stork (1963) discusses and reviews these methods, which have been given the name "lichenometry." To obtain reliable moraine ages, the growth rate of the lichen must be determined for each area. In Europe, where moraines have been dated historically, this is possible; in North America it is more difficult. In Alaska, Reger and

Péwé (unpublished manuscript) have determined lichen growth rates by using tree ages in the terminal moraine below the treeline and lichen diameters on the same moraines above the treeline. Andrews and Webber (1964) used aerial photographs and willow ages on Baffin Island to determine growth rates of lichens. Once the lichen growth rate has been determined, it can be applied to other moraines in the same general area.

Minimum estimates of the number of years since a glacier was extended beyond its recent maximum may be obtained as follows. It is often possible to find old trees just beyond the trimline or terminal moraine that are 600 to 700 years old. Sometimes these trees grow on decayed remains of a tree of equal diameter, indicating that at least twice this period has elapsed since a glacier occupied the point. Table 1 gives dates of the oldest trees or estimates of maximum time since deglaciation as determined by this method. For the Lemon Glacier adjacent to the Juneau Ice Field, Heusser and Marcus (1964) obtained a carbon-14 date of 10,000 years from a peat section only 375 m down-valley from the recent terminus. This date gave a more accurate estimate of elapsed time since previous glaciers had extended beyond their most recent maxima.

RESULTS

In addition to summarizing the published data on recent glacial fluctuations in North America as obtained by botanical evidence, this paper includes the results of my own dating of recent glacier fluctuations in Alaska. The field work was done in 1957 for the American Geographical Society as part of the International Geophysical Year. A large number of glaciers in central and south-central Alaska were visited briefly, but only those at which reliable data were obtained are reported in this paper. The methods used were those described above, except that no reliable lichen measurements were obtained. Locations of glaciers are shown in Figs. 2 and 3.

Portage Glacier

Portage Glacier originates in the ice fields adjacent to Prince William Sound and flows north and west to a terminus that drains into Turnagain Arm of Cook Inlet. Portage Pass was apparently free of ice until the glacier advance in the late 18th century that continued through the 19th century (Barnes, 1943). The glacier was near its maximum in 1898 (Mendenhall, 1900).

Trees cored on the terminal moraine were 42 years old. Allowing for a 20-year establishment period, the retreat would have started about 1890 to 1900, as Mendenhall's observation also indicates. Above the trimline on the north side of the valley, the 250-year age of the

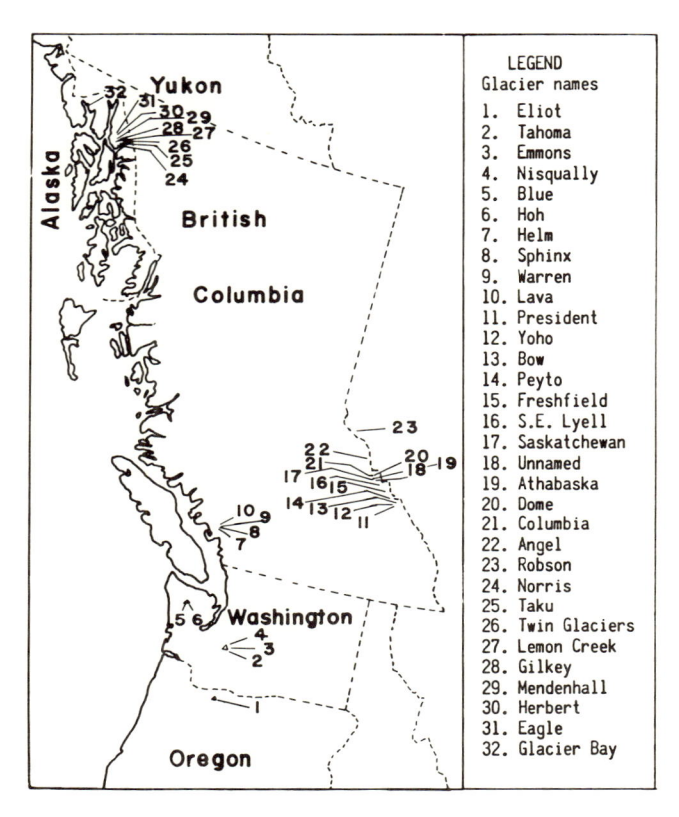

Fig. 2. Location of 32 glaciers in western United States, Canada, and southeastern Alaska that have had moraines dated by botanical methods.

oldest tree indicated that no greater maximum had been reached since at least 1700 and probably much earlier, judging from the mature aspect of the timber stands.

Spencer Glacier

The Spencer Glacier is located 15 km southwest of the Portage Glacier and flows from the same general ice field. Tarr and Martin (1912) believed the Spencer Glacier to have reached its maximum in the late 1890's. A log collected from till associated with the terminal moraine about 1 mile from the front of the glacier was dated by carbon-14 as "post-A.D. 1650" (Karlstrom, 1964). No spruce grow on this moraine but a balsam poplar (*Populus balsamifera* L.) on the terminal moraine was 64 years old in 1957. Allowing 5 to 10 years for the establishment of balsam poplar, a light-seeded pioneer species, recession would have begun in the mid- to late 1890's, as Tarr

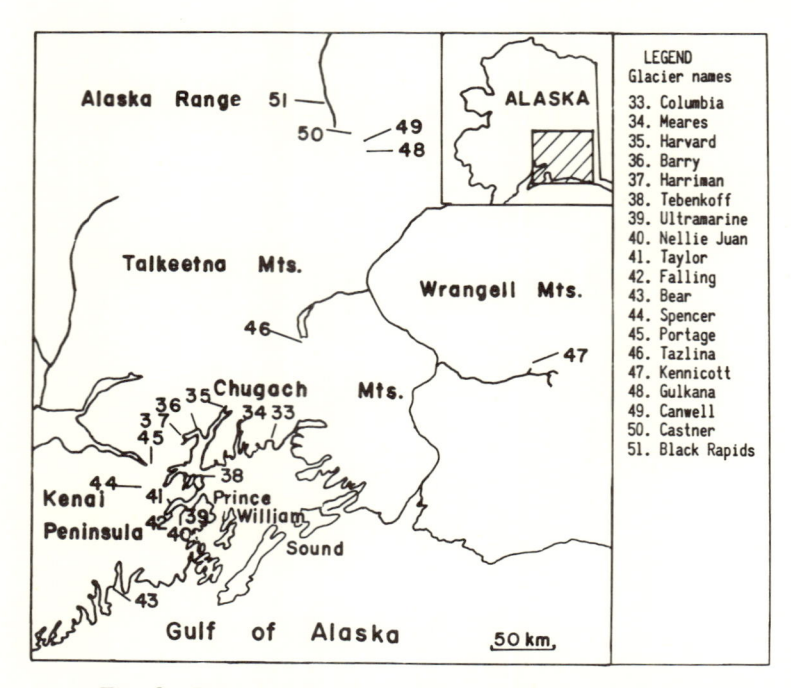

Fig. 3. Location in south-central Alaska of glaciers that have had moraines dated by botanical methods.

and Martin (1912) suggest. A 250-year-old mountain hemlock [*Tsuga mertensiana* (Bong.) Carr.] grew just above the trimline on the north side of the glacier.

Bear Glacier

Bear Glacier originates in the Harding Ice Field of the Kenai Peninsula and flows southward to a broad terminus at Resurrection Bay. Grant and Higgins (1913) estimated that the recession began about 1880. However, a 99-year-old Sitka spruce [*Picea sitchensis* (Bong.) Carr.] below the trimline indicates that recession probably began between 1835 and 1845 on the northeast side of the terminus. A 350-year-old mountain hemlock just above trimline shows that this recent advance of the Bear Glacier was its greatest since at least 1600.

Tazlina Glacier

Tazlina Glacier, flowing northward from the main snowfields of the Chugach Mountains, is of special interest because it flows from the same accumulation area as the Columbia Glacier, the largest glacier flowing into Prince William Sound.

The trimline, about 120 m above the present ice level on the west side of the glacier, is complicated by a recent fire, so no dates of maximum advance were obtained from it. The outwash and moraines in front of the glacier are only sparsely vegetated; strong winds blowing northward down the glacier have probably been detrimental to vegetation development. About 1.5 km from the present terminus is a conspicuous terminal moraine. The oldest tree on the outer edge of this moraine, stunted and only 2 m tall, was 105 years old. If 40 to 50 years is allowed for its establishment, the probable date for the beginning of recession of the glacier was 1800 to 1820.

Protruding through the outwash about 1 km beyond the terminal moraine is a rock outcrop. On the leeward side several white spruce [*Picea glauca* (Moench) Voss] were growing in an extremely windswept form. One of these, 57 cm in diameter, was too rotten to core. The other was 24 cm in diameter and 260 years old, from which I estimate the older tree to be at least 500 years old and conclude that the Tazlina Glacier has not been beyond the terminal moraine position since at least 1450 A.D.

Kennicott Glacier

Kennicott Glacier originates in the high peaks on the south side of the Wrangell Mountains and flows southward to a terminus near the town of McCarthy. The terminal area of the glacier is now stagnant, with vegetation growing on 1 to 1.5 m of gravel debris above the ice. A 67-year-old spruce tree grew 1 km back from the present terminus, and a 29-year-old white spruce was found growing on gravel above ice over 1.5 km up-glacier from the terminus.

Along the west side of the glacier is a conspicuous trimline 55 m above the 1957 level of the ice and cutting through mature stands of white spruce over 200 years in age. Along the trimline were groups of living trees that had been undermined by the glacier advance; one of the trees showed a definite change of rings in 1860, indicating that it had been tipped at that time.

White spruce up to 63 years in age grow on the terminal moraine and outwash. If 30 years is allowed for the invasion of spruce, a reasonable figure for this relatively dry site, these ages agree well with the 1860 date obtained from the western trimline as the time of maximum advance of the glacier.

A 360-year-old stand of black spruce [*Picea mariana* (Mill.) B.S.P.], about 1.5 km in front of the 1860 terminus and partially buried by outwash, indicates that the Kennicott Glacier has not been beyond its 1860 maximum since at least 1600.

Nellie Juan Glacier

Nellie Juan Glacier originates in the Sargent Ice Field on the

Kenai Peninsula and flows northeast to tidewater in Prince William Sound. Grant and Higgins (1913) reported that the glacier had receded 100 to 500 feet (30 to 150 m) from a maximum that occurred at least 20 years before 1908.

From a trimline on a granite knoll along the northwest side of the valley, I obtained a cross section of a mountain hemlock that had been tipped by a push moraine in front of the ice. A branch of the tree had bent upright and developed into a new tree. From the cross section it was evident that the branch grew as a normal branch until 1882, when it began to grow more rapidly and asymmetrically. The maximum advance of the Nellie Juan Glacier at its western terminus would thus have occurred about 1880. Inside this push moraine, 51-year-old mountain hemlocks indicated a 20- to 25-year period between the maximum advance and the establishment of trees on the moraine. On the east side of the granite knoll another hemlock was pushed over in 1863, indicating that the ice was at or near its maximum for 20 years with minor fluctuations at various parts of the terminus. Six meters from the terminal moraine a 355-year-old hemlock demonstrates that the 1860-1880 advance was the greatest since before 1600.

As is indicated by the ages of trees growing on their terminal moraines, several other glaciers in the western part of Prince William Sound have had maximum advances coinciding with that of the Nellie Juan Glacier. These include the Taylor, Falling, Tebenkoff, and Ultramarine Glaciers.

Columbia Glacier

Columbia Glacier is the largest glacier entering Prince William Sound from the snow fields of the Chugach Mountains. Photographs and observations show that it had a maximum from 1914 to 1922 that fluctuated along its 11-km front and then a recession with minor advances ending sometime after 1935. In 1935 Cooper (1942) found a 420-year-old tree just beyond the trimline on Heather Island in the center of the front and concluded that the 1914-1922 maximum was the greatest for at least the last 500 years.

At the center of the Heather Island front there is an extensive area where trees were pushed over by ice when the glacier was at its maximum. Five leaning mountain hemlocks were cross-sectioned in an attempt to determine if the tree-ring results correlated with the known history of the glacier. All five trees showed a definite break in the rings between 35 and 40 years before 1957; they thus indicated that on Heather Island the maximum was between 1917 and 1922 — a conclusion that correlates well with the observed maximum fluctuations between 1914 and 1922.

An examination of spruce and hemlocks on the deglaciated terrain of known ages showed a variation of from 6 to 13 years for the period required for the establishment of trees.

Three glaciers (Meares, Harvard, and Harriman) visited in 1957 were either at their maxima or had been so within a few years. The Meares and Harvard glaciers were advancing into mature forests at least several hundred years in age. The Harriman glacier was advancing into tundra, but a tree 2 km from the glacier was dated at 425 years. These three glaciers had not been beyond present maxima for several centuries.

Table 1 summarizes data obtained on recent glacier activity through the use of botanical methods in western North America, the Canadian mountains, and Alaska. Dates of major advances or beginning of recessions are given, along with the method used for obtaining the date. Where possible, the length of time required for tree establishment and estimated age of the vegetation beyond the maximum advance are given.

CONCLUSIONS

Botanical dating of glacier activity provides evidence for a glacier advance in North America in the past 300 years that is greater in most cases than any since the late glacial time. These advances climax a period that has been called the late postglacial by Heusser (1960), Little Ice Age by Matthes (1939), and Hypothermal by Cooper (1958). In northern Europe, the Alps, and Iceland there is historic evidence for an advance in the late 16th century greater than any during the Middle Ages (Matthes, 1942). History also records readvances in Europe in the mid-17th century, the 1770's, and the 1820's. In South America, according to Heusser (1961), the glaciers do not show a maximum advance in the 1600's but did advance in both the 18th and 19th centuries. Lawrence and Lawrence (1960) report a general synchrony between South American and Northern Hemisphere glaciers.

Heusser (1961) has summarized the recent glacier activity for the northwestern cordillera: (1) a maximum in the mid-1600's; (2) a second maximum in the early to mid-1700's that in most cases exceeded the 1600 advance, with retreat taking place at various times up to 1785; (3) readvances in the 1800's with a maximum, in some cases, exceeding those of the previous two advances; and (4) a general recession from the late 1800's to the present.

Counter to the findings of Heusser and others that the recent historical advances are the greatest since late-glacial times is the evidence reported by Karlstrom (1964) that at least two of the glaciers on the Kenai Peninsula, the Bartlett and Tustumena, have a series of moraines formed during what Karlstrom has called the Tustumena advances of Alaskan glaciation. These moraines have been dated from 3500 B.C. to 300 B.C. by carbon-14 methods. Karlstrom also reports two Tunnel advances for the Bartlett and Tustumena glaciers that date about 550 A.D. and post-1550 A.D.

TABLE 1

List of Glaciers in Western North America That Have Had Moraines Dated by Botanical Methods

Number	Glacier name	Location	Date of maxima and advances	Methods of determination	Minimum age beyond maximum advance	Tree invasion years	Source
Oregon and Washington							
1	Eliot	Mt. Hood, Oregon	1740	Ice-scarred tree	650		Lawrence, 1948
2	Tahoma	Mt. Rainier, Washington	1635	Trees on moraine	320+	5	From Lawrence, 1958 Sigafoos and Hendricks, 1961
			1835	Trees on moraine			
3	Emmons	Mt. Rainier, Washington	1745	Trees on moraine	700+	5	Sigafoos and Hendricks, 1961
			1859	Trees on moraine			
			1895	Trees on moraine			
4	Nisqually	Mt. Rainier, Washington	1840	Trees on moraine	600-700	5	Sigafoos and Hendricks, 1961
5	Blue	Olympic Peninsula, Washington	1650	Trees on moraine	500	12	Heusser, 1957
			1815-1820	Trees on moraine			
6	Hoh	Olympic Peninsula, Washington	1809-1812	Trees on moraine	450+		Heusser, 1957
British Columbia							
7	Helm	Mt. Garibaldi map area	1845	Trees on moraine Lower growth rate			Mathews, 1951
8	Sphinx	Mt. Garibaldi map area	1720	Trees on moraine			Mathews, 1951

RECENT GLACIAL ACTIVITY

9	Warren	Mt. Garibaldi map area	1715	Trees on moraine			Mathews, 1951
10	Lava	Mt. Garibaldi map area	1705-1725	Trees on moraine			Mathews, 1951
11	President	Banff-Jasper	1714	Trees on moraine	400	30	Bray, 1964
			1832	Trees on moraine			
12	Yoho	Banff-Jasper	1844	Trees on moraine	450+	28	Bray and Struik, 1963
		Wapta Ice Field		Growth rates			
			1858	Trees on moraine	400+	10	Heusser, 1956
13	Bow	Banff-Jasper	1669	Trees on moraine	600	14	Heusser, 1956
			1847	Trees on moraine			
14	Peyto	Banff-Jasper	1711	Trees on moraine			Heusser, 1956
			1863	Trees on moraine			
15	Freshfield	Banff-Jasper	1853	Trees on moraine	300	12	Heusser, 1956
16	S. E. Lyell	Banff-Jasper	1840	Tipped tree		12	Heusser, 1956
17	Saskatchewan	Banff-Jasper	1807	Tipped tree	300	10	Heusser, 1956
			1854	Tree on moraine			
			1893	Tipped tree			
18	Unnamed	Banff-Jasper	1790	Tree on moraine	350	17	Heusser, 1956
19	Athabaska	Banff-Jasper	1714	Tipped tree	350	17	Heusser, 1956
20	Dome	Banff-Jasper	1870	Trees on moraine		17	Heusser, 1956
21	Columbia	Banff-Jasper	1724	Trees on moraine	400	14	Heusser, 1956
			1842	Tipped tree			
22	Angel	Jasper National Park	1723	Trees on moraine		10	Heusser, 1956
23	Robson	Jasper National Park	1783	Trees on moraine	400	12	Heusser, 1956

Alaska

24	Norris	Juneau Ice Field	1750's	Trees on moraine	550+		Lawrence, 1950
25	Taku	Juneau Ice Field	1750's	Trees on moraine			Lawrence, 1950

Number	Glacier name	Location	Date of maxima and advances	Methods of determination	Minimum age beyond maximum advance	Tree invasion years	Source
26	Twin Glaciers	Taku Inlet	1775-1777	Trees on moraine	500		Cooper, 1942; Field, 1932
27	Lemon Creek	Juneau Ice Field	1750	Trees on moraine	10,000	10	Heusser and Marcus, 1964
28	Gilkey	Juneau Ice Field	1783				Heusser and Marcus, 1964
29	Mendenhall	Juneau Ice Field	(middle) 1767-1769 (east) 1786-1788	Trees on moraine	630	3-5 in depr. 5-7 ridge top	Lawrence, 1950
30	Herbert	Juneau Ice Field	1765	Trees on moraine	600		Lawrence, 1950
31	Eagle	Juneau Ice Field	1785	Trees on moraine			Lawrence, 1950
32	Glacier Bay glaciers	Glacier Bay	1735-1785	Trees on moraine		17-67 50-100	Cooper, 1937 Lawrence, 1958
33	Columbia	Prince William Sound	1914-1922	Direct observation	500		Cooper, 1942
			1917-1922	Direct observation			Field, 1932
			1917-1922	Tipped trees		6-13	Viereck
34	Meares	Prince William Sound	1957+ 1964+		280		Viereck Field, W. O. (in letter)
35	Harvard	Prince William Sound	1957+ 1964+		250		Viereck Field, W. O. (in letter)
36	Barry	Prince William Sound	1898	Direct observation	350+		Tarr, 1914; Viereck

RECENT GLACIAL ACTIVITY

37	Harriman	Prince William Sound	1957+ 1964+		425		Viereck Field, W. O. (in letter)
38	Tebenkoff	Prince William Sound	1875-1885	Trees on outwash		20	Viereck
39	Ultramarine	Prince William Sound	1880-1890	Trees on moraine		20	Viereck
40	Nellie Juan	Prince William Sound	1860-1885	Tipped trees	355	20	Viereck
41	Taylor	Prince William Sound	1865-1875	Trees on moraine		20	Viereck
42	Falling	Prince William Sound	1875-1885	Trees on moraine	525	20	Viereck
43	Bear	Southern Kenai Peninsula	1835-1845	Tree on moraine	350+	10-20	Viereck
44	Spencer	Kenai Peninsula	1890's 1890's	Estimated Tree on moraine	250	5-10	Tarr and Martin, 1912 Viereck
45	Portage	Kenai Peninsula	1900 1890-1900	Direct observation Trees on moraine	250	20	Barnes, 1943 Viereck
46	Tazlina	Northern Chugach Mts.	1800-1810	Tree on moraine	500	40-50	Viereck
47	Kennicott	Wrangell Mts.	1860	Tipped trees	360+	30	Viereck
48	Gulkana	Alaska Range	1580? 1650? 1830 1875	Trees on moraine Lichen diameters Lichen diameters Lichen diameters Lichen diameters			Reger and Péwé (unpubl. ms.)
49	Canwell	Alaska Range	1650? 1830	Trees on moraine Trees on moraine			Reger and Péwé (unpubl. ms.)
50	Castner	Alaska Range	1650? 1830	Trees on moraine Trees on moraine			Reger and Péwé (unpubl. ms.)
51	Black Rapids	Alaska Range	1650? 1830 1937	Trees on moraine Trees on moraine Direct observation	350-500	20	Reger and Péwé (unpubl. ms.)

The various geographical areas in western North America show distinct patterns that may eventually help explain the climatic factors affecting glaciers. In the northwestern United States advances have been recorded in all three of the past centuries, but not on any one glacier. The Nisqually Glacier shows only an 1840 maximum, the Eliot a 1740 maximum; the Blue and the Hoh both show advances in the mid-1600's and early 1800's. None of the glaciers in that area has had an advance in the late 1800's or 1900's greater than earlier advances.

Many of the British Columbia glaciers had maximum advances in the 18th century, but only the Bow has evidence of a mid-17th century maximum. Eleven of the British Columbia glaciers show a maximum or readvance ending between 1830 and 1870. Only the Saskatchewan Glacier advanced as late as 1890, and none has had a recorded maximum in the 20th century.

In Alaska some distinct patterns are revealed. The glaciers in the Alaska Range show evidence of advance in the late 1500's or mid-1600's. In the vicinity of the Juneau Ice Field and at Glacier Bay the most commonly recorded maximum is in the mid-1700's, an advance that has not been recorded in the Alaska Range. On the Kenai Peninsula and in Prince William Sound a major advance in the late 19th century to mid-20th century has destroyed most evidence of earlier advances.

SUMMARY

Tree-ring analysis and lichen growth rates are useful tools for dating glacial events during the past five centuries. Botanical dating shows that the glacial advance in the past 300 years is the greatest in the past 5 to 10 centuries and probably the greatest in postglacial times. All regions have some indication of an advance in the 1600's, 1700's, and 1800's, although local areas may lack evidence for one or more of these advances.

REFERENCES

Andrews, J. T., and P. J. Webber, 1964, A lichenometrical study of the northwestern margin of the Barnes Ice Cap: A geomorphological technique: Geograph. Bull; v. 22, pp. 80-104.

Barnes, F. F., 1943, Geology of the Portage Pass area, Alaska: U.S. Geol. Surv. Bull., v. 926-D, pp. 211-235.

Beschel, R. E., 1957, Lichenometrie im Gletschervorfeld: Ver. Schutz. Alpenofl. Jb., v. 22, pp. 164-185.

_____ 1961, Dating rock surfaces by lichen growth and its application to glaciology and physiography (lichenometry), *in* Geology of the

Arctic, G. O. Raasch (ed.): Toronto, Univ. Toronto Press, 1196 pp.

Bray, J. R., 1964, Chronology of a small glacier in eastern British Columbia: Can. Sci., v. 144, pp. 287-288.

―――― and G. J. Struik, 1963, Forest growth and glacial chronology in eastern British Columbia and their relation to recent climatic trends: Can. J. Botan., v. 41, pp. 1245-1270.

Cooper, W. S., 1937, The problem of Glacier Bay, Alaska: A study of glacier variations: Geograph. Rev., v. 27, pp. 37-62.

―――― 1942, Vegetation of the Prince William Sound Region, Alaska; with a brief excursion into Post-Pleistocene climatic history: Ecol. Monographs, v. 12, pp. 1-22.

―――― 1958, Terminology of Post Valders time: Bull. Geol. Soc. Am., v. 69, pp. 941-945.

Field, W. O., Jr., 1932, The glaciers of the northern part of Prince William Sound, Alaska: Geograph. Rev., v. 22, pp. 361-388.

Grant, U. S., and D. F. Higgins, 1913, Coastal glaciers of Prince William Sound and Kenai Peninsula, Alaska: U.S. Geol. Surv. Circ., v. 526, pp. 7-72.

Heusser, C. J., 1956, Postglacial environments in the Canadian Rocky Mountains: Ecol. Monographs, v. 26, pp. 263-302.

―――― 1957, Variations of Blue, Hoh, and White Glaciers during recent centuries: Arctic, v. 10, pp. 139-150.

―――― 1960, Late Pleistocene environments of North Pacific North America: New York, Am. Geograph. Soc., 308 pp.

―――― 1961, Final report, American Geographical Society Southern Chile Expedition, 1959: New York, Am. Geograph. Soc., 22 pp.

―――― and M. G. Marcus, 1964, Historical variations of Lemon Creek Glacier, Alaska, and their relationship to the climatic record: J. Glaciol., v. 5, pp. 77-86.

Karlstrom, T. N. V., 1964, Quarternary geology of the Kenai Lowland and glacial history of the Cook Inlet region, Alaska: U.S. Geol. Surv. Prof. Paper, v. 443, 69 pp.

Lawrence, D. B., 1948, Mt. Hood's latest eruption and glacier advances: Mazama, v. 30, pp. 22-29.

―――― 1950, Estimating dates of recent glacier advances and recession rates by studying tree growth layers: Am. Geophys. Union Transl., v. 31, pp. 243-248.

―――― 1958, Glaciers and vegetation in southeastern Alaska: Am. Scientist, v. 46, pp. 89-122.

―――― and Elizabeth G. Lawrence, 1960, Recent glacier variations in the southern Andes: Washington, D.C., Am. Assoc. Advan. Sci. (abstract).

Mathews, W. H., 1951, Historic and prehistoric fluctuations of alpine glaciers in the Garibaldi Map area, southwest British Columbia: J. Geol., v. 59, pp. 357-380.

Matthes, F. E., 1939, Report of Committee on Glaciers, April 1939: Am. Geophys. Union Transl., v. 20, pp. 518-523.
────── 1942, Glaciers, Physics of the earth, Hydrology, O. E. Meinzer (ed.): New York, McGraw-Hill, 712 pp.
Mendenhall, W. C., 1900, A reconnaissance from Resurrection Bay to the Tanana River, Alaska, in 1899, *in* Explorations in Alaska in 1898: U.S. Geol. Surv. 20th Anniversary Rept. 1898-99, Part 7, pp. 265-340.
Sigafoos, R. S., and E. L. Hendricks, 1961, Botanical evidence of the modern history of Nisqually Glacier, Washington: U.S. Geol. Surv. Prof. Paper, 387-A, 20 pp.
Stork, A., 1963, Plant immigration in front of retreating glaciers, with examples from Kebnekajse area, northern Sweden: Geograph. Ann., v. 45, pp. 1-22.
Tarr, R. S., and Martin, Lawrence, 1912, An effort to control a glacial stream: Ann. Assoc. Am. Geograph., v. 2, pp. 25-40.
────── 1914, Alaskan glacier studies: Washington, D.C., Natl. Geograph. Soc., 498 pp.

ARCTIC AND ALPINE ENVIRONMENTS (H. E. Wright, Jr., and
W. H. Osburn, eds.), 205-213, © 1967 Indiana University Press

11
Observations on the pH of Melting Snow in the Southern French Alps

PIERRE CLEMENT AND JEAN VAUDOUR
Laboratoire de Géographie Physique
Université d'Aix en Provence
Provence, France

Abstract

Observations in the southern French Alps show the acidity of melting snow. Its pH values, which change with time and with type of snow, are lower in winter and for recently fallen snows; this fact might be explained by the variation of the CO_2 content. The observations show very low pH for high-altitude snow and ice and a general decrease of the pH with increase of temperature for meltwater. An attempt was made to test the extent of meltwater chemical erosion upon rock and soil. Some suggestions are given in the conclusion about the climates in which this kind of weathering occurs most, and a comparison is briefly made with the pH values of rainwater in temperate climate.

Landforms such as alpine lapies and nivation hollows are attributed to weathering by snow, in which chemical action combines with mechanical phenomena. Therefore, the pH of snow and meltwater was measured during the winter and spring of 1964-1965 in the southern French Alps.

METHODS

Observations were made from December 1964 to June 1965 in the upper Drac valley between 1100 and 2200 m, the Montagne de Lure at 1600 m, and the Glacier Blanc between 2000 and 3000 m (Hautes et Basses Alpes, France).

A portable pH meter was used with a BRV glass electrode; its normal running was verified before each measuring with the pH 7 check. Samples were taken in Pyrex beakers with no contact whatsoever with outside materials that could change the measurement. Melting was produced by artificial means in order to make readings on the spot. Readings were made from the time when the melting had produced sufficient liquid so that the electrode was immersed. Internal and external temperatures were taken throughout the experiment.

For some samples, Ca^{++}, Mg^{++}, and Fe^{++} content in meltwater was determined in the laboratory; the quantitative analyses were made by complexometry for Ca^{++} and Mg^{++} and by spectrophotometry for Fe^{++}. Only the analyses of calcium seemed to be always satisfactory.

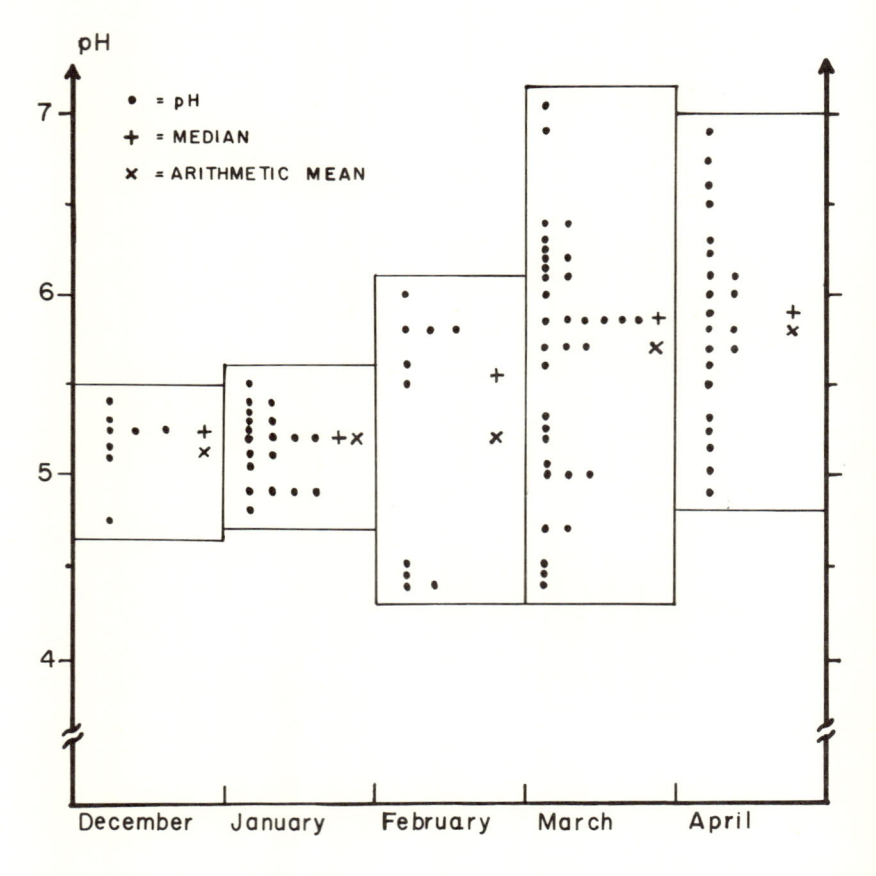

Fig. 1. Evolution of melting snow pH from December 1964 to April 1965.

RESULTS

Melting snow is clearly acid; the most frequent readings were around pH 5.4, the limits being 4.4 and 7.0. But it is more interesting to consider the variations of the data with time and snow type (Figs. 1 and 2).

The most acid snows occur particularly during winter. In spring the pH approaches neutrality, but the greatest contrasts are found in this season. The newest snows are clearly the most acid (fresh and powdery snows); older snows, changed by thaw-and-freeze (crust and granular), are less acid. Thus we can explain the consistent acidity of winter snows, which have changed less.

Recently fallen snows have a low density and are rich in air content; carbon dioxide can easily spread into the crystals and dissolve in meltwater in large amounts, as its solubility is in inverse ratio

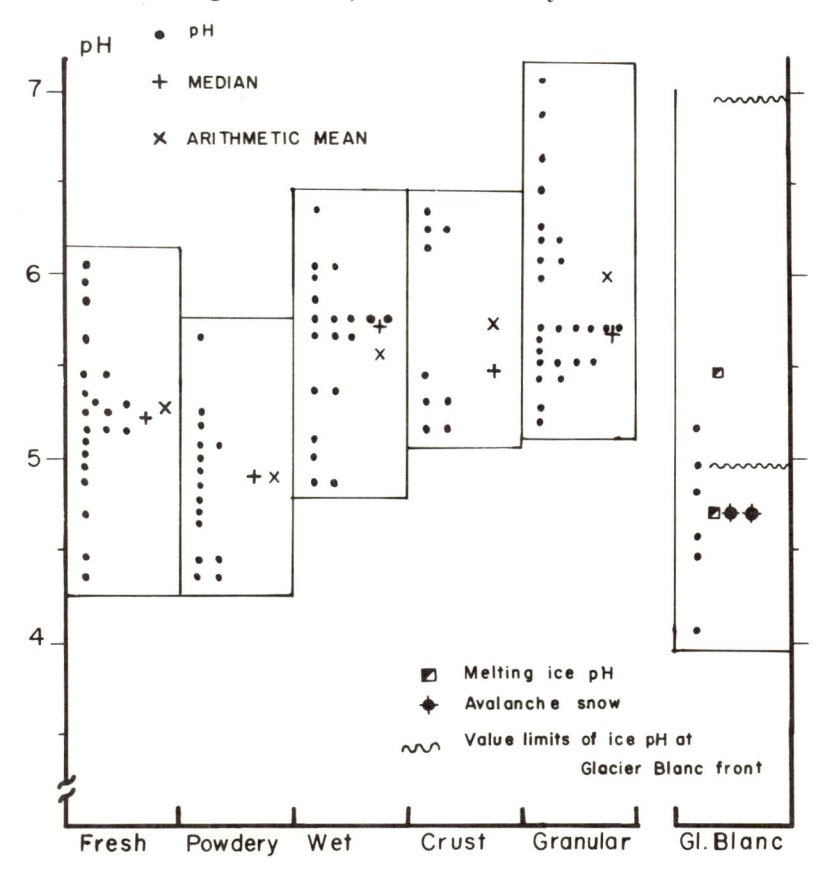

Fig. 2. pH according to snow type.

to its temperature (the temperature of the water-snow mixture is slightly above 0°C). This carbon dioxide produces a carbonic acid, never isolated, to which the low pH values can be attributed. It might happen that other elements, such as atmospheric acids, have an influence, but the relation between pH and snow type indicates that the important fact is the solution of CO_2 in liquid. While this snow is transformed and settles, the trapped air progressively escapes, and the dissolution of CO_2 is less abundant.

Snows that have been on the ground for a long time pick up dust and debris that can also modify the pH. The quantitative analyses indicate the results shown in Table 1 for some samples.

It appears that at least the calcium content is higher for samples with pH above 5.5.

On the Glacier Blanc at high altitude in June (Fig. 2), the pH values are very low for snow and even for ice; but snows, wet at that time, were loose and at the beginning of their transformation. This

TABLE 1

Place, altitude(m), and date		pH	Snow type	Ca^{++} [a]		Mg^{++}		Fe^{++}	
Drac Valley									
1400	2/14/65	5.8	Melting	3.2	0.16	18.0	1.5	0.90	0.03
1750		4.5	Crust	2.0	0.10	10.6	0.9	0.64	0.02
—		6.4	Melting	3.6	0.18	16.8	1.4		
Lure									
1600	3/17	6.2	Crust	5.2	0.26	6.5	0.5	0.76	0.03
—		5.8	Crust	4.4	0.22	6.1	0.5		
—		6.3	Ice	4.8	0.24	4.2	0.4	0.72	0.03
—		6.3	Crust	4.0	0.20	4.0	0.3	1.20	0.04
Drac Valley									
1750	3/24	5.0	Fresh	1.2	0.06	5.3	0.4		
2100		7.0	Granular	4.0	0.20	6.9	0.6		
—		6.8	Granular	4.4	0.22	5.3	0.4	2.16	0.08
1500	4/8	5.3	Fresh	0.0	0.00	7.7	0.6	2.75	0.10
1500	4/22	5.5	Fresh	0.0	0.00	4.8	0.4	1.96	0.07
Vallouise									
Pré de Mme Carle									
1850	6/12	5.4	Avalanche	0.0	0.00	4.1	0.3		
—		4.7	Snow	1.6	0.08	2.5	0.2		
Glacier Blanc									
3000	6/13	4.6	Wet	0.0	0.00	1.8	0.15		
—		5.2	Granular	0.8	0.04	1.9	0.16		
—		4.7	Bubbly	0.8	0.04	1.3	0.11		
—		4.7	Glacier ice	2.0	0.10	1.9	0.16		

[a] For each ion two numbers are given, the first in mg/liter, the second in meq/liter.

pH OF MELTING SNOW

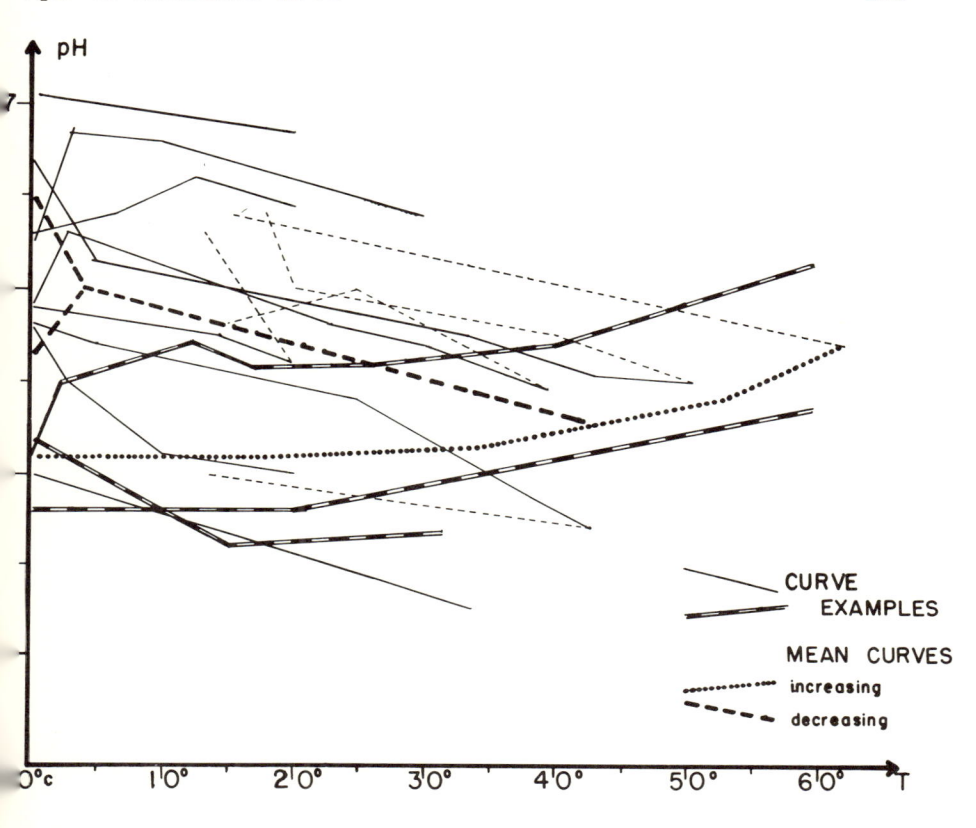

Fig. 3. Principal types of curves showing pH evolution with temperature.

explanation is reinforced by the fact that numerous snowfalls occurred in this area after April. The low values are more surprising and seem to contradict Ek's findings (1964) of neutrality for glaciers of Haute Maurienne, France. However, our ice was very clear, whereas Ek's measurements were made on glacier fronts in September, probably on highly transformed and dirty ice.

Distilled water measured in the same conditions on the spot (Glacier Blanc) was truly acid (pH 4.2), a fact that implies an equilibrium between the atmosphere and the liquid, for the same water was closer to neutral when measured in the laboratory. At high altitudes the UV radiation may be an important factor.

One fact we cannot explain — the evolution of the meltwater pH with increase of temperature (Figs. 3 and 4). In a great number of cases, the pH curve decreases, with sudden changes between 0 and 5°C. We think that these phenomena may be explained by the gas exchange between atmosphere and liquid and by chemical reactions in the liquid with temperature changes.

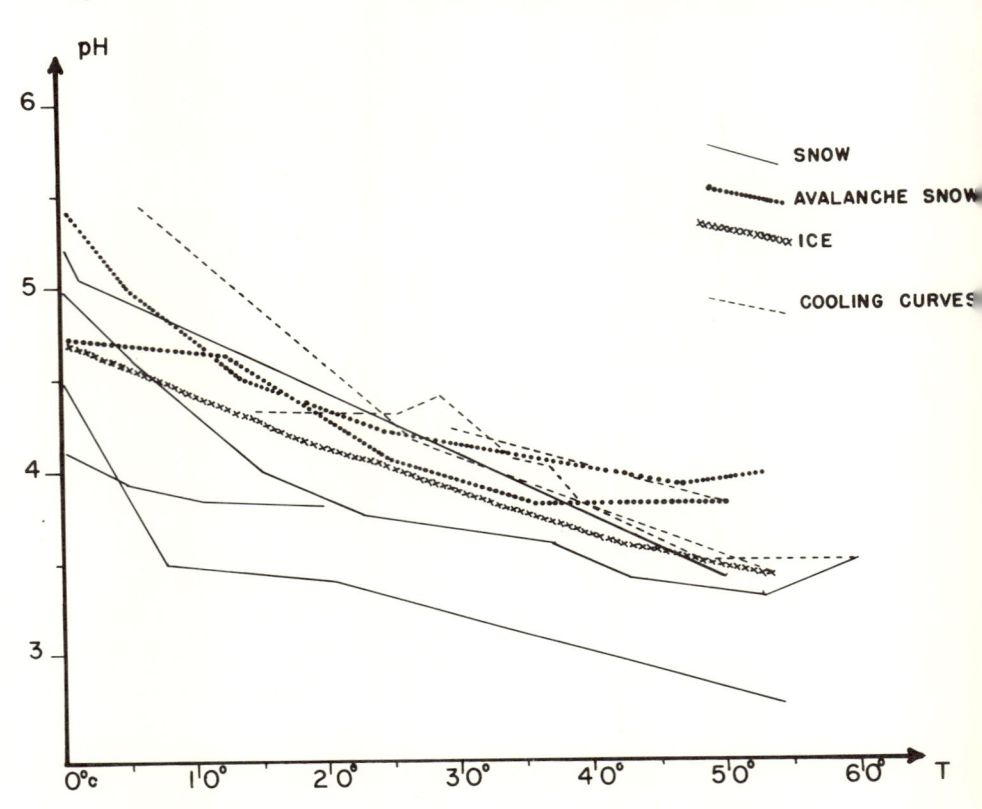

Fig. 4. pH evolution with temperature, June 1965, Glacier Blanc.

EXPERIMENTATION ON MELTWATER EROSION

Meltwater might have a precisely determinable chemical action upon rocks because of its acidity. We have begun to study this action; our methods have been progressively transformed, and, in spite of their imperfection, we think it could be useful to describe and criticize them and to give preliminary results.

Lightly compressed snow was laid upon soil or rock fragments placed on filter paper in a plastic funnel; snow was renewed until 1 liter of liquid was obtained. The sample was placed in an oven with variable temperature and humidity, with intermittent melting (for the apparatus permits the reproduction of thaw-and-freeze cycles); the melting occurred between 17 and 48 hours, at temperatures between 10 and 20°C, and between 72 and 107 hours, at temperatures between -20 and +10°C. At a high altitude (2200 m in the Drac valley) the experiment lasted 10 days, during which occurred insolation, heavy

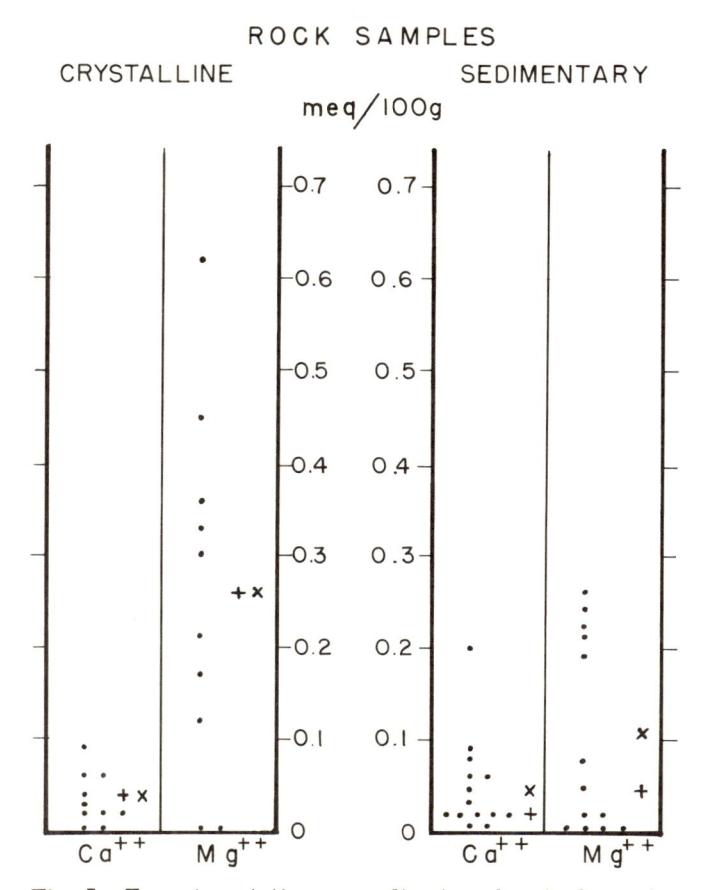

ROCK SAMPLES
CRYSTALLINE   SEDIMENTARY
meq/100g

Fig. 5. Experimentation on meltwater chemical erosion.

snowfalls, and dry, cold weather. Only this last experiment was close to natural conditions; in the others, snow structure was changed by artificial means such as compaction above the funnel and transformation in the oven into ice that did not completely cover the rock samples.

The samples were either unconsolidated and soft formations (calcareous soils screened to 2 mm diameter, and shales) or cohesive and hard rocks (sedimentary and crystalline); the average weight was about 400 g.

The results are shown in Fig. 5. For soil samples they are as shown in Table 2.

We assumed that the meltwaters themselves contained the measured elements, and we therefore subtracted the average content of water from the rough results. The subtracted values are not important because of the low surface area of rocks and the small volume of water.

TABLE 2

	Ca^{++}[a]		Mg^{++}[a]	
1	38.25	0.81	25.92	1.08
2	25.09	0.63	20.88	0.87
3	66.00	0.82	7.68	0.16

[a] First figure in mg/liter, the second in meq/100g.

It would be better to use unconsolidated sediments with such equipment (or with a column used for the extraction of cations) or to reproduce the experiment on a larger scale with larger rock fragments — for example, in a large tank with samples upon which a snow layer can melt according to natural conditions. It would be necessary to have the complete chemical analyses of the samples and to determine the other common ion contents.

The calcareous sedimentary rocks do not seem to release more calcium than the crystalline rocks, but the limestones we used were cohesive and uncracked. The Mg ion is more abundant and seems to be still more so in crystalline samples. In spite of their small content, the crystalline rocks that are relatively heterogeneous give out nearly as much calcium and magnesium as the less complex limestones. The values are, of course, higher for soil samples.

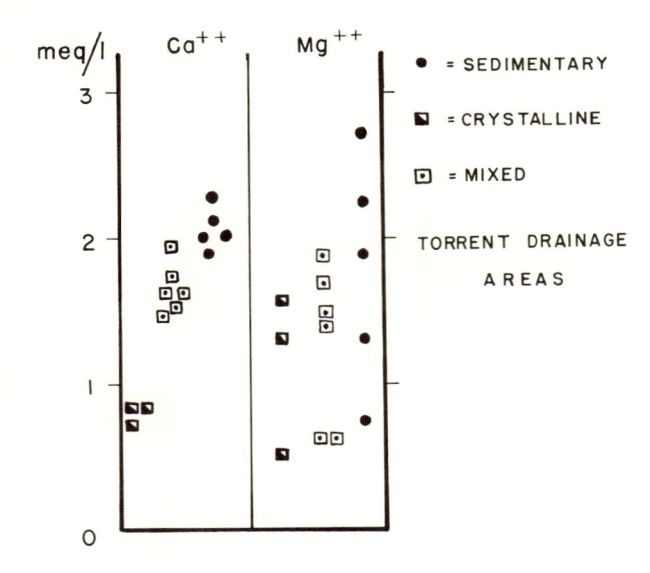

Fig. 6. Calcium and magnesium content in torrential waters, Drac valley.

We compared these results with those found in torrential waters during the melting period. The torrential drainage areas are relatively small, and the rocks within the drainage areas are homogeneous. Figure 6 shows a more obvious difference: The most calcareous waters are from sedimentary basins. This difference is also caused by the fact that the sedimentary areas either are larger or include more unconsolidated formations, such as glacial and torrent deposits. The complexity does not permit an exact estimate of the effect of any particular phenomenon, except through its experimental isolation.

CONCLUSION

According to our observations, the chemical action of meltwater might be more effective in the climates where snowfalls occur frequently (cold oceanic climates) and in high mountains during rapid melting, when large lengths of slopes are cleared. It might be less effective where snow can be transformed, such as firns and glacier fronts. On the other hand, thick snow layers prevent thaw-and-freeze cycles, which break rocks into smaller fragments. They also block UV radiation; the effect might be stronger in high tropical mountains, where the melting is very fast and occurs every day and where solar radiation is maximal.

Fine, cold rains also have low pH values (less than 6.0, according to our few observations in Provence during fall and winter), but their action is quicker than that of a snow layer melting on the ground. On the other hand, the fact that pH decreases with rising temperature from 0°C might give additional power to meltwaters that are warmed on sunny slopes, lapies hollows, etc. Such observations would profit from new and more systematic research in other areas.

REFERENCES

Barrère, P., 1964, Le Relief karstique dans l'Ouest des Pyrénées Centrales: Rev. Belge Géograph., 88e année, pp. 9-62.

Birot, P., 1962, Contribution à l'étude de la désagrégation des roches: Paris, C.D.U., 232 pp.

Ek, C., 1964, Note sur les eaux de fonte des glaciers de la Haute Maurienne, Leur action sur les carbonates: Rev. Belge Géograph., 88e année, pp. 127-156.

Grebine, T., 1963, Accumulation de poussière cosmique sur la terre: Compt. Rend. Acad. Sci., pp. 3735-3738.

Llibouvry, L., 1964, Traité de glaciologie: Paris, Masson, 428 pp.

Roques, H., 1962, Considérations théoriques sur la chimie des carbonates, 3e mémoire: Ann. Spéléolog., v. 17, pp. 463-467.

____, 1964, Contribution à l'étude statique et cinétique des systèmes gaz carbonique-eau-carbonate: Ann. Spéléolog., v. 19, pp. 255-484.

Shoeller, H., 1962, Les Eaux souterraines: Paris, Masson, 642 pp.

Geology

12
Erosion by Needle Ice in the Southern Alps, New Zealand

JANE M. SOONS
Department of Geography
University of Canterbury
Christ Church, New Zealand

Abstract

Runoff plots were established in a representative valley of the Southern Alps at localities with different aspects and contrasting vegetation. At a number of these plots, and particularly on one with an unvegetated surface, an inverse relationship between sediment yield and precipitation was noted. In winter, sediment yields are frequently high when rainfall is low. This apparent anomaly is attributed to the action of needle ice, and support for this view is offered by the reduction in runoff during the winter, associated with frost lifting of the surface soil.

The Southern Alps trend northeast for approximately 400 miles between latitudes 40°S and 46°S, forming the backbone of the South Island of New Zealand. Their width ranges between 50 and 100 miles, and the main divide between east- and west-flowing streams is close to the western coast of the island. Their height also varies, rising to 12,349 feet in Mt. Cook, the highest point, but most main divide peaks are between 8000 and 9000 ft above sea level. The front ranges on the eastern side are lower, rising to 5000 to 7000 ft. The rivers draining this mountain system are all swift and powerful, occupying broad and deeply cut valleys, in many cases structural basins of late Tertiary to early Pleistocene age. These conditions give rise to a number of climatic variations, the most striking contrast being across the main divide. To the west, rainfall is heavy, with annual totals of over 100 inches where complete records are available (Hokitika, 116 inches per year) and of about 400 inches near the divide (Dils, 1965). This rainfall, together with relatively mild temperatures and a limited incidence of high winds, is reflected in a dense rainforest which is remarkably effective in recolonizing any bare areas that have resulted from natural erosion or the activities of man. East of the divide rainfall totals decrease, dropping to 40 to 50 inches in basins about 20 miles from the divide, and to 30 to 40 inches in the foothill zone. With this decrease in rainfall is associated an increased temperature range, winter temperatures in particular being lower than west of the divide, and an increase in the importance of wind. In areas relatively unaffected by burning and grazing southern beech *(Nothofagus)* forms extensive forests, superseded by alpine vegetation at high altitudes. This vegetation has been replaced by grassland over wide areas, and the associated burning and grazing has resulted in severe erosion. In the prevailing climatic conditions, neither the native nor the exotic plant species found in the area are able readily to recolonize eroded surfaces.

The wide climatic range makes the Southern Alps a fascinating area for the study of most erosional processes, particularly east of the main divide, where the vegetation cover is less of an obstacle than to the west. There is scope for both investigation of the nature of such processes and for quantitative assessment of their effects. Two major erosive agents are involved, running water and frost, although others (e.g., glacier ice and wind) may be locally important. The effect of water action is immediately apparent in an abundance of erosional and depositional forms: the shifting channels of the broad, aggraded river beds; the deeply cut gullies that score the mountain sides and terraces; the ubiquitous and extensive alluvial fans. Frost action is evident in the expanses of active screes on nearly all mountain sides, but it is also important, through needle ice, over a much wider area. It is with this aspect of erosion that the present study is concerned, although studies made by New Zealand Forest Service personnel in the Craigieburn area suggest that other forms of soil ice, notably concrete frost, may have considerable hydrological importance.

The importance of ice needles has been very fully discussed by Troll (1944), and there seems to be no need to review their formation and general significance. Taber (1929) has produced them in the laboratory. Briefly, it may be noted that their formation requires an adequate water supply and freezing temperatures, and that they invariably form perpendicular to the cooling surface. A multitiered appearance is common, apparently as a result of a succession of freeze-thaw cycles. As far as I am aware, there is no evidence as to how cold it must be before needles will form, or any conclusive evidence as to whether slow or rapid freezing is the more effective in producing them.

The significance of needle ice as an erosive agent in the New Zealand mountains has been pointed out by a number of workers, although Gradwell was apparently the first to make any detailed study of them (1954, 1955). He observed that a close cover of growing plants, a layer of litter or a 3-inch-deep snow cover would prevent their formation, as would shading from the sky by overhanging foliage.

At the altitudes at which he was working (3500 to 4000 ft) ice needles did not form in midwinter on continuously shaded slopes, although they might develop in such sites in autumn and spring. Their absence in midwinter was associated with solidly frozen soil, with no segregated ice. In a further study he noted that vegetation surrounding bare patches was undermined by needle-ice development (Gradwell, 1960). No attempt was made to assess the amount of material moved, although Gradwell recognized that the ice needles played a part in sorting loose material into stone stripes, and that an appreciable downslope movement could occur. On an 11° slope some stones moved as much as 25 inches in a year, although the average movement was less (Gradwell, 1957). The stones used in these experiments were between 1 and 3 inches in diameter.

The size range of material that may be lifted by ice needles is wide. Needles less than $\frac{1}{2}$ inch in length will raise fine material, including grit and tiny pebbles, but larger stones about 2 inches in length appear to be unaffected and apparently insulate the soil beneath them. This insulating effect diminishes as frost intensity increases, and needles approximately 6 inches long will raise boulders 9 to 12 inches long. Presumably longer needles are capable of raising still larger fragments. As long as the soil surface is horizontal, the erosional effect of frost lift is limited, although patterned ground may develop. Under New Zealand conditions, however, this does not occur throughout the whole range of altitude affected by needle ice, but has to date been recorded only above approximately 3500 to 4000 ft above sea level. At lower altitudes the most marked effect of needle ice on flat or gently sloping surfaces is the raising of surface soil that is left in a characteristically "puffy" and friable state after drying. In this condition it appears to be very susceptible to further forms of erosion. Gradwell has suggested that it may be readily removed by rainwash, and it appears probable that it may also be susceptible to wind action. No attempts have been made to observe or isolate the effects of wind on frost-lifted material, but it should be noted that the area is subject to frequent strong winds. Pebbles up to $\frac{1}{4}$ inch diameter and occasionally larger may be picked up from unsealed road surfaces, and clouds of sand and silt from ploughed fields and riverbeds.

On slopes, the effect of needle ice in moving material is naturally greater than on horizontal surfaces. The figure of 25 inches of downslope movement on an 11° slope has been quoted, and Gradwell (1957) calculated that a pebble raised on ice needles $\frac{3}{4}$ inch long will travel 0.15 inch downslope as the needles thaw. On steeper slopes the amount of movement is naturally greater. It may be calculated that for a 29° slope the minimum amount of movement in one freeze-thaw cycle, producing ice needles $\frac{3}{4}$ inch long, will be 0.42 inch, and at least 0.84 inch if the ice needles are $1\frac{1}{2}$ inches long. The writer has observed stones $\frac{1}{2}$ inch long fall slightly more than 1 inch from melting ice needles $\frac{3}{4}$ inch long on such a slope, while others slid lesser

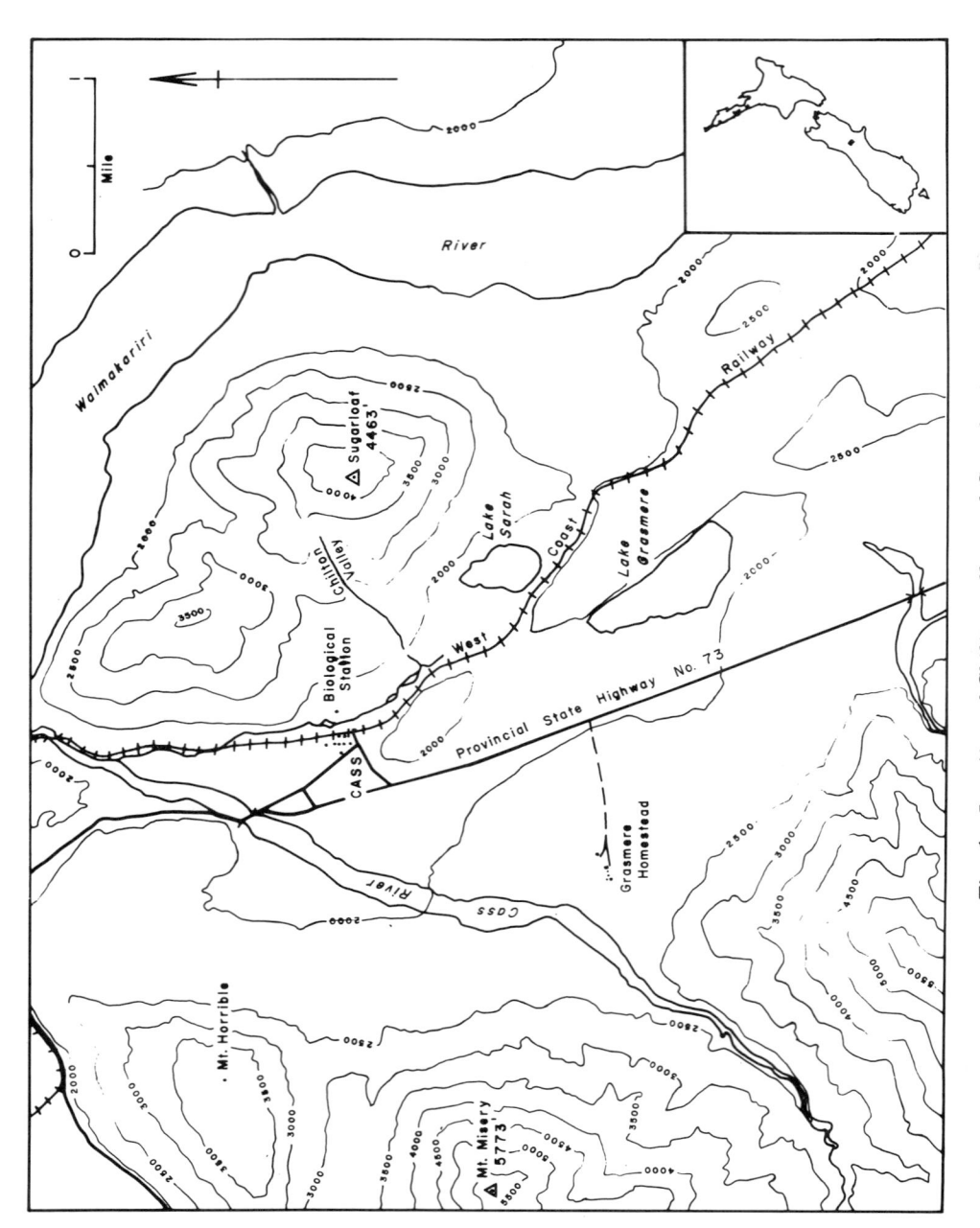

Fig. 1. Location of Chilton valley and Cass basin.

distances, rotating as they did so. Evidently, when stones fall on a slope of this degree of steepness they are likely to bounce and roll for a greater distance than the theoretical minimum. Finer material raised on longer ice needles has been observed to slump (J. N. Rayner, personal communication), and it is probable that even fine material may move appreciably farther than a simple calculation would suggest, because of the amount of water present as the needles melt, converting the soil surface into a wet, slippery mud that will readily flow downslope at least short distances.

There is some evidence of the amount of material that can be moved by this type of frost action. In late 1963 the Geography Department of the University of Canterbury began a program of observations involving the installation of a wide range of instruments in a small valley at Cass within the Waimakariri drainage basin. These were intended to amass information about climatic and geomorphic phenomena in a mountain environment (between 2500 and 2800 ft above sea level), and to examine interrelationships between the two.

The area selected for this study is known as Chilton valley, on the flank of an isolated hill situated between the Waimakariri River and the broad basin drained by the Cass River (Fig. 1). With respect to the categories of slopes found within it, its vegetation cover, and the climatic conditions, the Cass Basin is typical of wide areas of the South Island "high country." The average precipitation recorded at the University Biological Station at Cass is 51.09 inches. This includes some snow, but at the height of the station (about 2000 ft) it is unusual for snow to lie for more than a few days at a time. Temperature conditions are not so well known, but a range from 3 to 93°F has been recorded. Conditions in the Chilton valley, about 1 mile from the Biological station, are similar, although it appears that temperatures (at 2800 ft) are slightly less extreme, and precipitation may be slightly lower. This last effect may be due to shielding from heavy rainfall accompanied by very strong northwest winds.

In addition to the meteorological equipment, several runoff plots were established, to examine the relations among precipitation, runoff, and sediment yield on a variety of aspects and vegetational types. One such plot was established on an eroded area practically bare of vegetation and with most of the topsoil removed, leaving a yellowish subsoil in which fines were still abundant, although rock fragments of varying sizes were much in evidence. The slope of 29° faced northwest, thus in the Southern Hemisphere receiving long periods of sunlight even in midwinter. Other plots had better vegetation covers and were scattered around the valley with a variety of aspects (Table 1). A rain gauge of standard 5-inch size was placed by each plot, with the funnel mouth as nearly as possible parallel to the ground surface. Data on temperature conditions were available after August 1964 from recordings taken at the main recording station in the center of the valley. Temperature probes were also placed on slopes adjacent

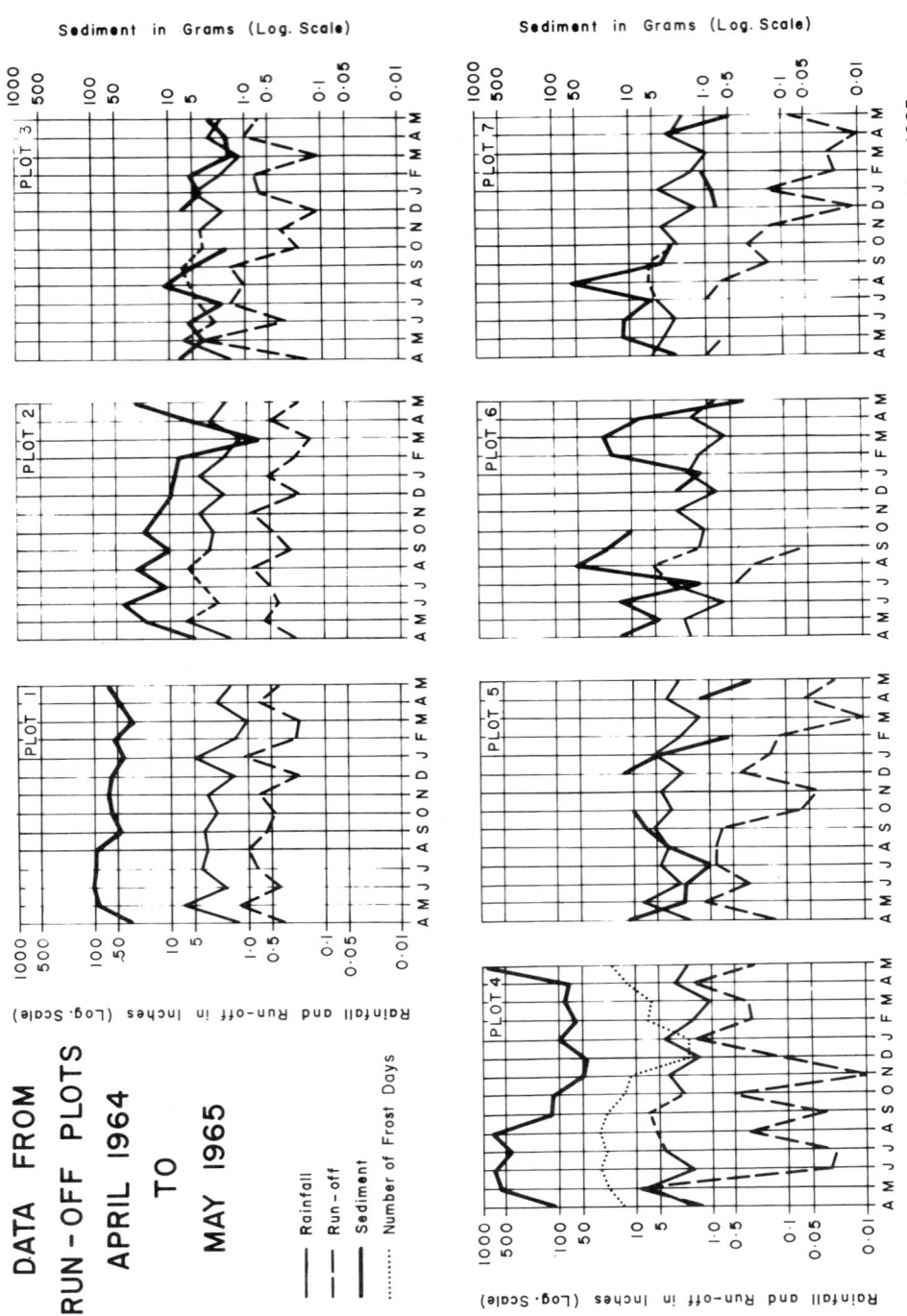

Fig. 2. Precipitation, runoff, and sediment collected at Chilton valley runoff plots, April 1964 to May 1965. Dashed lines on precipitation graph indicate that records at that particular plot were incomplete, and figures from the rainfall recorder have been interpolated.

TABLE 1
Runoff-Plot Characteristics

Plot	Slope°	Aspect	Vegetational cover
1	36	E.S.E.	Mountain daisy *(Celmisia spectabilis)* and tussock *(Festuca novae-zelandiae* and *Poa caespitosa)* with bare patches
2	32	S.E.	Continuous cover of mountain daisy and tussock
3	30	E.	Continuous cover of mountain daisy and tussock
4	29	W.	Bare ground
5	14	S.S.E.	Tussock, with some mountain daisy and tauhinu *(Cassinia fulvida)*
6	24	W.S.W.	Manuka scrub *(Leptospermum scoparium)* and some snow totara *(Podocarpus nivalis)*
7	22	W.S.W.	Tussock with some tauhinu and matagouri *(Discaria toumatou)*

to plots 1 and 4, i.e., on opposite sides of the valley, immediately below the soil surface and at depths of 2 and 15 cm.

Precipitation, runoff, and sediment have been collected at the runoff plots since April 1964, giving a total of 14 months data to the time of writing. The plots have been visited at least once a month, more often when opportunity offered and weather conditions made a visit desirable. More frequent observations were made during a 3-week period in August-September 1964, when the plots were inspected at least every 3 days. On an average the area has been visited twice a month over the past 2 years.

As a working hypothesis it was assumed that high rainfall would be associated with high runoff and high sediment yields, although some variation according to the type of vegetation cover and slope was expected. This was confirmed by preliminary observations, and the graphs in Figure 2 show a general correspondence between runoff and rainfall. The graph for plot 1 is a particularly clear example of this.

Runoff and sediment yields from plot 4 on bare ground were markedly higher than at any of the others, runoff amounting to over 60% of the monthly rainfall, when the maximum recorded at any other plot was 22% (for plot 1 on a 36° slope). Sediment yield was likewise high, being more than three times that of any other plot, and more than 10 times the amount from most plots. However, during the winter months (June, July, August, September) a marked and unexpected change was observed. While precipitation figures ranged from 2.4 to 6.6 inches per month, including some snow, runoff from plot 4 decreased and was never more than 2% of the precipitation. Sediment yields were high, however, never falling below 400 g a month, or between four and seven times the yield of any other plot. Only one other plot in fact produced sediment yields of anywhere near the same amount. This was again plot 1, on a shady site but with a poor vegetational cover. Other, better vegetated plots did not yield more than 50 g of sediments for any month during the same period, and only two produced more than 10 g per month. An examination of the graphs (Fig. 2) indicates that there was an inverse relationship between runoff and rainfall amounts on the one hand and sediment yields on the other. This was understandably most apparent in the case of plot 4, where the moderating effects of a vegetational cover were absent.

It is probable that this inversion might be explained in one of two ways. Either relatively heavy short-period rainfall in months with a low precipitation was highly efficient in transporting surface debris downslope, or low precipitation during those months was associated with a decrease in cloud cover and therefore an increase in radiation and freeze-thaw cycles. In these conditions needle-ice development would be favored, and maximum downslope movement of debris by this means would occur. Rainfall records for low and high precipitation months revealed no great variation in intensity of rainfall. It therefore appears probable that needle ice was responsible for the high sediment yields. It is also possible that needle ice might simply leave the surface in a state in which even light rainfall would readily wash sediment downslope. This view is not supported by the very low runoff figures recorded at plot 4 for the critical period, especially when their relationship to rainfall is considered. It seems probable that the frost-lifted surface allows ready infiltration of rainfall, rather than favoring runoff. It was noted that frost-lifted surfaces retained their puffy, friable character through the spring and early summer months (October to December) but thereafter became compacted. Runoff from plot 4 showed an increase after the end of November. Schumm (1964) has described a similar situation on the Mancos shales in Western Colorado.

Observations during the early winter of 1965 reinforced the evidence on the importance of needle ice in moving debris. Data from the runoff plots are usually collected at the end of each month, but an extra visit was made in mid-May, a fortnight after the regular collection. The month had been unusually dry, only 9.8 mm of rain having been recorded by the automatic rain gauge installed in the center of the valley. At those plots where runoff had occurred amounts were small, and some plots showed no runoff whatsoever. Amounts of sediment at plots 1-4 were, however, significantly increased (Table 2).

Bare ground throughout the Chilton valley was covered with small loose crumbs of soil, indicating that needle ice had been present, although none was observed at the time of the visit. The absence of ice needles at this time, in spite of temperatures below freezing point, appeared to be due to the dry conditions. After the second half of the month with an increased amount of rainfall (50.2 mm), which nevertheless produced a below-average total for the month as a whole,

TABLE 2

Sediment and Runoff Yields for Two Months of Similar Precipitation

		Plot						
		1	2	3	4	5	6	7
A[a]	Runoff, in.	0.24	0.24	0.69	0.52	0.125	Nil	0.02
	Sediment, g	57	7.7	5.0	60.6	0.5	17.9	Nil
B[b]	Runoff, in.	0.35	0.195	0.67	0.24	0.023	0.025	0.08
	Sediment, g	66.9	32.6	2.8	1040.5	0.2	0.2	0.4

[a] Feb. 1965, 2.27 in.
[b] May 1965, 2.4 in.

three plots (1, 2, and 7) yielded less sediment than in the first half of the month, while plot 4 yielded a greatly increased amount. Evidence of needle-ice action was again abundant when the plots were visited, and further confirmation of its importance is provided by comparison with sediment yields for February 1965, when the amount of precipitation was similar (Table 2). Figure 2 shows evidence of inversion of rainfall and runoff amounts at four plots.

An attempt has been made to assess rates of movement of stones within plot 4. In March 1965 paint lines were sprayed across the plot at distances of 6, 4, and 2 feet from the collecting tray. By the end of May individual stones had moved up to 3 ft from their point of origin, and a few had been found in collections from the tray, indicating a movement of up to 6 ft. There were indications that some of this movement might have been due to disturbance by animals, and further results are awaited.

A graph of numbers of occurrences of ground frost has been incorporated in Fig. 2. These have been derived from numbers of screen frosts recorded at an elevation of 3000 ft at the New Zealand Forest Service experimental area in the Craigieburn Range, about 15 miles from Cass. Comparison with the records available from Chilton valley suggest that the frequency of ground frosts may be lower, but that trends are similar. It will be noted that there is a close correspondence between sediment yields and frequency of ground frost.

Table 3 gives the amounts of sediment collected in the Chilton valley runoff plots during the period of operation of the plots. The range is wide, and the effect of a good vegetational cover in inhibiting downslope movement is apparent. In all cases, more sediment was collected in the winter 6 months than in the summer, although the proportion ranged widely, from 58% of the annual total at plot 5 to 94% at plot 7. About 60% of the precipitation for the year fell in this period. Runoff percentages showed a wide variation for the same period, and a longer period of data is required before a satisfactory

TABLE 3

Sediment Yield from Runoff Plots,
April 1964 to May 1965 Inclusive

Plot	1	2	3	4	5	6	7
Yield, g	909.5	214.5	59	4253.7	59.3	162.5	95.8

attempt can be made to determine the relationships between rainfall and runoff. For example, it may be necessary to eliminate the effect of snowmelt from the runoff figures. Snow drifting across plot 4 appears to account for the excessive runoff figure in May 1964. Nothing is known of the extent to which snowcreep may assist the downslope movement of loose material, although the limited period during which snow lies in a normal year suggests that this is slight compared with the movement caused by needle ice.

Although it is necessary to obtain more observations of the effects of needle-ice development, and further quantitative expression of the amounts of material moved and of the rates at which it is moved, the evidence presented in this paper gives an indication of the importance of this process in the erosion of New Zealand mountain areas. Intermittent and relatively localized events, such as mudflows and the severe stream erosion consequent on sudden storms, will undoubtedly move more material when they occur, but needle-ice erosion is persistent, and, apart from its direct effect in downslope movement of debris, it also inhibits the establishment of a protective vegetational cover on bare surfaces and leaves such unvegetated areas in a state in which they are only too susceptible to other forms of erosion.

Acknowledgments

The writer wishes to thank both Professor R. S. Waters and Professor M. Gage for reading early drafts of this paper, and for the helpful suggestions which they made. She would also like to express thanks and deep appreciation to Dr. J. N. Rayner, her co-worker in the Chilton Valley project, from which so much of the information in this paper has been derived. The financial assistance of the University of Canterbury and the University Grants Committee in establishing the Chilton Valley research project is gratefully acknowledged.

REFERENCES

Dils, R., 1965, Watershed management in New Zealand, status and research needs: Tussock Grasslands and Mountain Lands Inst. Spec. Publ. No. 4, 28 pp.

Gradwell, M. W., 1954, Soil frost studies at a high country station. Pt. 1: New Zealand J. Sci. Tech., sect. B, v. 36, pp. 240-257.
_____ 1955, Soil frost studies at a high country station. Pt. 2: New Zealand J. Sci. Tech., sect. B, v. 37, pp. 267-275.
_____ 1957, Patterned ground at a high country station: New Zealand J. Sci. Tech., sect. B, v 38, pp. 793-806.
_____ 1960, Soil frost action in tussock grassland: New Zealand J. Sci., 3, pp. 580-590.
Schumm, S. A., 1964, Seasonal variations of erosion rates and processes on hillslopes in western Colorado: Z. Geomorphol., v. 5, pp. 215-238.
Taber, S., 1929, Frost heaving: J. Geol., v. 37, pp. 428-461.
Troll, C., 1944, Strukturboden, Solifluktion, und Frostklimate der Erde: Geol. Rundschau, v. 34, pp. 545-694.

13

Fundamental Processes of Freezing and Thawing in Relation to the Development of Permafrost

ERWIN SCHENK
Giessen, West Germany

Abstract

The force of crystallization of water into ice causes all the structures in the freezing and thawing of soils, through deformation, sorting, cracking, etc. They are generally called *cryoturbations*. The essential process that is controlled by this force is determined by dehydration of the soil particles during freezing and hydration during thawing. All the phenomena that produce structures in the soil by freezing may be designated as cryoturbation. The question of what forces cause cryoturbation has been solved now that the movement of water in the freezing soil has been explained by hydration (Schenk, 1954, 1955a, 1955b).

HYDRATION

Hydrates are chemical compounds that are formed from another compound through deposit or take-up of water molecules. This water is the water of hydration, and the process is often combined with the release of heat, called *hydration heat,* an exothermic reaction.

Many salts, for example, calcium sulfate, form not only a simple water-free crystal form but also water-containing crystals. They thus form crystallized hydrates, for example, $CaSO_4 + 2H_2O$. This water of hydration is called *water of crystallization.*

The water molecules in an ice crystal take a very specific place. As a result of the tetrahedral bond of the hydrogen atom with the oxygen atom at an angle of nearly 109°, a tridymite lattice is formed (Pauling, 1958). Each oxygen atom with its positive charge is combined with two negatively charged hydrogen atoms. Each oxygen atom consequently belongs to two tetrahedrons. On the basis of the crystal lattice one can define the ice as an oxyhydrate with tridymite lattice. Accordingly, depending on the type of composition, the water formerly has been defined as a monohydrate, dihydrate, and trihydrate. This is important for research in frozen ground, insofar as the strength of the ice-crystal formation and of the frost effects must be determined from this knowledge. The compounds of free-moving ions and of water molecules in a solution are also called *hydrates*. The process of fixing is termed *hydration*. The term hydration is therefore clearly defined by both chemists and physicists. For decades the term has been in use in agronomy, particularly to describe and understand the attachment of water molecules to negatively and positively charged ions (Scheffer and Schachtschabel, 1960; Vageler, 1932).

In research in frozen ground one can then speak of hydration in a twofold sense, because the water of crystallization in ice appears through the hydration of hydrogen oxide. Just as in other crystallized hydrates, the characteristic exothermic reaction appears also in the formation of ice crystals, that is, during the formation of hydrated H_2O molecules.

The growth of the ice crystals, as of all other crystals, results from the electric attractions of one stable ion for another from the surrounding medium (Kossel and Stranski, 1960; Everett, 1961). The attraction is particularly strong at the end of a still incomplete lattice line. This attraction is particularly effective with the water molecule, because the molecules represent dipoles. Because the dielectric constant of water is only 2 and that of fluid water is more than 80, the result is a potential that is 40 times greater for ice than for liquid water (Schenk, 1955a, 1955b). With this explanation the forces can be calculated, not only those that move the water but also those that cause the frost effects. Further experimental investigations of Czeratzki (1956) confirm this. Reference to suction could have been abandoned many years ago. The explanation is in accord with the first law of thermodynamics (Eggert, 1960, p. 484) as well as the theory of electrostatics (Eggert, 1960, p. 591).

MICROCRYSTALS

Everett (1961) proved that the melting point of ice is not only dependent upon pressure but also on the size of the ice crystal. If the ice crystals are very small, they are less stable, and the smaller their diameter the lower their melting point. Large ice crystals can be formed in cracks and large ground pores at a temperature at which water in the fine pores cannot freeze, because the small ice crystals would not be stable yet. Table 1 shows how sensitively a very small ice crystal must react to temperature changes and what pressures are caused in the absence of large crystals.

TABLE 1

Diameter of pores, microns	0.1	1	3	10	30
Melting point of the ice crystal, °Celsius	-0.4	-0.04	-0.01	-0.004	-0.001
Possible pressure in large pores, atm	4	0.4	0.13	0.04	0.013

The smaller crystals also have a larger vapor pressure than the larger ones. Consequently, the growth of larger ice crystals is influenced by this difference of vapor pressure. The resulting movement of water particles in this steamlike form, and equally in liquid form (Fig. 1), causes a drying, which is a frost drying (Fig. 2). It must necessarily manifest itself through a decrease in the volume of the layer from which the water was transported away to be built into the lattice of the ice crystals on the frozen surface layer. This shrinkage is also combined with the formation of cracks and tears, while simultaneously a pressure is exerted by the growth of the ice crystals.

FORCE OF CRYSTALLIZATION

This force, as is well known, can lead to pressures (Fig. 2 and Table 1) over 2000 kg/sq cm (Everett, 1961). All forms of cryoturbation within the ground layer and the structure formation on their surface are to be ascribed to these pressures (Stackelberg, 1964; Schenk, 1955a, 1955b). It is therefore superfluous to speak of a suction force, because these forces have been exactly defined for a long time (Schenk, 1955a, 1955b). It is exactly as great as the pressure which the growing ice crystal can exert. Consequently, the sorption water of the negatively charged ions, in other words, of the clay-mineral particles with the ion upon their surfaces, is stripped to those layers (water films) that are attached with more than 2000 kg/sq cm (Scheffer and Schachtschabel, 1960). Frost drying is therefore considerably higher than the drying effect of air and sun and lies far below the point with which hygroscopic water is bound (Fig. 2). The cryoturbation and the structural formation in clay-containing ground must develop best and strongest under these forces and with a large content of sorption water.

HYDRATION THROUGH DEGELATION

Thawing of these cryoturbations must therefore be the most conspicuous. They are catastrophic when they affect streets, airports, and buildings. In thawing a reversal of the process of hydration occurs.

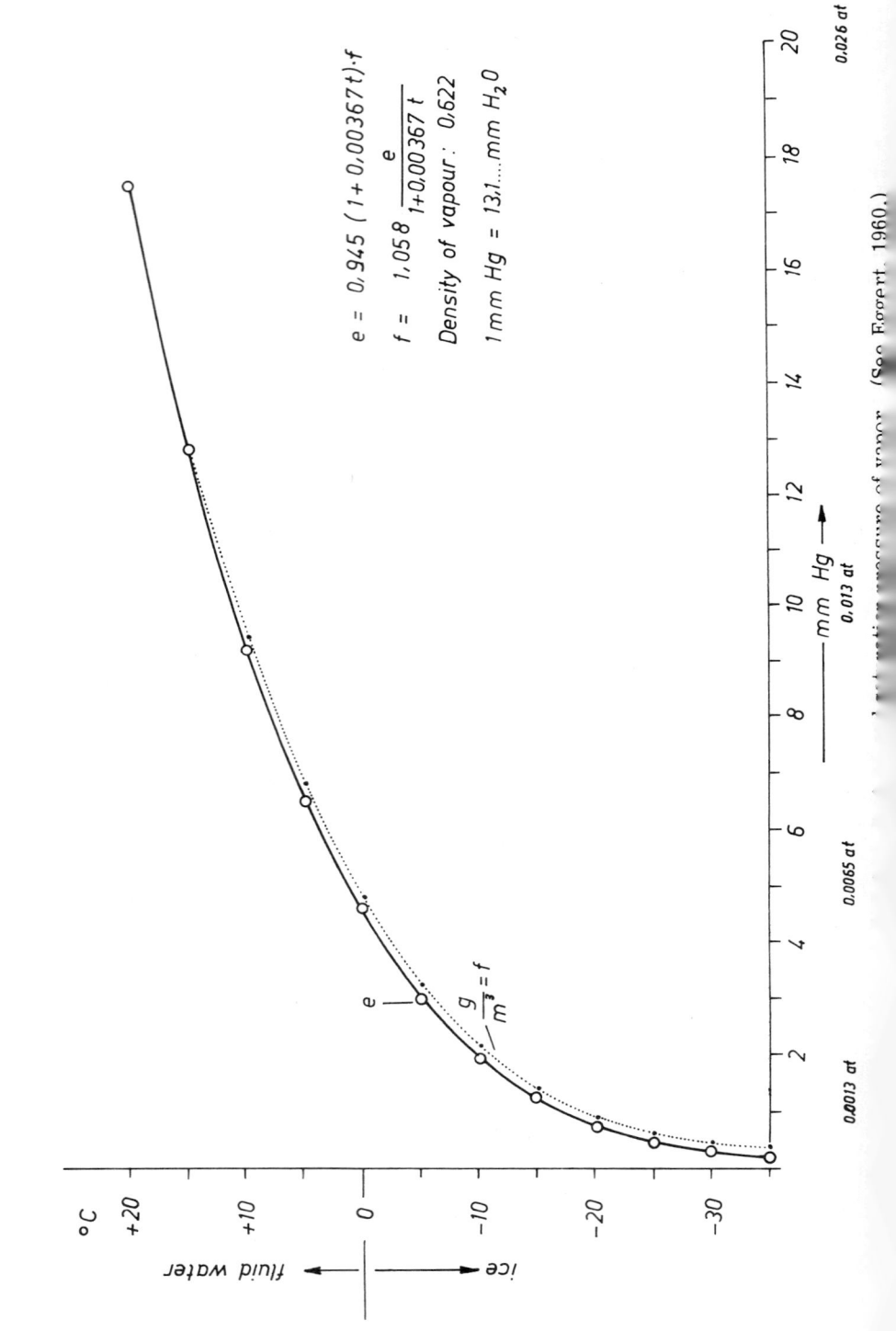

Force of water bond in soils

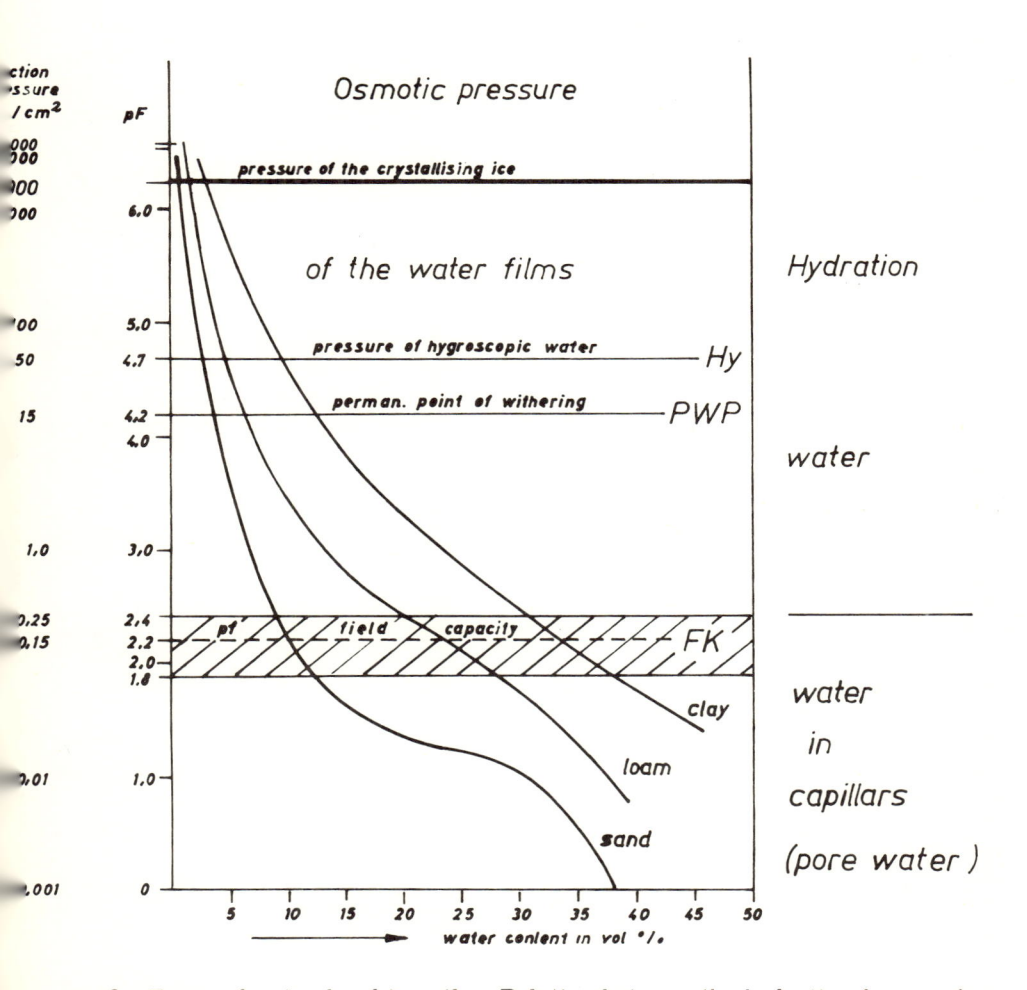

Fig. 2. Force of water bond in soils. Relation between the hydration forces of il particles and water content. (After Scheffer and Schachtschabel, completed by e author.)

The soil particles, more or less isolated by the freezing process, sink into the layer of water that is formed by the melting ice lenses and layers. They even sink to the bottom of such thin water layers, thereby becoming fully hydrated, because they have water-absorbing ions on their surface, so that they deposit themselves loosely on top of each other with thick water films. Any application of stress upon this ground, loosely packed through the water film, must lead to boils and to a collapse of the original ground-layer arrangement. Therefore we find in all periglacial areas an abundance of specific structures of the permafrost ground.

THERMAL CONTRACTION

The multiple structures of cryoturbation, especially of ice wedges, have also been explained by the diminution of the soil volume as a consequence of very low temperatures. This theory was developed by Middendorf (1864-67) and Bunge (1884, 1902) nearly a hundred years ago. It was used especially by Leffingwell (1915) to explain the formation of ice wedges. In recent years one worker has tried to develop a thermophysical theory for mathematical calculations (Lachenbruch, 1961, 1966). Many others (Black, 1954, pp. 839-856; Washburn, 1956, pp. 823-866, 1963; Péwé, 1959, 1962, 1966; Svensson, 1963) agree with this theory.

The older scientists could not know the forces and processes of hydration, however, and it is a fundamental error to refer to such calculations to explain the development of cracks and ice wedges without considering the forces of hydration and crystallization, that is, the first fundamental law of thermodynamics.

The observations undertaken by Brewer (1958) in the permafrost of northern Alaska show that the zero-degree level penetrates the soil only when all the accessible water in the underground has been used for the formation of ice crystals. From all these observations and numerous others based on frost experiments, it follows that the diminution of the volume of the soil that is connected with the formation of cracks takes place before the thermal contraction caused by low temperatures can become effective. The experiments of Czeratzki (1956) confirm the objections of Taber (1943), Dücker (1951), and Schenk (1955).

REFERENCES

Black, R. F., 1954, Permafrost - A review: Geol. Soc. Am. Bull., v. 65, pp. 839-856.

Brewer, M. C., 1958, Some results of geothermal investigations of permafrost in northern Alaska: Trans. Am. Geophys. Union, v. 39, pp. 19-26.

Bunge, A. von, 1884, Naturhistorische Beobachtungen und Fahrten im Lena-Delta: Acad. Sci. St. Petersburg, Bull., 29, pp. 422-476.
_____ 1902, Einige Worte zur Bodeneisfrage: Russ. K. Mineral. Ges. Verhandl., 2. Ser., v. 40, pp. 203-209.
Czeratzki, W., 1956, Bodenstrukturbildung durch Frost (Modellversuche): Göttingen Inst. Wiss. (film).
Dücker, A., 1951, Über die Entstehung von Frostspalten: Kiel, Schr. Naturwiss. Ver. Schleswig-Holstein, 25, Karl-Gripp-Festschr., pp. 58-64.
Eggert, J., 1960, Lehrbuch der physikalischen Chemie: Stuttgart, Hitzel Verlag, 844 pp.
Everett, D. H., 1961, The thermodynamics of frost damage to porous solids: Trans. Faraday Soc., v. 57, pp. 1541-1551.
Kossel, W., and J. N. Stranski, 1960, *in* Lehrbuch der physikalischen Chemie, J. Eggert (ed.): Stuttgart, Hirzel Verlag, p. 777.
Lachenbruch, A. H., 1961, Depth and spacing of tension cracks: J. Geophys. Res., v. 66, pp. 4273-4292.
_____ 1966, Contraction theory of ice wedges polygons. A qualitative discussion: Proc. Intern. Conf. Permafrost, Lafayette, Ind., 1963.
Leffingwell, E. de K., 1915, Ground-ice wedges. The dominant form of ground-ice on the north coast of Alaska: J. Geol., v. 23, pp. 635-654.
Middendorf, A. T. von, 1864-1867, Reise in den äußersten Norden und Osten Sibiriens: Petersburg, Kaiserl. Akad. Wiss., 739 pp.
Pauling, L., 1958, Chemie, eine Einführung: Weinheim-Bergstr., Chemie Verlag, 624 pp.
Péwé, T. L., 1959, Sand-wedges polygons (tesselations) in the McMurdo sound region, Antarctica. A progress report: Am. J. Sci., v. 257, pp. 545-552.
_____ 1962, Ice wedges in permafrost, lower Yukon River area near Galena, Alaska: Buil. Peryglacjalny, No. 11, pp. 65-76.
_____ 1966, Ice wedges in Alaska. Classification, distribution, and climatic significance: Proc. Intern. Conf. Permafrost, Lafayette, Ind., 1963.
Scheffer, F., and P. Schachtschabel, 1960, Lehrbuch der Agrikulturchemie und Bodenkunde, I. Teil Bodenkunde: Stuttgart, Enke Verlag, 332 pp.
Schenk, E., 1954, Solifluktion: Z. Deut. Geol. Ges., v. 105, pp. 197-202.
_____ 1955a, Die Mechanik der periglazialen Strukturböden: Abhandl. Hess. Landesamtes Bodenforsch., v. 13, 92 pp.
_____ 1955b, Die periglazialen Strukturbodenbildungen als Folgen der Hydratationsvorgänge im Boden: Eiszeitalter Gegenwart, v. 6, pp. 170-184.
Stackelberg, M. von, 1964, Die physikalische Deutung der Frostaufbrüche: Frankfurt-Main, Umschau, v. 3, p. 68.

Svensson, H., 1963, Tundra polygons. Photographic interpretation and field studies in north-Norwegian polygon areas: Lund Studies Geograph. Ser. A., Phys. Geograph., No. 29.

Taber, St., 1943, Perennially frozen ground in Alaska. Its origin and history: Bull. Geol. Soc. Am., v. 54, pp. 1433-1548.

Vageler, P. 1932, Der Kationen- und Wasserhaushalt des Mineralbodens: Berlin, Springer Verlag, pp. 60-220.

Washburn, A. L., 1956, Classification of patterned ground and review of suggested origins. Geol. Soc. Am. Bull., v. 67, pp. 823-866.

———, D. D. Smith, and R. H. Goddard, 1963, Frost cracking in a middle-latitude climate: Biul. Peryglacjalny, No. 12, pp. 176-189.

ARCTIC AND ALPINE ENVIRONMENTS (H. E. Wright, Jr., and W. H. Osburn, eds.), 237-240, © 1967 Indiana University Press

14
Features of Deposits Formed under Permafrost Conditions

E. M. KATASONOV
Permafrost Institute
Siberian Division of Academy of Sciences
Yakutsk, USSR

Abstract

Deposits formed under permafrost conditions are characterized by very high ice content and distinctive cryogenic structures, which depend on the conditions of accumulation and freezing of the sediments. Cryogenic structures are additional genetic features that can help in studying the permafrost.

Two types of perennially frozen deposits may be distinguished. The first comprises sedimentary rocks that accumulated and froze without being influenced by permafrost. Having been thawed for a long time, they underwent great diagenetic changes, with the formation of fissures that were later completely or partially filled with ice. The second type comprises deposits formed under the influence of shallow permafrost. Such deposits, originally talik (active layer), contain cryoturbations, ice wedges, and ice layers, as well as cryogenic structures composed of ice interlayers and lenses. Frozen Siberian Quaternary deposits are mainly of the second type. When compared with recently frozen sediments, these deposits were shown to have frozen slowly, layer by layer, as sediments accumulated. Deposits formed under permafrost conditions are either subaqueous or subaerial, according to the mechanisms of their freezing and their cryogenic structures.

Sediments in shallow lakes are not frozen initially, so they become consolidated. As the basins fill with sediment, the permafrost table under the water shifts upward, and the unfrozen sediments gradually decrease. The unconsolidated deposits thus freeze from the sides and bottom and, because of the redistribution of moisture in the deposits, discontinuous ice schlieren are formed (Fig. 1), inclined or

Fig. 1. Discontinuous ice lenses.

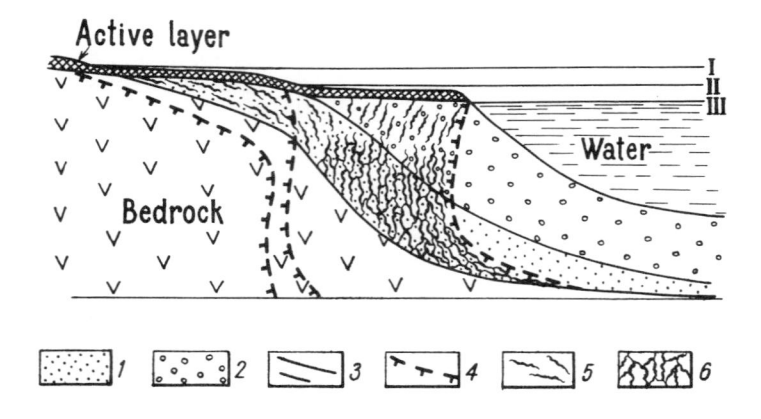

Fig. 2. Formation of ice schlieren in bottom sediments. I, II, III, water surface at different stages of the development of the basin; 1, bottom sediments of the first generation; 2, bottom sediments of the second generation; 3, bottom of the basin at different stages during its development; 4, permafrost table at different stages of the development of the basin; 5, discontinuous ice lenses which form inclined cryogenic structures; 6, discontinuous ice schlieren which form vertical latticelike cryogenic structures

Fig. 3. Regular ice layers.

almost vertical, depending on the position of the freezing front (Fig. 2). The clayey bottom sediments, subjected to early diagenesis at the moment of freezing, form latticelike cryogenic structures that are obviously connected with the appearance of tiny cracks ("syneresis"). In my opinion the inshore deposits with ice layers freeze in the same way, i.e., from the side of the frozen substratum.

Subaerial deposits that accumulate on slopes in floodplain and delta, where the depths of summer thaw do not exceed 1 to 2 m, do not undergo any diagenetic changes and thus have diverse cryogenic structures. By the time they become permafrost, they have moisture

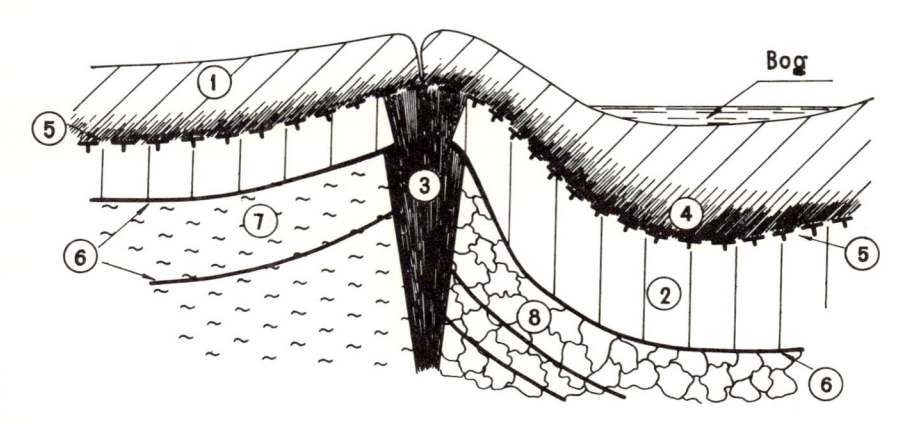

Fig. 4. Formation of cryogenic structures in subaerial deposits. 1, active layer; 2, active layer recently turned into permafrost; 3, ice wedge; 4, water-saturated rock on the permafrost table; 5, permafrost table; 6, ice layers forming bedded cryogenic structures; 7, lenticular cryogenic structures; 8, reticulate cryogenic structures.

characteristic of an active layer under certain landscape conditions. Therefore few if any ice inclusions are found in deposits that once were a waterless active layer. But if the active layer contains enough water, the perennially frozen deposits have lenticular or reticulate cryogenic structures and regular ice layers (Figs. 3 and 4).

Ice layers that form because of water refreezing on an uneven permafrost table occur horizontally, concavely, or in gentle waves, and they thus reflect the unevenness of the table. Through these occurrences, deluvial, floodplain, and solifluction deposits can be distinguished.

Thus we can point out the following features of continental deposits formed under permafrost conditions: (1) few or no diagenetic changes; (2) diverse, and often very high, ice contents; and (3) a variety of cryogenic structures, which depend on the conditions of accumulation and freezing of the sediments.

Cryogenic structures and ice and soil veins, additional genetic features, can also help in the study of permafrost.

15
Divided Elimination
by Glacial Erosion

DAVID L. LINTON
Department of Geography
University of Birmingham
Birmingham, England

Abstract

Divides of two kinds are considered those between adjacent corries (cirques) and those between adjacent troughs. Observations by M. J. Battey on sheet jointing in two Norwegian corries suggest a mechanism of corrie growth by plucking, with removal of shells of rock that are concentric about a vertical axis. Progressive destruction of the intervening divides would result in stages that may be designated as interrupted grats, shortened grats, and vestigial grats; subdued grats and residual pyramidal peaks are readily recognized in European mountains. The process leads to scenically impressive forms, but as a mode of bulk erosion it is much less important than the elimination of divides between troughs. Common observation shows that here again sheet jointing is important, but in this case the detached shells of rock are concentric about a horizontal axis. Convergence of adjacent troughs produces shortened, vestigial, and subdued divides. Such forms are unusual in temperate mountains, but in regions with a snowline around sea level, enlargement of the cross section of a trough is continuous downstream and involves progressive elimination of divides. Instances are cited from Antarctica and in some detail from Spitzbergen.

Most observers of glaciated mountains from Willard Johnson (1904) onward have agreed that the amphitheatral hollows that we call corries or cirques grow progressively with time. A well-known sequence of diagrams by Davis (1912, pp. 419-421) shows the imagined consequences of such growth through youthful and mature phases, which are abundantly matched in nature, to an old-age phase, in which the whole summit of the preglacial mountain is supposed to be consumed down to the level of the regional snowline. Field observation fails to reveal the existence of such truncated mountains but offers instead numerous examples of isolated pyramidal peaks of the Matterhorn type. The edges of such pyramids are continued by low arêtes, either still separating the ice of different corrie glaciers or overrun by ice and now worn down to a subdued form. These pyramids must be regarded as having formerly been the junction points of divides between opposed corrie walls that have since suffered progressive destruction and elimination. Examples of intermediate forms in this process are abundantly available, and we may conveniently recognize such stages as the *interrupted grat*,* where the ridge has been broken and overrun in its central portion but rises again to a peak at its distal end; the *shortened grat*, where the distal end of the divide has been eliminated; the *vestigial grat*, where only the articulation with the triangular walls of the pyramid remains; and the *subdued grat*, for those portions of all the above that were overrun and ice-molded before being uncovered.

All these forms are readily recognized in European mountains, while the most advanced of them (the vestigial grat and the pyramidal peak) are ubiquitous in the Antarctic and afford a valuable clue to the genetic status of the mountain forms now seen there. Along many Antarctic coastlines vestigial grats may be observed behind the coastal glacier fringe. That corrie glaciers have played an essential part in producing this scenery was recognized by Otto Holtedahl (1929, pp. 15-22, 149-153) in the Palmer Archipelago, but he did not grasp that the corrie glaciers themselves eliminated the divides between them, and he invoked an ice mass of continental origin to "smooth the mountain sides and remove the local ridges typical of a coast with cirque glacier erosion." On such inland mountain groups as the Tottan Mountains (Fuchs and Hillary, 1958, plate following p. 20) we see little but a complex of residual pyramids and vestigial divides, while elsewhere archipelagoes of isolated pyramids project through the ice and are almost certainly connected by subdued grats beneath it. Good examples are seen, for example, on sheets W 7070 and W 7068 of the British Antarctic Survey's 1960 1/200,000 map of Alexander Island. Occasionally one finds a single massive, round-topped mountain standing up among them and overtopping them by a thousand feet or more, still carrying a remnant of the preglacial surface. Mt. Taylor in the Palmer Peninsula is one such (British Antarctic Survey 1960 map of Graham Land, scale 1/25,000, Hope Bay sheet). Mt. Bechervaise in Australian Antarctic Territory is another (Crohn, 1959, pl. 22).

---

*Grat is the term used throughout the German-speaking Alps (both in common and in place-name usage) for the sharp ridges known in French as *arêtes*. The monosyllable *grat* is obviously more convenient in making compound terms.

Observations by Battey (1960) on the sheet jointing of two Norwegian corries throw some light on the nature of corrie growth implied by the foregoing sequence of forms. He showed that in the small corrie of Veslgjuvbreen in Jotenheimen the strike of the major vertical joints passes from east-west to north-south and back again to east-west if the corrie wall is followed from the south side round the head to the north side, and that similar relations characterize a neighboring corrie (Vesl-Skautbreen). He concluded from this that the joints arise by spontaneous dilatation of the rock in a direction normal to the corrie wall as the stresses in that direction are relieved by erosion. But the new joints encourage further removal and progressive enlargement of the corrie. Battey's observations represent a real contribution to our knowledge of the plucking process, and it is to be hoped that they will be widely extended by similar careful examinations of the joint systems of corrie walls elsewhere. In the light of this work we can see that when the walls of two adjacent corries approach, the rock between them may be traversed by two sets of joints intersecting at an acute angle; the divide thus becomes very vulnerable, and breaching and shortening can be expected to be rapid. But in the pyramid that is thus outlined the rock has probably reached equilibrium. It has for some time been free to expand outward toward each of the defining corries and is probably not liable to much further change of this kind. So its core may long remain sound and unjointed, and the reduction of such a residual pyramid may be comparatively slow.

A similar hypothesis may be outlined in relation to glacial troughs. Many troughs, such as that of Loch Coruisk in Scotland or Tyssedalen in Norway, show on their naked rock walls conspicuous sheet joints, markedly concave upward. Removal of rock from the center of the trough in the early phases of erosion, and its replacement by ice only one-third as dense, may be expected to lead to dilatation normal to the rock wall and the production of sheet joints and so to progressive deepening and enlargement. Where two troughs lie parallel and adjacent, or converge to a junction, the intervening wall may be expected to be attacked from both sides and progressively demolished from its distal end upstream. *A shortened divide* should result and, as it is shortened, a *subdued divide* should remain in front of it. Such forms are common in the Antarctic, and two instances may here be referred to.

Near Hope Bay at the extremity of the Palmer Peninsula, a larger and a smaller glacier converge and are separated by a rock ridge called the Steeple (Fig. 1). The two rock faces of the Steeple are nothing but the curving walls of two troughs of unequal volume, depth, and radius of curvature (R1 and R2). Clearly it is simply a rock remnant between the two troughs and must once have extended much farther down valley. Its distal end towers up like the prow of a ship, and in front of it is a low ice-molded ridge — the subdued divide.

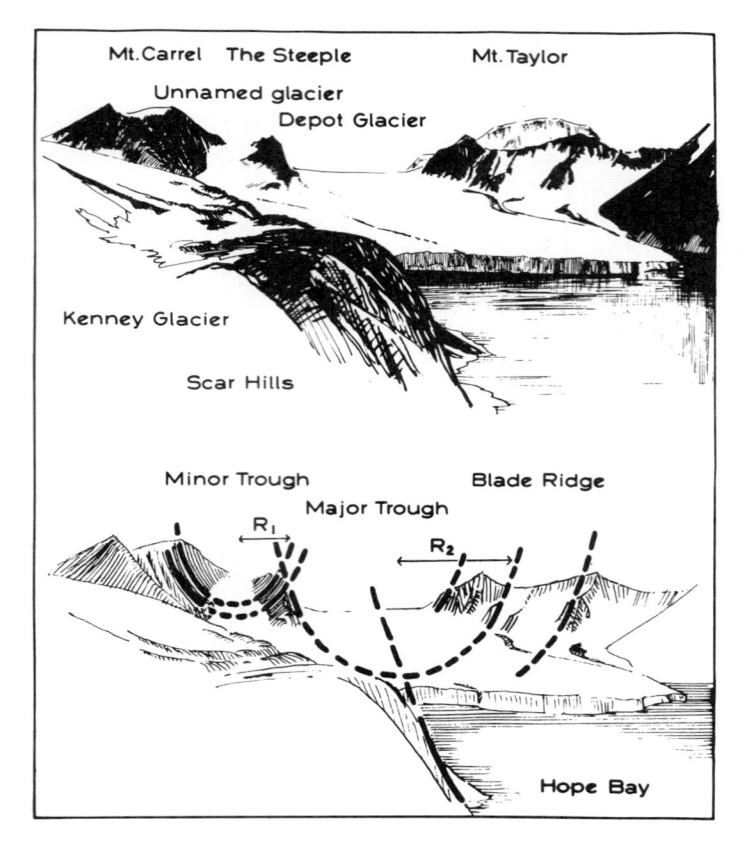

Fig. 1. Progressive divide elimination between subparallel troughs exemplified by the Steeple, Hope Bay, British Antarctic Territory. (Drawn from photographs by the author.)

From this low ridge it is clear enough why the Steeple is so called (Linton, 1963, pl. 6). The second example, called Stenhouse Bluff, is a great rock buttress between the East and West Stenhouse glaciers in King George Island in the South Shetlands (Fig. 2). It is the distal end of a shortened divide that lies concealed beneath the ice. In front of it is a low, glacially subdued rock spur.

In mountainous regions in high latitudes where the regional snow-line is at sea level this type of divide shortening and elimination is widespread. The confluence of valley glaciers is not accompanied by any reduction in ice volume by melting, and the cross-sectional area of the main glacier must increase progressively downstream. An excellent example is furnished by Reindalen in Vestspitsbergen at about 78°N (Fig. 3). Today Reindalen is without a glacier, although some tributary glaciers deploy their moraines on the floor in the upper

Fig. 2. Shortened divide with subdued divide in front of it. Stenhouse Bluff between West and East Stenhouse Glaciers, Admiralty Bay, King George Island, British Antarctic Territory. (Author's photograph.)

part. Here the valley is $1\frac{1}{2}$ to 2 miles wide, but below Kokbreen the valley sides diverge visibly, and where Tverrdalen comes in between strikingly ice-tapered spurs the width has increased to 4 miles in a distance of only 6 miles. Where Semmeldalen enters from the north, 7 or 8 miles downstream, the width increases abruptly from $4\frac{1}{2}$ to 6 miles. In the next mile or so Reindalen receives Litledalen on its southern side from behind Litledalsfjellet, a 6-mile-long ridge that is spectacularly smoothed, tapered, and recurved away from the main valley. Almost immediately Reindalen enters Van Mijenfjord on a 7-mile front, yet the whole valley is less than 30 miles long.

These relationships are without parallel in water-cut valley systems. They become explicable when we envisage the ice streams that used this valley system at the periods of heaviest glacierization. Figure 4 attempts representation of such a situation. It has been constructed by drawing margins against the existing rock walls of an ice surface that had a level about 200 m above sea level at the confluence with Van Mijenfjord (which was, of course, ice-filled for 30 miles or more downstream to the open sea), rising to about 300 m near the confluence of Tverrdalen, and to heights about 100 m above the levels of the existing remnant glaciers. "Medial moraines" have been shown on Figure 4, although these would have been concealed deep below the

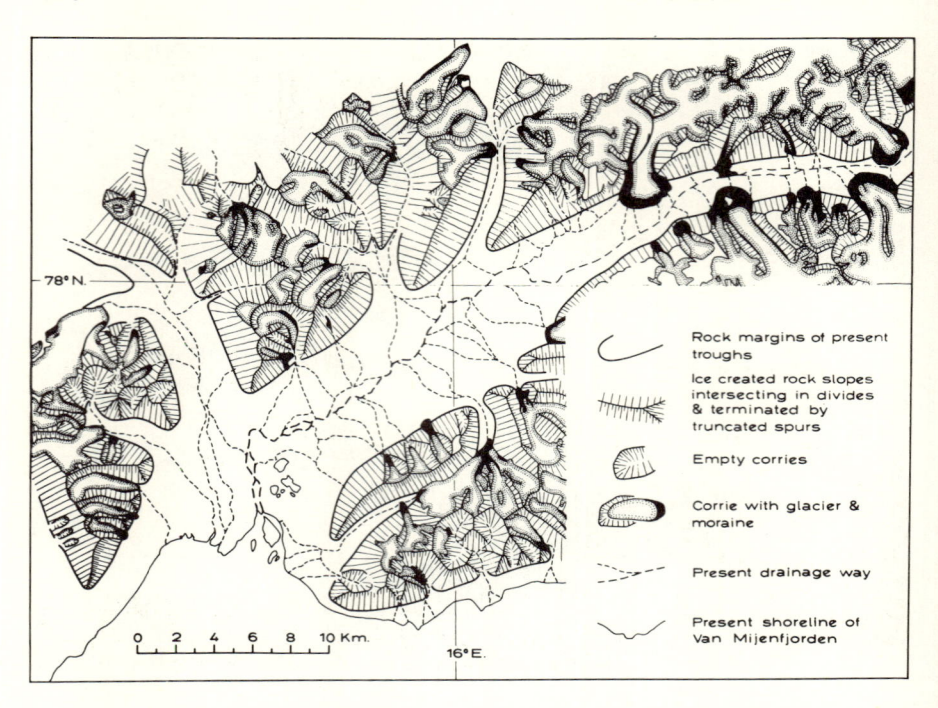

Fig. 3. "Valley" widening by shortening and elimination of lateral spurs, Reindalen, Vestspitsbergen. Maps B-10 and C-10, scale 1/100,000, Norges Geografiske Oppmåling.

ice surface at the time imagined. They serve to show how the increases in trough width have been necessitated.

Figure 5 carries the reconstruction a stage further. It shows by contours at 200, 400, 600, 800, and 1000 m the topography of a region whose drainage lines are those of Reindalen and its tributaries, whose summits have the location and altitude of the present mountain peaks, and whose landforms and slopes are those characteristic of fluvial erosion descending to a main valley that reached sea level only at the mouth of the present Van Mijenfjord. Comparison of Figs. 4 and 5 reveals how the creation of Reindalen as it is today has involved cutting back many of the preglacial lateral divides by several miles, and how no part of the present landscape remotely resembles that which we must suppose to have existed preglacially.

This instance has been cited from a region built wholly of level-bedded Tertiary sediments and we may assume that, geological considerations being simple and uniform, they may be safely ignored. But in fact the same features are still developed in areas of massive rocks and strongly developed linear structures. Dunderdalen is cut obliquely across the strike of the resistant Hekla Hook formation to

DIVIDE ELIMINATION BY GLACIAL EROSION

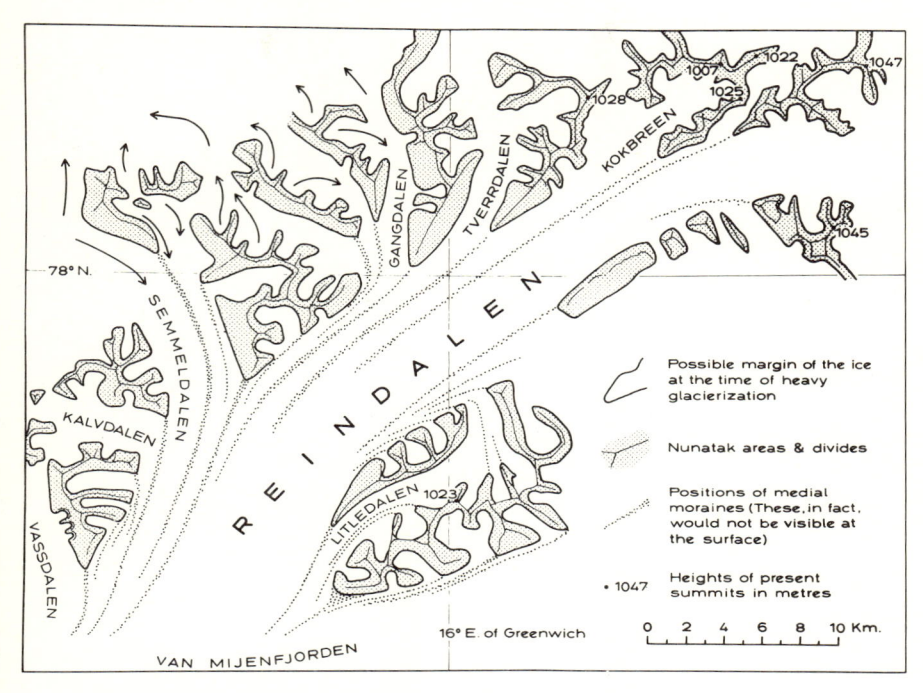

Fig. 4. Reconstruction of appearance of Reindalen during severe glacierization, showing streamlining of nunatak walls by removal of all lateral divides, and close adjustment of visible topography to channel requirements of ice streams. This reconstruction resembles the present picture at the head of Storbreen and Nathorstbreen (Map C-12, scale 1/100,000, Norges Geografiske Oppmåling).

open directly on the west coast at 77°28'N (Map B-11, scale 1/100,000, Norges Geografiska Oppmåling). In less than 10 miles it widens from only 1 to more than 3 miles by the steady recession of its streamlined walls and the tapering away to nothing of the 300-m-high Slettfjellet in 2½ miles. In fact, there is every reason to believe that under suitable climatic conditions divide elimination is quite general and essentially without respect to bedrock geology. If the ice volumes become large enough, lateral spurs may be shorn right back to their junctions with the main ridge, as is well seen in the Vestspitsbergen ridges Luciakammen and Sofiekammen (Map B-12). Indeed, in Antarctica, where ice streams achieve their grandest dimensions, there is reason to think that in some cases mountain ranges have been progressively cut back by the ice streams on each side until they have disappeared altogether.

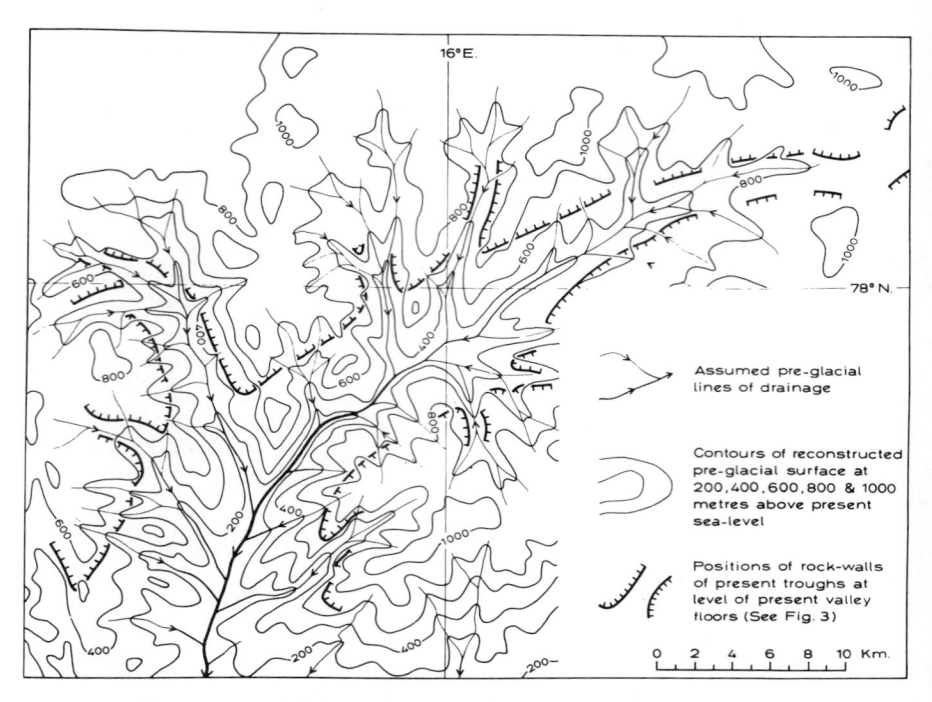

Fig. 5. Reconstruction of probable preglacial topography of the area draining to Reindalen, for comparison with Fig. 3.

REFERENCES

Battey, M. H., 1960, Geological factors in the development of Veslgjuvbotn and Vesl Skautbotn, *in* Investigations on Norwegian Cirque Glaciers, W. V. Lewis (ed.): Roy. Geograph. Soc. Res. Ser., No. 4, pp. 11-24.

Crohn, P. W. R., 1959, A contribution to the geology and glaciology of the western part of the Australian Antarctic Territory: Melbourne, Dept. External Affairs, Australian Nat. Antarctic Res. Exped., Ser. A, v. 3, 103 pp.

Davis, W. M., 1912, Die erklärende Beschreibung der Landformen: Leipzig, B. G. Teubner, 565 pp.

Fuchs, Vivian, and E. Hillary, 1958, The Crossing of Antarctica: London, Cassell, 337 pp.

Holtedahl, O., 1929, On the geology and physiography of some Antarctic and Sub-Antarctic islands, *in* Scientific Results of the Norwegian Antarctic Expeditions 1927-28 and 1928-29, No. 3: Avhandl. Norske Videnskaps-Akad. Oslo, 172 pp.

Johnson, W. D., 1904, The profile of maturity in Alpine glacial erosion: J. Geol., v. 12, pp. 569-578.

Linton, D. L., 1963, The forms of glacial erosion: Inst. Brit. Geograph. Publ. 33, pp. 1-28.

ARCTIC AND ALPINE ENVIRONMENTS (H. E. Wright, Jr., and W. H. Osburn, eds.), 249-254, © 1967 Indiana University Press

16
Tectonic and Lithologic Control on Trough and Cirque Features in Caledonian, Hercynian, and Alpine Mountains of Europe

THERESE PIPPAN
Salzburg, Austria

Abstract

Graphs based on statistical data from comparative glaciomorphological field and map studies in the Norwegian mountains, the Bohemian Forest, and the Austrian Central Alps show that the tectonic and lithologic conditions of these areas control shaping of cirques and troughs. Thus with the same orographic height of mountains but different ages of uplift these features may be marked by rather different intensity. The development of cirques is much favored by quick retreat of valley heads in culmination areas uplifted and dissected during the late Tertiary, where updoming brought their summits under the influence of long-lasting Pleistocene to Recent local glaciation. In the Bohemian Forest, where such youthful uplift did not occur, the shallow valley heads could hardly develop into typical cirques. If a latest preglacial cut was set into a broad preglacial valley floor, because of young updoming, as in the Hohe Tauern, shoulder troughs developed, but if the cut is into an old surface as in the inner Norwegian mountains, shoulderless valley cross sections occur. The influence of the different proportion of uplift on trough-shaping is shown by the asymmetric Norwegian mountains. There in the higher, western part, typical trough sections occur, because of rapid and straight flow of valley glaciers and ice caps in deep, narrow valleys of high gradient. But in the lower, eastern part the movement directions rarely coincided, and the ice occupied shallow, broad valleys of low gradient.

The shaping of typical steep, smooth walls of cirques and troughs is favored by planes, joints, faults, and bedding planes in hard, uniform granite or gneiss striking parallel to the valley and dipping

249

250　　　　　　　　　　　　　　　　　　　　　　　　　　　THERESE PIPPAN

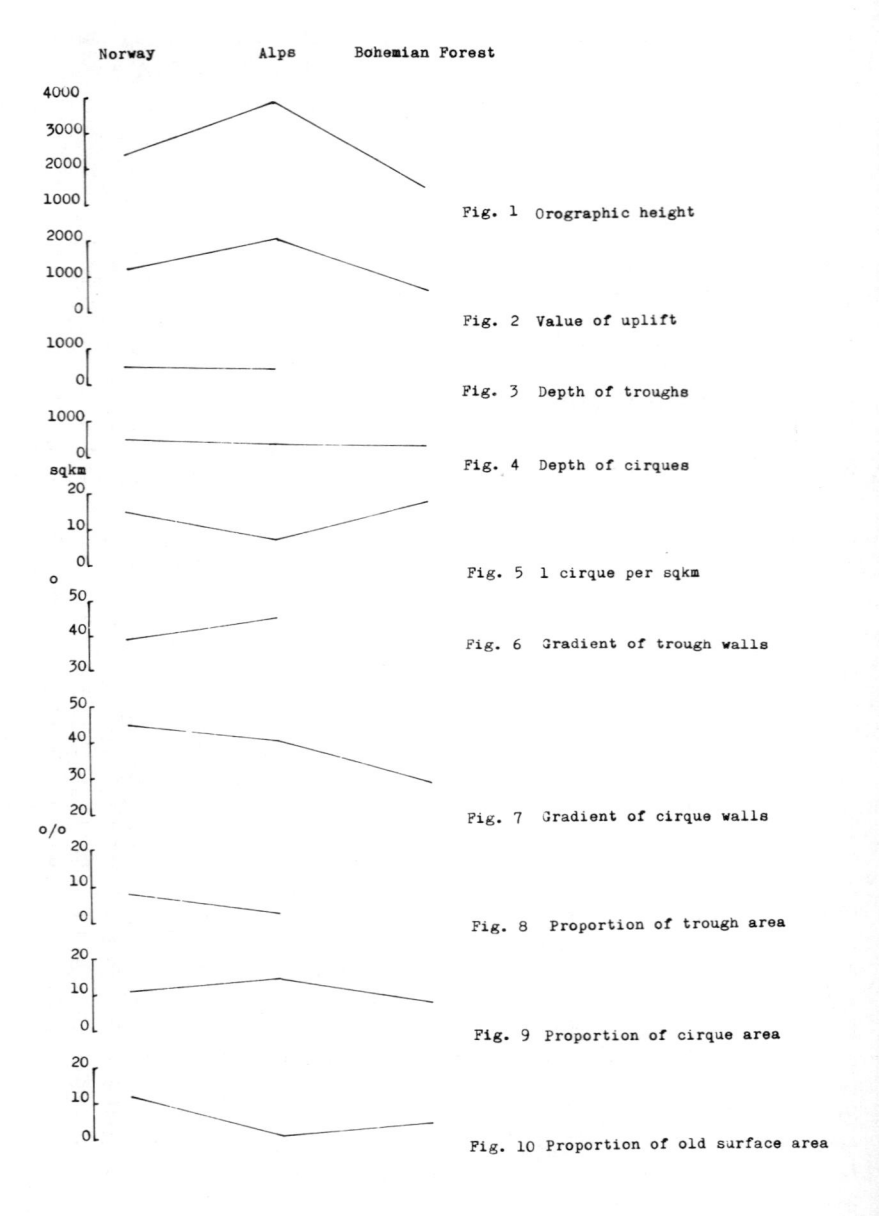

Fig. 1　Orographic height

Fig. 2　Value of uplift

Fig. 3　Depth of troughs

Fig. 4　Depth of cirques

Fig. 5　1 cirque per sqkm

Fig. 6　Gradient of trough walls

Fig. 7　Gradient of cirque walls

Fig. 8　Proportion of trough area

Fig. 9　Proportion of cirque area

Fig. 10　Proportion of old surface area

about the same amount as the mean slope angle of the walls. With rocks of variable resistance and transverse strike, the cirque and trough cross sections occur only at projecting bastions. Cirques can also be controlled by bends in folds.

Comparative glaciomorphological investigations of troughs and cirques in the Caledonian Mountains of Norway (2468 m), the Hercynian Bohemian Forest (1457 m), and the Alpine Hohe Tauern (3798 m), based on field work and studies of numerous local maps, have revealed a high degree of lithologic and tectonic control in their typical development (Fig. 1).

A favorable factor for the creation of *troughs* was the strong uplift of the late Tertiary to the Pleistocene, which encouraged fluvial dissection. In Norway this uplift amounted to 1200 m and in the Hohe Tauern 2000 m (Fig. 2), producing mean summit gradients of 37 and 40°, respectively. In the high western mountains of central Norway the initial surface for the incision of troughs was generally a shallow river valley cut directly into an older surface. The prevalent trough form in this area is therefore shoulderless. But near the coast and in the Hohe Tauern the preglacial valleys contained deep, narrow rejuvenation cuts with steep longitudinal profiles. In these areas, therefore, the glacial troughs possess shoulders composed of the remnants of the preglacial valley slopes and floors. In all these valleys there were glaciers of over 1000 m thickness, with steep sole gradients and intense erosional power. Trough depths average 400 m in the Hohe Tauern and 500 m in the high mountains of Norway (Fig. 3), when the erosive force of the glaciers was reinforced by the concordant movement of an ice cap. The troughs of the Norwegian high mountains cover about 8% of the total mountain area and those of the Hohe Tauern about 2.5% (Fig. 8).

In Norway the best-shaped troughs follow either the strike of the Caledonian folds or the direction of steep joint or fault systems. These ancient structural features are accentuated by valley-forming processes, as in the Romsdal.

In both old and young mountains trough formation is particularly favored where master systems of steeply dipping joints or faults happen to parallel the strike and the valleys. Such tectonic planing of the trough walls may be accentuated by glacial polishing. The classic trough head of the Kaefer Valley in the Hohe Tauern is in part associated with such faults. Slates which parallel the valley and are steeply tilted by the tectonic pressure of overthrust have a similar effect.

The Bohemian Forest, by contrast, shows tectonic conditions that are unfavorable for trough formation. There the amplitude of Miocene to Pleistocene uplift was only about 500 m (Fig. 2). Summits did not reach 1500 m (Fig. 1), and their mean gradient attained only 14°. As a result both fluviatile and glacial dissection were moderate. Preglacial rejuvenation did not penetrate far into the mountains, and mature valleys still prevail. However, glaciers did not exceed 3 km in length or 125 m in thickness, and this, combined with their gentle bottom gradient, means an absence of troughs.

In the Caledonian and Alpine Mountains, the glacial polishing of the trough walls may be prevented by the presence of shatter belts, microfolding belts, foliation, log structure caused by compression, or rocks that strike transversely to the valleys. Other conditions that contribute to the suppression of typical trough features are zones of relative subsidence that develop broad shallow longitudinal valleys of low longitudinal gradient, such as the Upper Pinzgau at the foot of the Hohe Tauern. The trend of valleys in a direction opposite that of the main movement of the ice cap, as to the east of the principal Norwegian divide, has had a similar effect in suppressing troughs.

As a general rule the Hohe Tauern troughs are less well formed than those of Norway. This results from stronger uplift, which caused more extensive removal of the old surface, leaving it to cover only 0.7% of the mountain area, as compared with 12% in the Norwegian Caledonians (Fig. 10). Hence ice accumulation was less heavy, and the erosive and polishing power of the glaciers was reduced in spite of the steep longitudinal gradient. Moreover, the E-W strike means that rocks outcrop transversely to the consequent valleys, whose sides therefore remain rugged. Steeply tilted thrust wedges of imbricate structure frequently strike across the valleys, and their fault planes guide deep gullies, as on the west side of the Bären gorge in the Fuscher Valley. On the east side of the same part of the gorge there are similar gullies along shatter belts between these wedges, and the trough shape is also modified by projecting bastions formed of the disturbed rocks.

Trough formation in both old and young mountains is also facilitated by favorable rock dispositions, including steep bedding planes, joint planes, or slab planes that continue for long distances or resume intermittently in parallelism with the valley. Glacial attack on surfaces such as these has perpetuated the steepness of the receding trough walls. An example is afforded by the lower Ködnitz Valley in the Hohe Tauern. There steep joints in granite or gneiss maintain the trough walls at a mean angle of 52°, which is 7° above the average for these mountains (Fig. 6). Similar conditions occur in Norway between Bonasjōn and the Aefjord and promote excellent glaciated polished walls in U-shaped valleys, which grade into convex upper and concave lower slopes. Where steeply dipping beds or slabs of rock strike transversely to the valley, they prevent the development of a smooth uniform trough wall, and in this case trough bastions occur. Gently dipping or horizontal beds produce rugged outcrop slopes with steps related to variations in rock resistance. These are likely to produce screes that obscure the shape of the trough.

The lithological influence is seen in the fact that the narrowest troughs with the steepest slopes occur in hard, uniform granite and gneiss, gabbro, quartzose slate, calcareous mica schist, and limestone. This can be illustrated by the Habach Valley in the Hohe Tauern and the inner Rombaksbotn near Narvik, both in gneiss. The metamorphism of several orogenies in the Caledonian Mountains has largely equalized the original differential resistance of the rocks, and well-formed troughs are therefore widespread. In the Alps, however, there is only a lower grade of metamorphism, with more retention of differential resistance, and well-developed troughs are rare.

Soft rocks are definitely unfavorable for trough development, e.g., the phyllite that produces flat slopes in the Fuscher Valley. In the Hohe Tauern there is a frequent change of rock type due to nappe structure, and this prevents the formation of long smooth trough walls. However, the intercalation of resistant beds results in the presence of bastions, and the valleys are more troughlike than those of uniform soft material. An example is provided by the lower Kaprun Valley, where calcareous mica schist occurs within phyllite.

Favorable conditions for *cirque* formation were also engendered by the strong uplift of Tertiary and Quaternary times and the resultant rapid headward erosion of valley heads up to elevations of 1900 m in Norway and 2300 m in Austria. Such initial features were reshaped into cirques by local glaciers, and these are also found close to sea level in the Norwegian coastal mountains, where the ice cap rapidly descended to low elevations. In this area, cirques average a density of one per 15 sq km and occupy about 11% of the mountain surface. Their depth averages 530 m, and the gradient of their walls 45°. Corresponding figures for the Hohe Tauern are one cirque per 7 sq km, occupying 14% of the surface with an average depth of 380 m and an average slope of 40° (Figs. 4, 5, 7, 9). Cirque stairways and cirquelike valley steps developed as a result of intermittent uplift.

In the Bohemian Forest, where uplift and preglacial dissection were moderate and where the valley heads possessed gentle slopes, only 12 cirques developed, e.g., at Rachel Lake, and some of these were not well developed, e.g., the Stubenbach Lake basin. The cirques are located between summits of at least 1300 m at a height of 925 to 1100 m and were occupied by cirque glaciers that developed into slope and valley glaciers. The mean density of cirques is one per 17 sq km; they occupy 7% of the respective mountain area. Their mean depth is 270 m, with a maximum of 500 m, and their backwalls slope at an average of 28°, with a maximum of 70° (Figs. 4, 5, 7, 9).

Cirque formation is favored along the sites of tectonic culminations, where granite or gneiss occurs beneath sedimentary rocks, e.g., the Gr. Venediger in the Hohe Tauern and the summits above the Aefjord in Norway. In all mountains steeply dipping bedding and fault planes help to produce high gradients in cirque walls. W. V. Lewis observed how cirque faces may follow tectonic foliation. In all such cases the tectonic smoothing is intensified by glacial polishing. In the Hohe Tauern, e.g., in the Fuscher Valley, very fine semicircular cirques coincide with the curve of folds.

Tectonically shattered rocks are unfavorable for the creation of steep cirque walls, because the faces become obscured by abundant scree produced along the structural planes.

Fairly steeply dipping flags between bedding or joint planes contribute toward smooth precipitous cirque walls and thresholds. The sapping action of the cirque glacier traces out those joint, sheet, or foliation structures that favor gelifraction and plucking. In the Bohemian Forest the granite and gneiss is rather steeply jointed, as at the Baerenstein, and this produces steeper cirque faces than the low relief would lead one to expect. An example is the Little Arber Lake.

On the southwest side of the Grossglockner crest, the northeast strike of the rocks governs the direction of the intercirque divides. The east faces of the Grossglockner itself, however, demonstrate that rock planes can be too steep for cirque formation, for snow and ice cannot gather. If such beds strike normally to the trend of the back walls, they may be dissected by gullies.

Lithologically, hard and uniform granite and gneiss offer the best conditions for cirque sculpture, as well as for trough formation. In these materials cirque faces in the Hohe Tauern attain gradients of 48°, which is 8° more than the general value for the area (Fig. 7). In the older rocks of Norway, where resistance is little differentiated, most of the cirques are of classic shape. Changes of lithology permit the development of cirque stairways, with the steps associated with harder material and the basins with softer. Where such rock alterations occur, smooth cirque walls cannot be formed, and soft rocks occurring alone are unlikely to produce precipitous faces at all.

ARCTIC AND ALPINE ENVIRONMENTS (H. E. Wright, Jr., and
W. H. Osburn, eds.), 255-266, © 1967 Indiana University Press

17
Extent of Pleistocene Glaciation
in the Pyrenees

FRANÇOIS TAILLEFER
Institut de Géographie de l'Université
Toulouse, France

Abstract

The Pyrenees Mountains, located a little south of the 43° N lat. and not exceeding 3404 m in elevation, were affected only by a local glaciation. At the time when the glaciers reached their widest extent, the area of the zone of snow accumulation covered approximately 7000 sq km, 3800 on the northern side, 3200 on the southern side. This area was broken into many individual basins of accumulation, 17 on the northern side, 20 on the southern side, if only the most important are numbered. The areas of these basins were of very unequal size; three of them covered approximately 700 sq km, two on the northern side (Gave de Pau and Ariège), one on the southern side (Noguera Pallaresa). Only these basins, plus the Garonne basin (380 sq km), fed large composite glaciers, with tongues 50 km long or more. The area of the Valira basin (Andorra), on the southern side, was 330 sq km. All the other basins covered less than 300 sq km. From the largest of them issued tongues between 10 and 30 km long: 7 tongues flowed down on the northern side, 9 on the southern side. Beside these glaciers of appreciable extent, small individual glaciers were scattered at each end of the range and on its northern side, on mountains of medium elevation.

Located between 42° and 43°30'N lat., the Pyrenees are situated in the latitude of the Mediterranean. The Mediterranean climate, dry in summer, affects their eastern extremity and a part of their southern slope, whereas the western end of the range and most of its north slope are under the influence of an oceanic temperate climate with warm summers. The snowline, variable according to exposure, scarcely extends below 2600 m in the west and rises above 3000 m in the east. But because the altitude does not exceed 3404 m and is almost everywhere under 3000 m, the catchment area of the present glaciers is limited to the higher massifs of the central and western Pyrenees. It is not very extensive, and it is much broken up. But in Pleistocene times the snowline was much lower, and the zone of glacier equilibrium was 1000 to 1200 m below its present level, depending upon the place. Snow fields were very extensive and nourished ice streams several tens of kilometers long and several hundred meters thick, comparable to the dimensions of the present glaciers of the Himalayas. Before describing the characteristics of these glaciers, whose importance varied according to the epoch, their evolution should be briefly retraced.

PYRENEAN GLACIATIONS

Major Glaciation

The landscape of the Pyrenees bears the clear marks of a great glaciation, in which three stages may be distinguished.

The first is related to a glacial advance mainly characterized by erosional forms, whose limits are delineated by erratics that allow retracing with sufficient precision the outline of that maximum extent. In fact, these limits have never been exceeded or even attained. A second stage, markedly retreatal from the preceding with regard to the volume of the glaciers rather than the area which they covered, consists of a prolonged stationary phase, marked by large moraines and alluvial deposits at the glacial margin, such as terminal moraines, and the associated principal terrace of the valleys (or lower terrace), as well as lateral moraines blocking small tributary valleys.

A third stage, still more recessional, consists of a probably shorter stationary phase, with thin glacial tongues located at the bottom of the mountain valleys. It is represented by inner moraines, generally smaller than the outer moraines, and abundant deposits at the margin of the glaciers. Terraces of variable number, generally cut into the principal terrace or covering it with a thin layer of alluvium, are connected with the inner moraines. This glaciation occurred at a time when the mountain valleys had already been cut out and when the land forms were little different from the present ones. The deposits of this glaciation are but little altered, and the soils over them are immature, having developed under conditions not very different from those of today. This glaciation appears to have ended at the time of the climatic optimum, which probably raised the climatic snow line above the highest summits.

Neoglaciation

Within the cirques and along the walls of the higher mountains, far upstream from moraines of the last stages of the major glaciation, lie moraines and old rock glaciers, at present inactive. They belong to a glacial advance that followed the climatic optimum. Evidence for two stages can very often be noted: a stage of advance before the historic period, and a less important stage, which appears to have culminated in the middle of the 19th century before the recession that characterizes our time. The features of the high mountains are mostly due to the stages of the Neoglaciation, whose existence has been recognized only in the last years (Taillefer, 1964).

Problem of Older Glaciations

The major glaciation appears, in the mountains, to have destroyed or obliterated the remnants of older epochs of the Quaternary, and only downstream from the outer moraines can some older Quaternary erosional features and deposits be found. These are mostly alluvial gravels and terraces, generally higher than the terraces related to the stages of the major glaciation. An important phase of dissection and valley cutting therefore separates the construction of the latter from the deposition of the older alluviums, which are always, moreover, strongly altered, by rubification on the north side of the range and calcification on the south side. The older alluvia never have a morainic topography. The characteristics of their material (shape of the pebbles, composition of the fines) do not exclude a fluvioglacial origin but do not demonstrate it either.

It is often possible to observe three ancient alluvial beds, at lower levels than Pliocene gravels: The two higher (higher levels) perhaps represent Villafranchian, the next (higher terrace) an intermediate level between the latter and the terraces connected with the major glaciation (Table 1). If correlation of these alluvial deposits with glaciations older than the major glaciation is still a subject of discussion, it is admitted today that they are of climatic origin and that variations of marine base level did not have notable consequences for the morphologic evolution of the piedmont, which is too far from the coasts. It seems preferable not to apply to these different periods of the Quaternary, defined by the phases of morphologic evolution, the terminology commonly used in Europe. In fact, because the nomenclature of the Quaternary subdivisions does not have definitions so precise as that of older geologic stages, a great uncertainty reigns on the subject. Thus the same alluvial bed was correlated with Mindel, Riss, or Würm glaciations, according to various authors. The confusion is still greater for the older Quaternary.

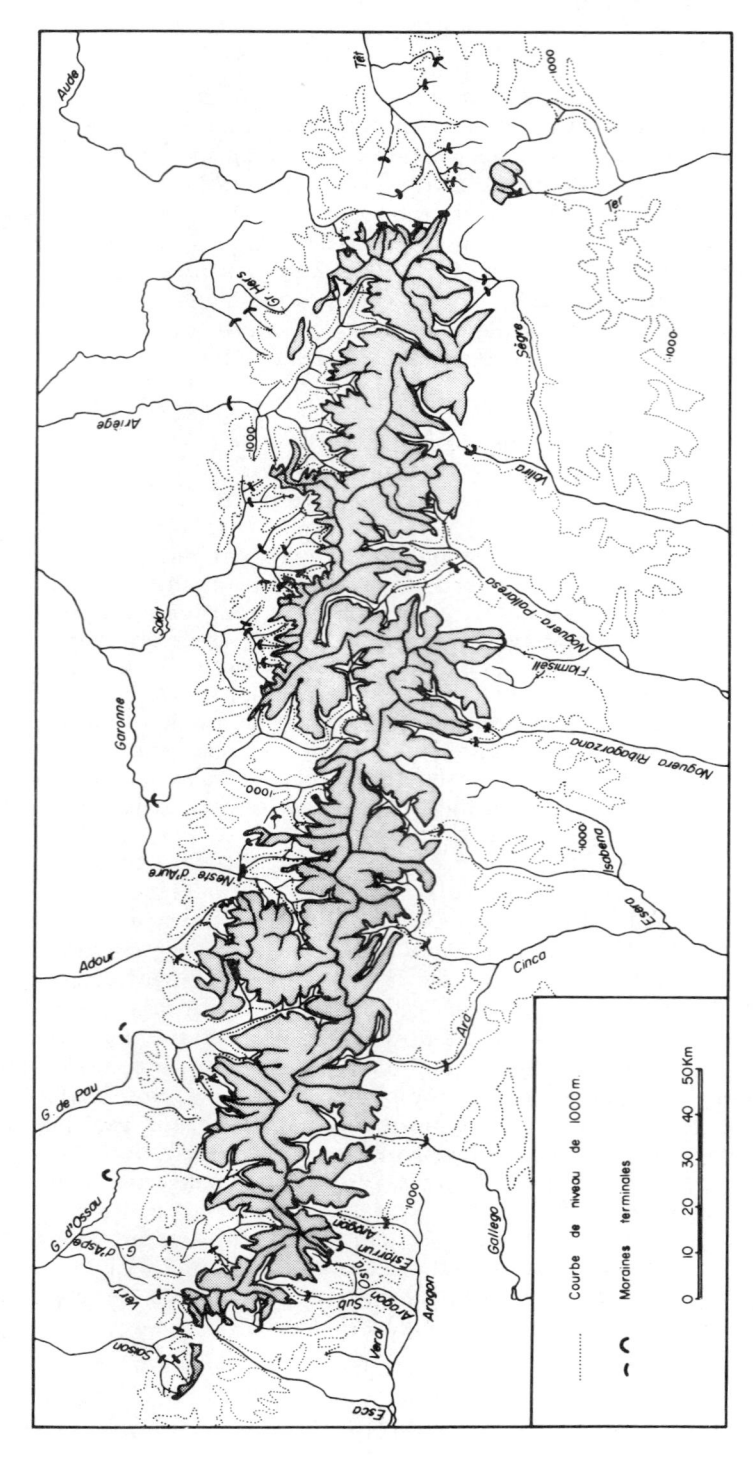

Fig. 1. Map of collecting basins of Quaternary glaciers in the Pyrenees. Gray pattern shows zones above the snow line.

TABLE 1

Morphologic Evolution of the Pyrenees and
Their Piedmont During the Pleistocene

Mountains	Piedmont
Neoglaciation	Resumption of erosion
Major glaciation	
inner moraines	Terraces cut into the low terrace or alluvial deposits covering it
outer moraines	Low terrace
maximum extent	High terrace
Older glaciations?	High levels
	lower
	upper
	Pliocene gravels

I shall ordinarily refer below, unless otherwise indicated, to the second stage of the major glaciation, which built the outer moraines. In fact, the first stage left too scanty deposits and appears to have been of rather short duration. The existence of earlier glaciations is hypothetical. As for the neoglaciation, its much more modest extent requires separate consideration.

CATCHMENT AREAS OF THE GLACIERS

To measure the catchment areas of the Pleistocene glaciers, in the fluvial basins of the Pyrenees where glaciers have existed, the surfaces situated above the limit of equilibrium of the glaciers at the time of the major glaciation have been planimetered (Fig. 1). The planimetry has been made on the 1:200,000 contour map of the Institut Géographique National, the only one that covers all the area studied. The precision of this map is rather poor, and it was necessary to approximate the line of glacial equilibrium to make it coincide with one of the contours of the map; depending on the basin, the altitudes adopted were 1400, 1600, or 1800 m. Therefore, the areas measured on the map are the projected areas, smaller than the actual ones. This discrepancy is of little importance, for the regions where the slope is very steep are not much involved in snow accumulation. The numbers obtained are therefore very approximate, but they are comparable from one basin to another.

The alimentation area, following the main axis of the range, formed a continuous area between the Carlit mountain, near the sources of the Aude, Têt, and Carol Rivers, which are tributary to the Sègre, and the mountains of the Upper Soule (Pic d'Orri), a length of as much as 240 km (Fig. 1). Its width, greatly variable, is greatest in the upper valleys of the Ariège River and the Valira River (30 km) and in those of the Gave de Pau and of the Gallego River (35 km). In the middle of the range, the upper valleys of the Garonne and of the Noguera Pallaresa, very oblique with respect to the axis of the range, divide the alimentation area in two parts, whose ice fields did not always join. Therefore, the Pyrenees, during the time of the major glaciation, were covered by an ice cap extending two-thirds of their length. Numerous transsections can be identified, not only between watersheds on one side of the range but between those on the north and south sides, across the main divide.

At the periphery of this wide alimentation area, the highest mountains bore small isolated glaciers, in particular on the north and east slopes (Canigou). The "north slope" is the side of the Pyrenees situated north of the present divide. In glacial times this divide probably was farther to the north, as transsections occurred toward the south side. Moreover, these terms should not be taken in their strictest meaning with regard to exposure; as the range is broken into many massifs, all exposures can be noted on both "slopes." But the catchment basins were much less extensive with respect to the area covered by the major ice cap, which extended on about 6836 sq km. The north slope accounts for 3713 sq km, the south slope for 3123 sq km. The latter figure is certainly too large, for the line of glacial equilibrium that we have admitted for the basins on the south slopes (1800 m) is a little low. It shows, however, that the glaciation on the south slope is far from being negligible and that, if the glaciers of this slope did not attain a development comparable to those on the north slope, the main cause was the less favorable conditions in the ablation area. The alimentation area, because of the dissection of the topography, was broken into a great number of basins, and multiplicity is one of the characteristics of the Pyrenean glaciation. Many short ice streams were located in the upper cirques and valleys. Because of the dissected topography, the ice was diverted in various directions rather than joining in great glacier systems. Furthermore, frequently in one single fluvial basin, the glacial tongues that formed in the upper valleys did not join, and only the meltwaters merged in the main valley.

In Table 2 the principal alimentation areas of Pleistocene glaciers in the Pyrenees are given. They are more numerous on the south slope than on the north slope (20 basins compared to 17), but on the average are less extensive. This is normally the consequence of a greater division, because of a less general englaciation.

Figure 2 represents schematically the alimentation areas of the major glaciers on the north and south slopes. The smaller ones have not been drawn, except those of the Lez and Salat Rivers (north slope), which have been combined.

Only three glaciers had extensive alimentation areas of about 700 sq km: those of Gave de Pau (749 sq km) and of the Ariège (705 sq

TABLE 2

Major Glacial Alimentation Areas in the Pyrenees

	Area, sq km	Length, km		Area, sq km	Length, km
North side					
Saison	46	—	Lez	23	—
Gave d'Aspe	185	26	Ribérot	29	12
Gave d'Ossau	271	38	Estours	15	—
Gave de Pau	749	60	Upper Salat	18	—
Adour	127	—	Alet	27	14
Neste d'Aure	274	26	Garbet	28	18
Neste de Louron	61	25	Ariège	705	52
Garonne	378	66	Aude	75	—
			Upper Têt	52	—
South side					
Esca	26	—	Isabeña	15	—
Rio Veral	27	—	Baliera	40	—
Aragon Subordan	120	20	Noguera Ribagorzana	104	20
Estarrun	22	—	Noguera de Tor	168	24
Aragon	86	23	Flamisell	61	18
Gallego	213	35	Noguera Pallaresa	688	40
Ara	176	32	Valira	330	25
Cinca	130	22	Carol	108	11
Cinqueta	112	20	Freser	72	—
Esera	261	26	Upper Ter	30	—

km), both on the north slope, and that of Noguera Pallaresa (688 sq km) on the south slope. In fact, the latter rather consists of adjacent but indeed separate alimentation areas, except in the highest mountains. The alimentation area of the Garonne River glacier was appreciably smaller (378 sq km), exceeding only slightly that of Valira (330 sq km) on the south slope. No other alimentation area attained 300 sq km, the main other ones being those of the Ossau glacier (271 sq km) and of the Neste d'Aure glacier (274) on the north slope, of the Gallego glacier (213) and of the Esera glacier (261) on the south slope.

A single glance at Fig. 1 (on which are indicated the glacier termini) and Table 2 shows that there is no direct relation between the extent of the alimentation areas and the length of the glacier tongues. According to the factors of accumulation, related to climate, and the relief pattern, the Pleistocene glaciers can be classified into three types (Table 2).

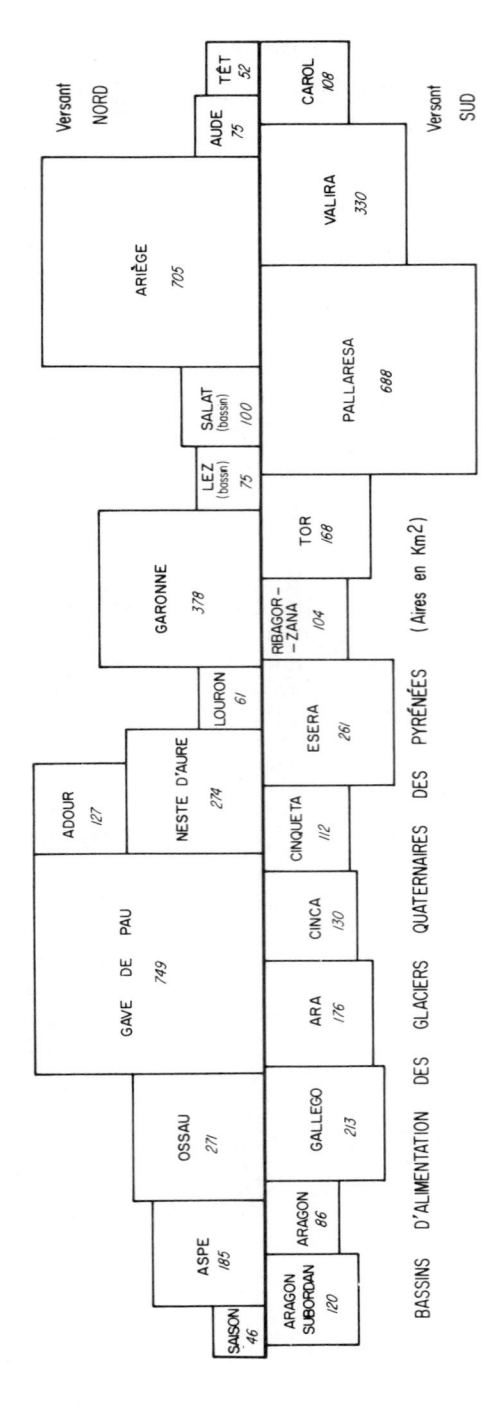

Fig. 2. Principal collecting basins of Quaternary glaciers of the Pyrenees (schematic).

TYPES OF PLEISTOCENE GLACIERS

Because of the fact that the alimentation area was broken into many parts, local glaciers were numerous. This is the first type. When the conditions of alimentation were good, however, some valley glaciers of the alpine type formed. Third, where good conditions of alimentation combined with a physiographic pattern that favored confluences, great composite glaciers, of the Himalayan or Alaskan type, were constituted.

Local Glaciers

They were especially numerous at the two ends of the range, where the glaciation was less extensive — to the west the mountains are too low (in the Vert and Saison valleys on the north slope and in the Rio Esca, Veral, and Estarrun valleys on the south), to the east the mediterranean climate prevails (the Aude and Têt valleys on the north slope and the Sègre, Ter, and Freser valleys on the south slope). But even in the middle of the range, some areas only possessed local glaciers: the Isabeña and Baliera valleys on the south slope, and the Adour and Salat valleys on the north slope.

The case of the Salat valley is particularly characteristic. In spite of high altitudes (the ridges that form the southern limit of the river basin often pass 2600 m and reach 2880 m at Pic de Maubermé), a wet climate, and north-facing or northwest-facing slopes that make rain and snowfalls most effective, the Salat valley had only small scanty glaciers (Chevalier, 1954). Their alimentation areas were occasionally coalescent and joined by cross-flowage, but the tongues were too short to attain confluence in the valleys, so that composite glaciers could not form. The principal cause of this type is the extreme dissection of the topography by a many-branched dendritic river system ("leaves of fern" pattern) carving Paleozoic rocks less resistant than the crystalline rocks within the Ariège mountains. Steeply sloping ridges hang above narrow deeply cut valleys. Hardly any high surfaces exist upon which snow could persist and be transformed into ice.

The alimentation areas are therefore very small and discontinuous (no less than 32 can be numbered). They fed 16 small glaciers, of which only two, the Garbet and the Alet, attain 14 to 18 km in length, followed by that of Ribérot (12 km). These are relatively well fed by the shallow cirques formed on granitic batholith; they occur as an exception in the Salat valley. Except for these three valleys, the Salat mountains are thus little marked by glaciation.

Valley Glaciers

Glaciers occupying the head of a main valley are the most common form on the south slope. In fact, the climatic conditions were not so good as to allow a major development of glacial tongues, and the latter have not joined to form great composite glacier systems, even with favorable physiographic conditions, as in the longitudinal Aragon Valley. Below is a list of the major valley glaciers from the west to the east on the south slope (length in kilometers):

Aragon Subordan	20	Esera	26
Aragon	23	Noguera Ribagorzana	20
Gallego	35	Noguera de Tor	24
Ara	32	Flamisell	18
Cinca	22	Valira	25
Cinqueta	20		

The Aragon glacier can be taken as an example. It followed one of those transverse linear and little branched valleys so frequent in the Pyrenees. It is fed mainly on the north by the mountains of the Axial Paleozoic Zone, of moderate altitude (2400 m), whose northern slope also supplies a distributary through the fairly low pass of Somport (1632 m). It is also fed on the east from the high but slightly glacierized calcareous range of Peña Collarada. It terminated at an altitude of 800 to 900 m near Castiello de Jaca, where a beautiful set of arcuate moraines was built (Taillefer, 1957; Barrère, 1963).

Some glaciers of the same type occurred on the north slope, but they were larger and longer and extended much farther downslope; some even attained the mountain front:

Gave d'Aspe	26	Neste d'Aure	26
Gave d'Ossau	38	Neste de Louron	25

The Ossau glacier even was, in some respects, a composite glacier of the Himalayan type, where three valley glaciers well fed by the high mountains of the Axial Zone were joining. The tongue thus formed extended out of the mountain to the piedmont zone. The terminal basin of Arudy, within a good morainic amphitheater, is much like the terminal basins of Bavarian piedmont glaciers, on the north slope of the Alps (Taillefer, 1948; Barrère, 1963).

Composite Glacier Systems

The last type, resulting from particularly favorable climatic and physiographic conditions, is represented by four composite glacier systems, three on the north slope — the Gave de Pau, Garonne, and Ariège — and one on the south slope — that of the Noguera Pallaresa.

As indicated above, the last-named, only 30 km long, results rather from the juxtaposition of several separate glaciers that have joined at their ends because of the disposition of relief multiplying the valley junctions (Nussbaum, 1956; Zandvliet, 1960). Thirty-two zones of accumulation can thus be numbered in the Noguera Pallaresa valley, just as many as in the Salat valley. But here high surfaces on granitic batholiths bore extensive snowfields and, in spite of climatic conditions not so good as those in the Salat valley, a widespread and often thick ice cap has developed. Once again the influence of landform pattern appears therefore decisive.

It is no less so in the case of the three composite glacier systems on the north slope, the Ariège glacier (52 km) as well as the Garonne glacier (66 km) and the Gave de Pau glacier (60 km). It is the junction of large ice streams fed by the snowfields of the high surfaces of the gneiss massives or granitic domes of the Axial Zone that formed tongues 700 to 800 m thick in the glacial equilibrium area, able to flow far downstream. They terminated at an altitude as low as 400 m, after sending out distributaries through the passes of the mountain front. The Ariège glacier and Garonne glacier thus terminated in the valleys of the Prepyrenees (Taillefer, 1960, 1953), whereas the Gave de Pau glacier spread out, north of Lourdes, in a piedmont lobe of about 10 km radius, and sent out, simultaneously or successively, its meltwater into five radial valleys on an old Pliocene alluvial fan (Taillefer, 1958; Alimen, 1964).

CONCLUSION

The Pleistocene glaciers of the Pyrenees, even at the time of their maximum extent, have been strongly subjected to the influence of exposure and landform pattern. The Pyrenees Range affected the wetter and colder climate of that epoch almost exactly as it does now. The climatic contrast between the two slopes was as obvious as today, and the glaciers on the south slope remain both less well developed and confined to higher altitudes than those on the north slope. But the development of these glaciers has been mainly controlled by topography, which determined the alimentation areas as well as outflow of the ice and the ice-stream pattern.

The best-nourished glaciers are those whose alimentation areas extended on massive mountains formed of hard rocks: high surfaces of gneissic massifs or granitic domes. On the contrary, the mountains of a very dissected topography have not been favorable to glacier development. On the whole, the linear character of the valley pattern in the Pyrenees favored the formation of valley glaciers of the alpine type, and the composite glacier systems were both exceptional and more extensive. Glaciation in the middle of the range has been effective enough to create, through the development of distributaries and transsections, an outflow pattern different from that of the present time. But the major land forms were preglacial and explain the distribution of the different types of glaciers and their extension.

REFERENCES

Alimen, H., 1964, Le Quaternaire des Pyrénées de la Bigorre: Paris, Mém. Carte géol. France, 394 p.

Barrère, P., 1963, La période glaciaire dans l'Ouest des Pyrénées franco-espagnoles: Bull. Soc. Géol. France, v. 5, pp. 516-526.

Chevalier, M., 1954, Le relief glaciaire des Pyrénées du Couserans: Rev. géograph. Pyrénées Sud-Ouest, v. 25, pp. 97-124, 189-220.

Nussbaum, F., 1956, Observations morphologiques dans la région de la Noguera Pallaresa: Zaragoza, Pirineos, No. 39-42, pp. 57-94.

Taillefer, F., 1948, Les Bassins glaciaires d'Arudy et de Lourdes. France méridionale et pays ibériques: Toulouse, Mélanges Faucher, v. 1, pp. 449-465.

―――― 1953, La terminaison du glacier de la Garonne au Sud de Montrejeau: Paris, Ministére Education Nationale, Sect. Géograph. Comit. Trav. Hist. Sci. Bull., 66, pp. 271-282.

―――― 1957, Glaciaire pyrénéen, versant Nord et versant Sud: Rev. géograph. Pyrénées Sud-Ouest, v. 28, pp. 221-244.

―――― 1960, Recherches récentes sur le relief glaciaire de la vallée de l'Ariége. Pays de l'Ariége: Auch, XVI Congrés Etudes Fédér. Soc. Sav. Languedoc-Pyrénées-Gascogne (Foix, 1960), pp. 211-224.

―――― 1964, Le modelé post-würmien des hautes montagnes françaises: Toulouse, Rev. géograph. Pyrénées Sud-Ouest, v. 35, pp. 129-138.

Zandvliet, J., 1960, The geology of the upper Salat and Pallaresa Valleys. Central Pyrenees, France-Spain: Leidse Geol. Med., v. 25, pp. 1-127.

18
Recent Natural Landscapes and Ancient Glaciation of the Pamir

I. P. GERASIMOV AND R. P. ZIMINA
Institute of Geography
Academy of Sciences
Moscow, USSR

Abstract

This report deals with the specific natural landscapes of the Pamir Upland. These so-called cold deserts were formed only in the second half of the Quaternary after Pamir became ice-free. Ice extinction proceeded due to the increasing orographical isolation of upland when the surrounding mountain ranges were uplifted. In the environment of high-mountain radiation and very low air humidity, the process of ice sublimation had a great importance. The flora and fauna of the Pamir Upland are very young and mostly represented by Tibetan elements.

The highest upland territory of the USSR — the Pamir — was named long ago the Top (or Roof) of the world, for the Pamir dominates, by its altitude, all adjacent mountain systems. It is perhaps paradoxical that a region with such an expressive definition and such massiveness should be so poorly known. The authors suggest a reconstruction of the paleolandscape and postulate subsequent landscape, floral, and faunistic development.

PRESENT APPEARANCE OF THE PAMIR

The Pamir landscape is characterized by youthfulness — not only in geomorphology but particularly in flora and fauna. Plant and animal communities have no stable composition or structure, and many areas appear biologically barren. Paucity of life results from a lack of specialized organisms found in other regions.

The general aspect of the Pamir landscape is that of undulating desert plains surrounded by low mountain ridges that are capped with snow and ice. Although no continuous cover of modern deposits occurs, evidence of glacial erosion may be found at all altitudes, from the relief sculpture of ancient cirques and troughs down to the lowest intermountain plains, where striations on stones and the presence of erratics are common. River valleys are very broad, meandering, shallow, and bordered by low terraces. Deposits revealed by scarps bear greater resemblance to morainal debris than to stratified alluvial deposits. High-elevation slopes may be nearly buried under their own deposits, while lower slopes bear the characteristic imprint of solifluction. The ground is largely mantled by a lag gravel deposit, and vegetation is sparse and restricted mainly to stream margins or to protected sites.

Evidence for a cold dry climate may be inferred from the geomorphology, soil-surface conditions, and plant types and forms. The unique combination of extreme aridity of climatic conditions (25 to 30 mm annual precipitation at Lake Kara-Kul) with very high radiation (10 kcal g/cm^2 during summer) and with winter temperatures reaching -40°C makes biological existence quite difficult. In these extreme conditions, as though on the outskirts of life, plants have special adaptive features. For example, most plants are dwarfed and ground-hugging, with their perennating organs buried below the ground surface, and their metabolic rhythm matches that of favorable periods in the environment.

Nearly all the eastern Pamir seems to have been covered during early Quaternary time by a cap of snow and ice that was not uniform in its activity, thickness, and other conditions. Occasionally summits of the inner mountains (nunataks) protruded. The ice cap was formed mainly because of the geographical position of the region. At this time the Pamir was exposed to moisture-laden air masses moving in from the north, west, and south. Modern mountain ridges such as the Darvas, Budakshan, and Hindukush, which now form an orographic barrier, were not present. During the Quaternary period the Pamir rose continuously to its modern elevation. A slow process of ice ablation probably started in the second part of the Quaternary. This wastage of ice was undoubtedly caused by the increasing aridity of the climate and a decrease in precipitation, both of which were caused in turn by an orographic blockade of the Pamir from western and southern moisture-laden air masses. Complete ice wastage has been delayed only by the low air temperature. A remarkable paradox — ice removal without landscape destruction — was associated with this ice wastage. Ice probably disappeared mostly by sublimation (under conditions of very low humidity) rather than by melting and thus left largely unchanged a landscape formed before the Quaternary. This thesis is substantiated by many geologic and geographic peculiarities of the Pamir landscape, among them the excellent preservation of an ancient peneplane surface, small amounts of fluvioglacial deposits, and weak erosion of modern glacial forms.

The reasons for the geologic youthfulness of the Pamir natural landscapes follow from this landscape hypothesis. Only quite recently, during the second part of the Quaternary, ice disappeared from the Pamir and exposed a nearly barren, hostile landscape. Masses of migrating plants and animals, confronted by numerous barriers, have undergone drastic selection. The most successful were the immigrants from Central Asia and especially from Tibet, which now predominate in the flora and fauna of the Pamir. However, during a relatively short period some species of plants and animals developed and are now well adapted to their environment.

Altogether, general geographic observations and the above paleogeographical reconstructions show the paradoxical character of the recent nature of Pamir and its processes of geologic development. The expressive definition of the Pamir as the Top (Roof) of the world has some basis in these paradoxes.

ARCTIC AND ALPINE ENVIRONMENTS (H. E. Wright, Jr., and
W. H. Osburn, eds.), 271-281, © 1967 Indiana University Press

19
Anthropogene Development of the Subarctic Lowlands of Northeast Asia

N. A. SHILO
Academy of Sciences
Magadan, USSR

Abstract

Vast lowlands, the largest of which is the Maritime, are situated in northeastern Asia along the Arctic seas. They have some features of alluvial plains. In the south they are fringed by a piedmont belt, and in the north they pass into the shelf of the Arctic basin. The surface of the lowlands is complicated by lakes that cover about 40% of its area.

The oldest unconsolidated Anthropogene deposits are composed of aleurolites, or locally of silts and clays with fresh-water fauna. They are overlain by a series of silts, sandy loams, and loams containing abundant vegetal remains and mammoth fauna. This series encloses numerous bodies of ice segregations and polygonal ice veins.

The Subarctic (Maritime and Kolyma) lowlands appeared as a result of tectonic activity of Asian orogenic belts at the boundary between the continental and oceanic crusts. The lowlands occupy a definite position in the structures of the Verkhoyansk-Kolyma region of folding.

Vast lowlands are situated along the Arctic Seas in the northeastern USSR. The largest of these, the Maritime (Yana-Indighirka) Lowland in the Lena-Indighirka interfluve, has some features of alluvial plains. In the south the lowland is fringed by the Polousny Range, and in the west by northern spurs of the Verkhoyana Mountains; it merges in the east with the Kolymian Lowland and in the north with the shelf that occupies a considerable part of the East Siberian Sea, part of the Laptev Sea, and the Chukotsk Sea. This shelf is fringed by a steep slope leading to the central depression of the Polar Basin.

The Kolymian Lowland occupies the Kolyma-Indighirka interfluve. It juts into the continent as a narrow strip. The mountains of the Ilin-Tas range are its southwestern boundary, and the Anjuy upland and Jukagira plateau are its eastern boundary. The small elevated Abiy plain, between the Ilin-Tas and Polousny ranges, forms the western sector of the lowland.

The origin of these lowlands was attributed by Toll (1897), who studied the Novosibirsk Islands, Vollosovich (1915), and others to relic glacier ice in the deposits of these lowlands. This hypothesis was opposed particularly by Figurin (1823), Lopatin (1876), Bunge (1903), and others, who argued that vein ice results from freezing in frost cracks. Subsequent discussions were made by Ermolaev (1932), Grigorjev (1932, 1946), and especially Kolosov (1947), who considered that even the modern extent of fossil ice in the regions of the Novosibirsk archipelago, the Maritime Lowland, and the adjacent part of the Polar shelf is like a blanket. The peculiarities of modern geomorphic processes in the northeastern USSR have been attributed by him to the presence of relics of ancient glaciation. In accordance with these views, many investigators associated lakes distributed throughout these lowlands with early Quaternary glaciation.

More recently, Shvetsov (1938, 1957), Popov (1953), Shumsky (1955), and Muchin (1955) demonstrated the multiple-vein origin of fossil ice and especially of so-called polygonal-vein underground ice during the Anthropogene (Pleistocene and Holocene). The alluvial origin of the Maritime and the Kolymian lowlands was widely recognized, particularly by Saks (1953), Popov (1953), Biske (1957), Katasonov and Biske (1959), and Romanovsky (1961). The alluvium of the subarctic plains and periglacial regions of continental glaciation was studied by Lavrushin (1962), who concluded that the formation of the alluvial strata of plains rivers is nearly the same in temperate and subarctic regions.

The study of some regions of Chukotka, and particularly of those lakes that reveal an ice origin, has convinced the author that the role of streams in the sedimentation of the subarctic lowlands has been grossly exaggerated. He has noted earlier, in regard to the Yana-Kolymian gold-bearing belt, that almost all river valleys from the mountain to the plain indicate the very important role played by the general Quaternary subsidence of the whole coast and of much of the Kolymian middle massif (Shilo, 1960). The ice-origin theory of the Chukotka lakes, although often considered indisputable and consequently given general paleogeographical significance, has no factual support.

The Maritime and Kolymian lowlands, misnamed "East Siberian" by Baranova and Biske (1964) (in spite of the well-known fact that eastern Siberia and the northeastern USSR are quite incompatible parts of Soviet Asia), occupy the coastal subarctic belt of the northeast and extend several hundred kilometers into the continent. Their general tectonic and geomorphic development in the Anthropogene has been confirmed, but only over an area of about 400,000 sq km. The surficial sediment of the continental shelf, the fossil fauna, the modern flora, and the Mesolithic artifacts show that the Maritime and Kolymian lowlands occupied great areas and spread far to the north, 500 to 600 km from the modern coast line of the Polar Basin. The absolute elevations of the lowland surface are below 200 m; the depth of the sea along the shelf ranges from several meters in the coastal zone to 150 to 200 m at the edge of the central depression of the Polar Basin. The exceptional uniformity of absolute elevations on great surfaces of the coastal area and the shelf is apparently closely connected with tectonic and geomorphic development in the Anthropogene.

The piedmont belt of the continental lowlands is possibly connected with pre-Quaternary surface of erosion. The lowlands, which slope toward the sea, have been slightly eroded by modern fluvial streams. The river net is not generally well developed, but the great rivers draining the lowlands (the Kolyma, Indighirka, and Yana) have cut valleys into the loose deposits. The oldest deposits are light-gray to dark aleurites, including silts and even clays, in some places about 30 m thick. They are still considered to lie on the surface of the original rocks of the geosyncline complex of the Yana-Kolymian and Chukotsk fold systems — not in a continuous belt, but more often in isolated but very large areas. They contain freshwater mollusks and are dated as Middle and even Upper Quaternary. The surface of this stratigraphic unit contains signs of polygonal depressions attributed by some investigators to thawing of vein ice.

The stratum of silts, loams, and sandy loams contains vegetal remains, either dispersed or in lenticular accumulations or thin streaks. The diverse fauna (with early and late mammoths) indicates an Upper Quaternary origin. The deposits are locally as much as 100 m thick. The whole monotonous sequence contains ice segregations and polygonal ice veins, which even form subsurface hillocks. The vein ice often penetrates to a depth of 40 to 50 m in steeply dipping veins that form the polygonal system in the sedimentary strata. These deposits have an upward limit at the foothills at an elevation of about 200 m, although they may be separated from the foothills by talus-solifluctional fans.

At present there are several points of view on the formation of this stratum, which comprises the unconsolidated cover of the lowlands. One view, held by Popov, Romanovsky, and other investigators, is that aleurolite, which forms the upper part of the loose deposits, is formed under lagoon conditions, and that a freshwater fauna is present because considerable desalinization occurred. These researchers believe the upper part of the section, which contains silty-clayey-sandy deposits with vegetal remains and mammoth fauna, is entirely alluvial, with subordinate channel deposits. The sedimentation probably occurred simultaneously with the growth of polygonal ice vein.

In spite of the apparent logic of this theory, its proponents fail to explain many features of the structure, composition, and distribution of the sediments. Even Popov noted that the contemporaneous formation of alluvium and polygonal ice veins is not fully explained.

The second view on the formation of the lowland cover is held by Biske, Katasonov, and others, who consider that the Upper Quaternary alluvial and alluvial-lacustrine deposits are the floodwater sediments of streams from the mountains. Biske notes that the process is no longer active because the tectonic subsidence of the lowland has ceased.

The third theory (Lavrushin, 1962) is that the relief was shaped only by streams that were controlled entirely by climatic conditions. Lavrushin uses Popov's theory of the formation of the vein ice in these deposits; the presence of polygonal ice veins in any part of the lowlands depends on recent climatic changes.

Vtyurin (1964) tried to resolve the conflict among the three theories of the formation and distribution of the surficial sediments of the lowlands by showing that all lithologic differences among sediments of the same age are indicated by cryogenic textures. Vtyurin's original error led to an incorrect explanation of the conditions of sedimentary accumulation. Even without specific investigations, cryogenic textures on the whole are obviously epigenetic and therefore have no relation to the process by which the main lithologic and structural features of this cover were formed.

Thus most investigators agree that the origin of the Asian subarctic lowlands is related to fluvial processes. However, even if this question is solved, we must recognize that the surficial development of the lowlands, among other great features of the earth, is closely related to inner forces in the earth and to the structural development of the earth's crust.

The lowlands and the adjacent shelf occupy a very definite position in the tectonic structures of the northeastern USSR and cover this whole slope of Asia to the Polar Basin, where the Yana, Indighirka, and Kolyma rivers appear. This slope is the main watershed between the river systems of the Polar and Pacific Basins, which approach the Ochotsk Sea coast in the western part of the northeastern USSR, and the Chukotsk Sea coast in the eastern part. The asymmetry of the watershed line is reflected in the main young relief forms (uplands and plateau), related genetically to oscillatory structural movements in the Ochotsk-Chukotsk volcanic belts and, apparently, even to the new movements that enveloped the Koryak-Kamtchatsk folded region and the modern Ochotsk and Bering Seas during the Quaternary.

Undoubtedly the main surficial features of the northeastern USSR are deeply rooted in the uplift of the late geosynclinal troughs during the Mesozoic in the Verkhoyana-Kolymian folded region and during the Cenozoic in the Koryak-Kamtchatsk. The concluding stages of this development were the formation of the volcanic belt and then, in the Quaternary, of the surrounding seas, such as the Ochotsk and the Bering. The formation of a new geosynclinal region changed the regime of transgression and regression in the zone adjoining the Pacific depression, as in northern Asia.

The Maritime and Kolymian lowlands could be contrasted tectonically with the Ochotsk-Chukotsk volcanic belt, in which deep faults localized in the great zones controlled different widespread magmatic complexes. In their later events, these lowlands can be contrasted with the whole Koryak-Kamtchatsk folded region, which has numerous depressions developed on structures under permanent, intensive tectonic subsidence.

For proof of the functional interdependence of these morphostructures, the paleogeographical history of prepolar and pre-Pacific Asian zones must first be considered. As is generally known, the pre-Pacific Asian zone, beginning with the upper chalk, developed under conditions of contrasting tectonic movements, intensive volcanic activity, and continuously alternating marine transgressions and regressions. Apparently, the concluding, Paleocene stage in the formation of the volcanic belt involved a maximum regression, which liberated eastern Asia from the sea almost as far as the modern oceanic depression. Many data show that in the Eocene, much of the Bering Sea and almost all of the Ochotsk Sea were dry and connected Asia with America. At this time, apparently, powerful orogenic movements enveloped most of the pre-Pacific continental zone.

During the Miocene, much of eastern Asia subsided below sea level. The transgressing sea separated Asia and America and penetrated as far as the modern bays of Korf and Olyutorsky and the Anadyr, Chatyrka, and Opucha river basins, among other places.

The boundary of Pliocene transgression is not very clear. Many data place it close to the modern coast line, which was formed by seas of the Pacific Basin. In the Eopleistocene the tectonic-geomorphic development of the pre-Pacific zone continued, and powerful orogenic movements caused the sea to regress far to the east, apparently to the boundaries of the oceanic depression. Tectonic structures of the areas liberated from the sea became more complicated; faulting renewed earlier fractures. The tectonic-magmatic evolution of the earth's crust brought intensive volcanism and the formation of the main relief features, especially in the pre-Pacific zone. Oscillations stimulated continued uplifts and orogenesis during the whole lower Pleistocene and possibly influenced glaciation of that period.

In the beginning of the Upper Pleistocene, the character of geological events changed sharply. The troughs of nearly all Far Eastern seas were formed; Asia and America were separated. Along with the Kuril and Aleutian Islands, the Japan, Ochotsk, and Bering Seas appeared, approximately within their modern boundaries. Volcanic activity shifted from west to east — that is, to the island arc of the Kuril-Aleutian ridge.

The geologic history of the Asian circumpolar zone, which contains the subarctic lowlands and the adjoining shelf, involves a rather quiet and prolonged process. Although the area was affected by sharply changed tectonic conditions, as were the center of the Polar Basin and the circum-Pacific zone, the earth's crust, on the whole, was comparatively stable tectonically; however, irregular oscillations of its separate blocks occurred and were reflected, at the top of the upper chalk, in prolonged oscillations of dry land and the encroaching epicontinental sea, which transgressed far to the north, where during the Tertiary and Quaternary the oceanic depression of the central Arctic clearly expanded and deepened.

The formation of different morphostructures in the circumarctic and circum-Pacific zones of Asia is undoubtedly connected with deep tectonic processes. In much of eastern Asia, the tectonic-magmatic evolution of the geosynclinal substratum proceeded differently, but the same process of intensive granitization influenced the formation of the continental crust and the tectonic evolution of the surface. The subarctic lowlands and the adjoining shelf experienced rather quiet processes of granitization that developed in the transitional zone between the continental and oceanic types of the earth's crust.

Besides having different tectonic histories, the circumarctic and circum-Pacific zones of Asia differ in the position of their coast lines. The sea in the latter zone ended near the modern coast line, which remained almost as far east as the oceanic depression, while the coast line of the circumarctic zone apparently coincided with the boundary of the continental slope until the Upper Pleistocene.

The comparatively simple outline of the Far Eastern Oligocene seas indicates the insignificant development of early-Tertiary deposition in much of the Koryak-Kamtchatsk folded regions; the whole territory of Mesozoic structures and the Ochotsk-Chukotsk volcanic belt contain no deposits from this period, according to Pogozhev and Semeykin (1957).

The Neogene marine deposits of the northeastern USSR are similarly restricted Miocene-Pliocene seas. The Neogene sea deposits occur in different areas of the Koryak-Kamtchatsk folded region, where geosynclines are also found in the Opuksko-Pikulneysk and Olyutorsk zones. Over the rest of the territory, postgeosynclinal depressions are believed to have formed (with fresh-water, occasionally coal-bearing, sedimentation), and intensive volcanism occurred in the circum-Pacific zone. During this time alluvial plains were formed in the inner continental regions.

In all valleys during the Anthropogene, the coast line of the Far Eastern seas coincided with the modern one. Boreal transgressions were either absent or quite minor and were related partly to disturbance of the isostatic equilibrium of the earth's crust by the ice sheet in Europe and perhaps in western Siberia, and partly to eustatic sea-level movements. The whole eastern Asian circumarctic zone, which was never glaciated, did not experience this disturbance and consequently was not submerged. This is one other indication of differential geomorphic development of northern Europe and northeastern Asia.

The continental development of the subpolar lowlands of the northeastern USSR has thus not been interrupted since the deposition of the upper chalk. These lowlands, widening in the chalk at the expense of the adjoining continental shelf, apparently became restricted only later in the Anthropogene, according to Lindberg (1946), Berg (1946), Udintsev (1955), and others.

Thus the endogenic relief processes in the lowlands are closely related to crustal structure. Data now available permit a more precise determination of the structure and age of the base of the lowlands.

Much of the Kolymian lowland, with the adjoining continental shelf, is a geomorphic expression of this structure and apparently is analogous to the west Siberian structural plate or, as Pushcharovsky (1960), Tilman (1962), and others believe, similar to the massif; it is therefore called the Chukochya plate (massif). This plate seems to have a crystalline foundation composed of pre-Paleozoic formations on a Mesozoic-Cenozoic shelf of slightly faulted rocks. Jurassic sedimentary rocks northwest of the Polousny Range and on the Indighirka-Alaseysk interfluve, as well as Jurassic and Cretaceous volcanic deposits, project through the surficial continental Anthropogenic deposits in various parts of the lowlands. Kuvaev has recently found small anomalies on the Kolymian median massif and has characterized the gravitational field of the plate within the Kolymian lowland and the adjoining shelf. The Kolymian median massif, genetically connected with the southern lowlands, experienced certain tectonic movements that prevent identification of it with type platform structures. Apparently the massif and the Chukochya plate developed differently in the pre-Paleozoic; the Verkhoyana-Kolymian geosyncline in the massif was later reworked, to some degree, and the Chukochya plate, separated from the massif by a deep fracture, controlled the Polousny Range of granitic rocks and continued to develop slowly in the Mesozoic and the Cenozoic. The rigid structures of Mesozoic consolidation contrast with the Kolymian median massif, which probably underwent pre-Paleozoic consolidation.

The Chukochya plate in the east is separated from the Chukotsk fold system by a deep fracture running along the lower part of the Kolyma River. Its western boundary might follow the Polousny fracture along the Indighirka River, as indicated by small fields of effusive rocks on the left bank. The plate is separated from the Kolymian median massif by an original structure similar in some ways to avlakogen; in the east this structure is closed, whereas in the west it widens and merges with the Yana-Kolymian fold system.

In the north the Chukochya plate is apparently separated from the Giperborean platform by a deep fracture, which seems to show a changing of the gravitational field (according to Kuvaev) and to correspond to a wide line that divides the shelf into two equal parts, northern and southern.

The structural features of the base of the Maritime (Yana-Indighirka) lowland were largely submerged west of the folded foundation of the Chukochya plate; the Oldzhoyskaya depression is apparently the transitional zone between the Kolymian massif and the Yana-Kolymian fold system, which has in the north a rigid structure called a Novosibirsk massif by Rozhkov and Mokshanzev. The tectonic structures are disturbed by the system of deep fractures, one of which runs toward Cape Saint.

Thus the different tectonic structures of the Maritime and Kolymian lowlands led to their unequal tectonic-geomorphic development, especially before permafrost in the Anthropogene essentially smoothed out the differences between these lowlands.

The pre-Anthropogenic tectonic stability of the Chukochya plate allowed the development of the modern Kolymian lowland and its adjoining shelf. It might be assumed that under the surficial deposits the bedrock was undissected. Instead, in the pre-Anthropogenic period the Maritime lowland was most likely an eroded mountain country. Because of this essential difference the Maritime lowland cannot be considered part of the Kolymian.

Thus the northeast Asian subarctic lowlands were formed on a different tectonic base, but they assumed their main features during tectonic-geomorphic evolution in the Anthropogene because of their subpolar location. In the Pliocene-Pleistocene they expanded considerably at the expense of the shelf, and the coast line in the far north apparently coincided with the continental slope to the central depression of the Polar basin. Well-established paleogeographical data indicate the large dimensions of the Kolymian and Maritime lowlands during the Eopleistocene. The transgression of the sea, beginning in the Neogene, is undoubtedly connected with the creation and expansion of the central depression of the Polar Basin and continues also at present to influence the formation of the continental cover of the lowlands, which apparently changed gradually, from the Eopleistocene, into accumulation plains. The formation of these lowlands as great morphostructures thus occurred against a background of tectonic activity in Asian orogenic belts at the continental edge throughout the Neogene and the Anthropogene.

The location of the subpolar lowlands was quite significant during the last stage of its formation, when the Pleistocene-Holocene sediments were deposited, for they contain fossils of the mammoth complex; at the same time the base of the lowlands remained stable tectonically; the transgression of the sea continued and contributed sediments to the young Anthropogenic shelf.

ANTHROPOGENE DEVELOPMENT

The subpolar situation and the accompanying permafrost of the subarctic lowlands, which were submerged by modern marine transgression, promoted the formation of the lakes area that covered more than half the dry area of the lowlands. The numerous lakes hampered the flow of the surface water and changed the radiation balance, for more solar heat was absorbed and transmitted to the rocks beneath, thus increasing the temperature contrast in the subsurface and promoting the development of thermokarst. The hampered flow of water on the vast surface of the lowlands disturbed the development of the cryogenic zone.

All these conditions promoted the intensive formation of vein ice in polygonal fractures in the unconsolidated sediments of the lowlands; thermokarstic processes became stronger everywhere — particularly in the formation of the lakes, which gradually accumulated much more heat than did the adjacent land area.

Many complex heat exchanges (Budyko, 1956) disturbed the established thermodynamic equilibrium, developed a deep thermokarst, caused a karst migration on the surface of the lowland lacustrine reservoirs, halted the underground formation of ice, and even eradicated permafrost. However, during this process the lakes were also disappearing. Thermal balance was gradually restored at the geothermal level characteristic for subarctic regions. Permafrost reappeared and renewed the formation of underground ice, undoubtedly in the polygonal net of fractures from the previous ice cycle. The polycyclic and inherited development of vein ice explains their deep penetration (to 50 m) and accounts for the uneven distribution of the permafrost within the subarctic lowlands, as is also demonstrated by a mathematical prognosis of thermal interaction of adjacent lakes with a common frozen base, and supported by the presence of a total zero curtain on their banks (Tomirdiaro, 1963).

The appearance, development, and disappearance of subarctic thermokarst lakes occurred during the neotectonic-geomorphic conditions of the Anthropogene and the marine transgression of the early Pleistocene, which influenced decisively the formation of the river net and sedimentation. All the alluvial deposits were reworked extensively by the lakes and thus became a flood plain with facies containing much organic matter. The effects of thermokarst lakes in the continental lithogenesis of the northeast Asian subarctic lowlands are obvious, for limnological sedimentation was very significant during the transgression of the sea along the coast, but even more significant in the formation of permafrost, when such sedimentation occurred throughout the lowlands. Limnological sedimentation can be compared in scale with maritime sedimentation.

This account of the formation and development of the subarctic lowlands in the northeastern USSR approaches the whole problem in a new manner, and only some of the details were exposed in the discussion. The ideas expressed here do not preclude the older approach to the study of morphostructures.

REFERENCES

Baranova, Yu. P., and S. F. Biske, 1964, Stratigraphy of the Cenozoic and the history of development of the East Siberian lowland relief: in Quaternary geology and geomorphology of Northeastern Siberia, V. A. Nikolaev (ed.) (in Russian): Novosibirsk, Inst. Geol. Geophys. Trans., No. 8, pp. 41-64.

Berg, L. S., 1946, Submarine valleys (in Russian): Moscow, All-Union Geogr. Soc. Proc., v. 78, pp. 301-302.

Biske, S. F., 1957, Quaternary deposits of the Kolymnian lowland: in Materials on the geology and useful minerals of the Northeastern USSR, B. B. Evangulov (ed.) (in Russian): Magadan, Geol. Prospecting Dept., No. 11, pp. 68-82.

Budyko, M. I., 1956, Thermal balance of the earth's surface (in Russian): Leningrad, Gydrometeoizdat, 254 pp.

Bunge, A. A., 1903, A few words on frozen ground (in Russian): Imperial Mineralog. Soc. St. Petersburg Mem. Ser., 11, pt. 40, 203 pp.

Ermolaev, M. M., 1932, Geological and geomorphological sketch of Bol'shoy Lyakhovskiy Island (in Russian): Leningrad, Acad. Sci. USSR, Council on the Productive Forces of the North. Trans., Yacut Ser. No. 7, pp. 147-228.

Figurin, A. E., 1823, Extracts from notes on a description of the banks of northeastern Siberia (in Russian): St. Petersburg, Notes of the State Admin. Dept., v. 5, pp. 259-328.

Grigor'ev, A. A., 1932, Glaciation of the Yakut territory in the Quaternary (in Russian): Moscow, Acad. Sci. USSR Comm. Study Quaternary, Trans., v. 1, pp. 31-42.

_____ 1946, The Subarctic (in Russian): Moscow, Acad. Sci. USSR Inst. Geogr., 171 pp.

Katasonov, E. M., and S. F. Biske, 1959, The problems of the geomorphology of the Yana-Indighirka and Kolymian lowlands (in Russian): Moscow, Acad. Sci. USSR, Second Geomorphol. Conf., 16 pp.

Kolosov, D. M., 1947, Problems of the ancient glaciation of the northeastern USSR (in Russian): Moscow-Leningrad, Mining-Geol. Dept. Glavsevmorput Trans., No. 30, 175 pp.

Lavrushin, Yu. A., 1962, Alluvium of the plains rivers of the subarctic belt and periglacial regions of continental glaciation (in Russian): Moscow, Acad. Sci. USSR, Geol. Inst. Ph.D. thesis, 23 pp.

Lindberg, G. U., 1946, Geomorphology of the bottom of the outlying seas of eastern Asia and the distribution of freshwater fishes (in Russian): Moscow, All-Union Geogr. Soc. Proc., v. 78, No. 3, pp. 279-301.

Lopatin, I. A., 1876, Information on the ice beds in eastern Siberia (in Russian): Moscow, Acad. Sci. Mem., v. 29, Suppl. 1, pp. 3-32.

Pogozhev, A. G., and A. I. Semeykin, 1957, Tertiary deposits of the northeastern USSR (in Russian): Magadan, Ministry of Nonferrous Metal Industry and Ministry of Geology of the USSR, Conf. Stratigraphic Schemes Northeastern USSR, pp. 105-107.

Popov, A. I., 1953, Features of the lithogenesis of alluvial plains in rigorous climatic conditions (in Russian): Moscow, Acad. Sci. USSR, Proc. Geogr. Ser., No. 2, pp. 29-42.

Puscharovskiy, Yu. M., 1960, The Near-Verkhoyanian foredeep and mesosoides of the northeastern Asia (in Russian): in Tectonics of the USSR, v. 5: Moscow, Acad. Sci. USSR, 235 pp.

Romanovskiy, N. N., 1961, The structure of the Yana-Indighirka (Maritime) alluvial plain and the conditions of its formation (in Russian): Moscow State Univ. Press Freezing Investigations, No. 2, pp. 129-139.

Saks, V. N., 1953, The Quaternary period in the Soviet Arctic (in Russian): Moscow-Leningrad, Sci. Res. Inst. Arctic Geol., v. 77, 626 pp.

Shilo, N. A., 1960, Geological structure and the original sources of the Yana-Kolymian gold-bearing placer belt (in Russian): Magadan, All-Union Sci. Res. Inst. Trans., Geol., No. 63, 108 pp.

Shumskiy, P. A., 1955, The principles of structural ice study. Petrography of fresh ice as a method of the glaciological investigation (in Russian): Moscow, Acad. Sci. USSR, 491 pp.

Shvetsov, P. F., 1938, Permafrost and the engineering-geological conditions of Anadyr region (in Russian): Leningrad, Glavsevmorput.

_____ 1957, History of the development of the Yana-Indighirka (Maritime) lowland in the Anthropogene (in Russian): Moscow, All-Union Interdept. Conf. Study Quaternary Period.

Tillman, S. M., 1962, Tectonics and history of the development of the northeastern Near-Kolymian (in Russian): Magadan, Siberian Div. Acac. Sci. USSR, Northeastern Complex Sci. Res. Inst. Trans., No. 1, 190 pp.

Toll, E. V., 1897, The relation of New Siberian Island fossil glaciers to mammoth carcasses and to the glacial period (in Russian): St. Petersburg, Russian Geogr. Soc. Mem. General Geogr., v. 32, No. 1.

Tomirdiaro, S. V., 1963, Thermal calculations of the bases in permafrost regions (in Russian): Magadan, Siberian Div. Acad. Sci. USSR, Northeastern Complex Sci. Res. Inst. Trans., No. 4, 104 pp.

Udintsev, G. B., 1955, The origin of the relief of the Ochotsk sea bottom (in Russian): Moscow, Inst. Oceanol. Trans., v. 13, pp. 5-16.

Vollosovich, K. A., 1915, The mammoth of Bol'shoy Lyakhovskiy Island (Novosibirsk Islands) (in Russian): Petrograd, Mineral. Soc. Mem., pt. 50, pp. 305-338.

Vtyurin, B. I., 1964, Cryogenic structure of Quaternary deposits (in Russian): Moscow, Acad. Sci. USSR, Pub. House "Nauka," 150 pp.

ARCTIC AND ALPINE ENVIRONMENTS (H. E. Wright, Jr., and
W. H. Osburn, eds.), 283-293, © 1967 Indiana University Press

20

Soils of Arctic Alaska

J. C. F. TEDROW
Department of Soils
Rutgers University
New Brunswick, New Jersey

J. BROWN
U.S. Army Cold Regions Research and Engineering Laboratory
Hanover, New Hampshire

Abstract

During the past 12 years a genetic approach to soil distribution has evolved for the Arctic Slope of Alaska. The region includes three physiographic provinces: the northern Brooks Range, Foothills, and Coastal Plain. In addition to Arctic Brown, Tundra, and Bog soils, other soils have been described: Podzol-like, Rendzina, and Shungite soils.

Ten soil zones are presently delineated on a mapping scale of 1:5,000,000. Zones are controlled largely by physiography and geology. More detailed soil mapping has been conducted at Pt. Barrow (Coastal Plain 1:20,000), Umiat (Foothills 1:10,000), Howard Pass (1:250,000), the Okpilak River (1:30,000), and other locations. An intricate aspect of soil mapping in northern Alaska is the ubiquitous occurrence of patterned ground. Ice-wedge polygons predominate on the low relief of the Coastal Plain. Sorted circles, nets, and polygons are major patterns on the bouldery valley and upland terrain of the mountains and foothills. Well-drained soils increase in areal coverage in areas of coarser-grained materials. Tundra and Bog soils occupy much of the Coastal Plain.

The Alaskan arctic, which is of considerable importance in pedology, consists of three physiographic provinces with varied landforms, substrates, and biotic and climatic gradients, which combine to produce many soil varieties. The ground is perennially frozen to depths of 1000 ft or more (MacCarthy, 1952), with an average seasonal thaw of generally less than 2 ft (Drew et al., 1958). Patterned ground and massive ground ice in the near-surface sediments are nearly always present, the abundance and type depending upon local conditions.

Soil studies have been conducted in northern Alaska since 1953. This report summarizes some findings of these studies, describes soil-forming processes, and, for the first time, presents a generalized soil map of Arctic Alaska.

Gorodkov (1939) initiated a realistic approach to the genesis of arctic soils when he stated that there were no unique pedogenic processes in arctic regions. These processes were, instead, qualitatively similar to those of the northern forests. Gorodkov's work gives us a framework for depicting those processes of the main arctic region that occur generally between the 40 and 54°F July isotherms. Nearly all land of northern Alaska, except that at the higher altitudes in the Brooks Range and the northern littoral fringes, lies between these two isotherms, and our discussion is confined primarily to this climatic belt.

MAJOR SOILS

Well-Drained Soils

Certain well-drained mineral soils of northern Alaska, designated as Arctic Brown, are in many respects similar to the brown-colored soils of the northern forests (Tedrow and Hill, 1955; Drew and Tedrow, 1957; Hill and Tedrow, 1961); iron weathering from the parent material and in association with humus produces a brown-colored solum. In the southern fringes of the Alaskan Arctic Slope, the surface horizons are mildly to strongly acid and have certain podzolic affinities (Hill and Tedrow, 1961; Brown and Tedrow, 1964), but farther north well-drained soils are less acid, and the podzolic character is less evident (Drew and Tedrow, 1957). In the high arctic, the so-called Arctic Brown soil is, in effect, a variety of cold-steppe soil (Tedrow and Douglas, 1964).

Within the Brooks Range, climatic-orogenic factors have a controlling influence on soil development and, accordingly, there is a suppression of soil formation with increasing altitude (Tedrow and Brown, 1962).

A Podzol-like soil has been described on some of the valley moraines of the Brooks Range (Brown and Tedrow, 1964). Its occurrence is closely related to acid parent material and the heath-birch vegetation of protected sites.

Mineral Gley (Tundra) Soils

Because Tundra soils mantle the greater part of the arctic landscape not orogenically controlled, this Great Soil Group has been given considerable prominence in the literature. Processes involve humus formation, mild leaching, a gley process, and frost displacement (Tedrow et al., 1958; Brown and Tedrow, 1958; Douglas and Tedrow, 1960). In the soils of the central sector of Arctic Alaska there is a tendency toward a thicker zone of seasonal thaw than is the case farther north. Despite low seasonal ground temperatures, Tundra soils of the arctic have strong affinities toward the mineral gley soils of the boreal regions (Tedrow and Harries, 1960). Tundra soils are usually mildly acid and predominantly silty in character, with no specific trend in particle size with depth.

Within the general grouping of Tundra soils the better-drained conditions have been designated as upland Tundra, and the wetter conditions as meadow Tundra (Drew, 1957; Tedrow et al., 1958).

Bog Soils

Bog soils are present throughout northern Alaska; the portion of land mantled by these soils increases from the Brooks Range northward to the shore of the Arctic Ocean. In the valleys of the Brooks Range the thickness of the organic deposits appears to be limited to 2 to 5 ft, but farther north isolated localities have organic deposits 20 to 30 ft thick. Bogs in northern Alaska are nearly always mildly to strongly acid, but there is reason to believe that some alkaline bogs are present, particularly east of the Colville River.

Miscellaneous Soils

Special mention should be made of the presence of certain arctic Rendzina soils (Ugolini and Tedrow, 1963) and the unique soil conditions on the black shales of the Brooks Range (Ugolini et al., 1963). In the latter condition the Shungite soils form under mesic drainage conditions with organic matter accumulating to a thickness of 15 to 30 inches. Soils of the flood plains and terraces were described earlier (Tedrow et al., 1958; Tedrow and Cantlon, 1958).

SOIL REGIONS

General

Few attempts have been undertaken to map soil conditions in this arctic region. Kellogg and Nygard (1951) made some generalizations as to soil distribution in northern Alaska, and Reiger (1963) recognized coastal and upland Tundra (gley) soils in this region along with Lithosols. Selected areas within each of the provinces have been mapped: Point Barrow on the Coastal Plain (Drew, 1957), and the Umiat area of the Northern Foothills (J. C. F. Tedrow and D. E. Hill, unpubl. ms.),

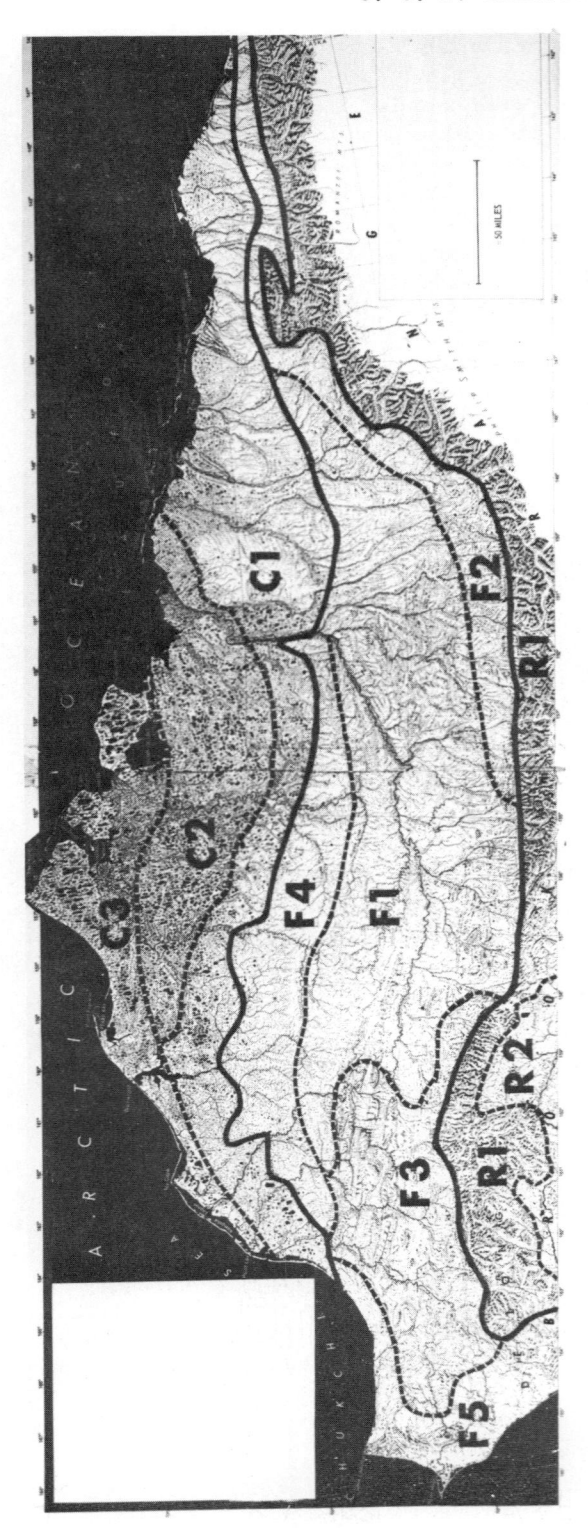

Fig. 1. Soil-distribution pattern of Northern Alaska. C1, tundra soils of the Coastal Plain; C2, tundra soils of the Coastal Plain with many sand dunes; C3, tundra soils of the Coastal Plain with extensive Bog-like soils; F1, tundra soils of the Foothills; F2, tundra soils of the Foothills with many stony conditions; F3, tundra soils of the Foothills with steep topography; F4, tundra soils on fine sands; Foothills-Coastal Plain transition; F5, tundra soils of the Foothills with dark-colored sola; R1, shallow soils of the mountains; R2, tundra soils of the Noatak Basin.

SOILS OF ARCTIC ALASKA

the Howard Pass quadrangle (MacNamara and Tedrow, 1966), and the northeastern portions of the Brooks Range (Brown, 1962a). In general, the approach has been to map both surface features or patterns and major genetic soils and soil conditions in the form of soil complexes or soil associations.

Specific soil units or complexes can generally be delineated on aerial photographs. The amount of detail depends on the scale and purpose of the mapping. Southward from the Coastal Plain toward the Brooks Range, the number of units and their interrelationship increase as a reflection of increasing complexity in topographic gradients, ground patterns, and parent materials.

Soil regions of northern Alaska can be conveniently described under three physiographic headings: Brooks Range, Arctic Foothills, and Coastal Plain. Since physiography and geologic material tend to play an important role in soil distribution, these physiographic separations serve, in part, as pedologic boundaries. The map shown as Fig. 1 is compiled from field observations made over the past 10 years. The line separating the Arctic Foothills from the Coastal Plain is more transitory.

Soils of the Coastal Plain

The Coastal Plain of northern Alaska is flat to undulating with the drainage pattern of the northern portion poorly developed (Figs. 1 and 2). Tundra soils predominate on both the Gubik and Sagavanirktok formations and generally consist of sandy loams, fine sandy loams, or silt loams (Douglas, 1961) (Fig. 3). From the Colville River east to Canada many of the rivers tend to have wide terraces with considerable gravel present. In the White Hills section, a number of streams have deposited carbonate-bearing sediments along the flood plains. Apparently they were transported in turn as eolian material over the landscape, and the attendant Tundra soils have an alkaline reaction (Drew, 1957; Douglas and Tedrow, 1960). Bog soils are also common throughout the C1 area.

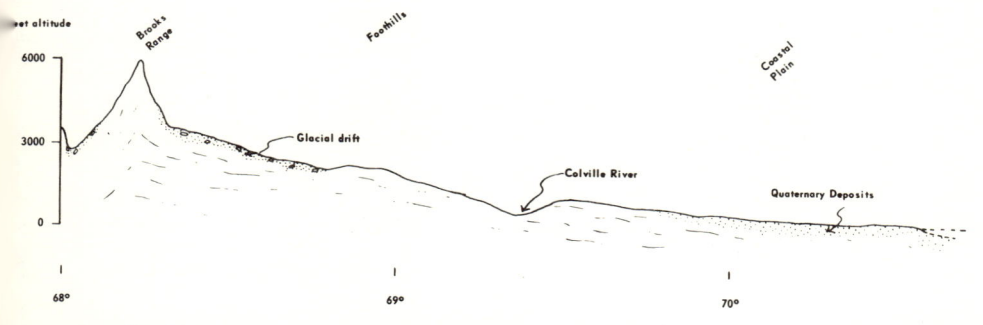

Fig. 2. Idealized north-south transect of Northern Alaska along the 154°W meridian.

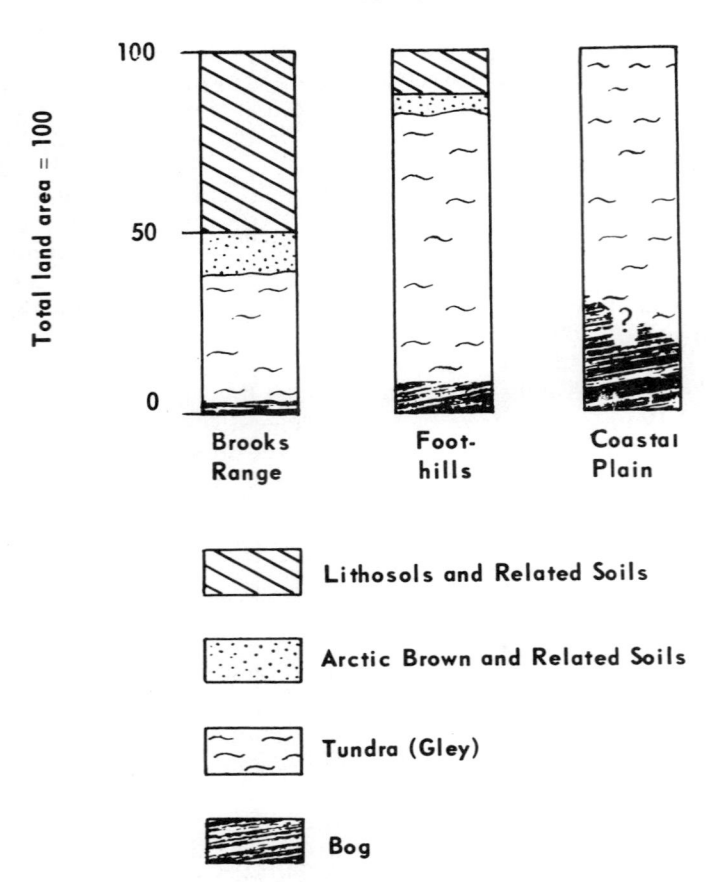

Fig. 3. Soil distribution in northern Alaska (highly generalized).

The area from the central Meade River basin eastward to the Colville River delta (Fig. 1, C2) is comprised of loam to sandy loam Tundra soils with prominent sand dunes, many of which are active (Black, 1951). The dunes tend to consist of medium sand.

The littoral area from the delta of the Utukok River through Barrow, Teshekpuk Lake, and the Colville Delta is low-lying and covered with many lakes and ponds. This area is characterized by a high percentage of Bog-like soils (Fig. 1, C3), with extensive areas of Tundra soils of silt loam and loam textures.

Patterned ground exists throughout the Arctic Coastal Plain, with various forms and varieties of ice-wedge polygons. Frost scars are present throughout the area (Fig. 4).

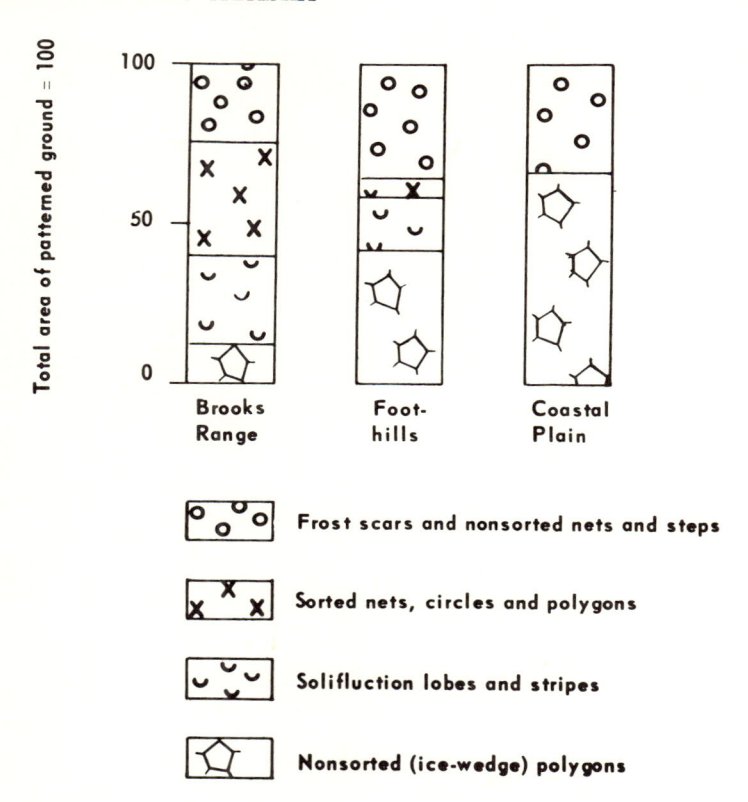

Fig. 4. Patterned-ground distribution in northern Alaska (highly generalized).

Soils of the Arctic Foothills

The Arctic Foothills consist primarily of folded sedimentary rocks, including sandstone and a small amount of limestone. Altitudes reach 4000 ft in the Southern Foothills sector and decrease to less than 1000 feet to the north. Glaciers moved northward from the Brooks Range for a distance of 10 to 30 miles into the Arctic Foothills (Leffingwell, 1919; Detterman et al. 1958; Porter, 1964). Drift in the most southerly part of the Foothills is relatively thick and continuous, except on isolated peaks and mountains where it occurs in a thin discontinuous pattern.

Soils of the Foothills consist mainly of Tundra soils, which mantle the landscape generally from ridge crest to valley bottom. Bog soils are present on many flat positions and along water courses. Arctic Brown soils are present in small quantity on ridge crests and equivalent stable, well-drained positions (Hill, 1957). Tundra soils are in general moderately acid and of silt loam texture. There appears to be little difference in morphology (excluding erratics) between the Tundra soils of the glaciated and nonglaciated areas (Tedrow and Harries, 1960).

For the purpose of this discussion, the Foothills Province is subdivided into five soil areas (Fig. 1). As outlined, the major soil conditions apply in particular to the F1 area.

The soils of the F2 area, while classified as Tundra, differ from those of F1 because of the stony character of the former. In the F2 area also, local well-drained soils commonly have Podzol-like features present (as is the case with the soils of the valleys of the eastern R1 area) (Brown and Tedrow, 1964). Very few Podzol-like soils have been recorded north of the F2 area, nor have they been observed west of Kurupa Lakes.

The F3 area (Fig. 1) is delineated from the prototype (F1) because the landscape is more hilly, with a larger percentage of well-drained and shallow soils, including bedrock outcrops, than is found in the F1 area.

Soils of the F4 area are quite similar to those designated as F1, but in the former there tends to be a discontinuous surficial deposit of fine sands. Excellent examples of the surficial sands are exposed near the lower Kogosukruk River.

The upper mineral horizon of the Tundra soils (F1) approximates a light olive-brown to gray color (Douglas and Tedrow, 1960), but on the extreme western portion (F5), especially near Cape Sabine, this horizon tends to be dark brown to black. Whether this dark color is a reflection of the maritime climate, the presence of montmorillonite clay minerals, or some other factor is unknown. This darker-colored solum of the F5 area (Fig. 1) is a condition within the Arctic Brown as well as the Tundra soils.

Special mention should be made of the heavy plastic bentonite deposits near Umiat, with no semblance of a developed soil profile (Tedrow, 1962; MacNamara and Tedrow, 1966).

Soils of the Brooks Range

The Brooks Range is a region of high, mountainous relief. Soils tend to be shallow and stony, with bedrock exposed over extensive areas. Over much of the area there is no developed soil; instead boulder fields, shattered bedrock, and organic mats mantle the landscape. Although the Brooks Range has been glaciated, apparently most of those portions of the mountains above an altitude of 4000 to 5000 ft stood above the ice. Figure 1 shows the general region of mountainous soils (R1). R2 designates a lower area within the Noatak basin that has predominantly Tundra soils. The major valleys of the R1 area are several miles wide, with altitudes approximately 2000 to 3000 ft. Soils of the valleys are predominantly Tundra and Bog (Brown, 1962b), but with the local elevated landforms as much as 15 to 20% of the area is mantled with Arctic Brown and Podzol-like soils (Brown and Tedrow, 1964) (Figs. 2 and 3). Ascending to higher terrain within the Brooks Range, the soils are well-drained to xeric. On slopes, solifluction processes are active. At altitudes of 3000 to 5000 ft much of the landscape is devoid of vascular vegetation, with isolated well-drained, brown-colored soils and scattered Ranker-like soils (Kubiena, 1953; Tedrow and Brown, 1962).

The eastern sector of the Brooks Range, particularly the Phillip Smith, Franklin, and Romanzoff Mountains, is more rugged and has a larger percentage of rocky, soil-free, conditions than does the western section, especially in the vicinity of Howard Pass and the DeLong Mountains.

Rendzina soils (Ugolini and Tedrow, 1963) have been described on the limestone deposits of the Brooks Range eastward from Howard Pass, as have the unique organic-like soils of the black shales in the vicinity of Porcupine Lake (Ugolini et al., 1963).

Within the Brooks Range and Southern Foothills, observations were made to determine if a chronosequence existed in soil development as one proceeded northward from youngest to oldest glaciated surfaces. Although no such sequence was observed, differences of parent material were clearly reflected in the soil profiles (Brown and Tedrow, 1964).

PATTERNED GROUND AND PERIGLACIAL ENVIRONMENT

Virtually all forms of patterned ground are present in Arctic Alaska (Drew and Tedrow, 1962; Brown, 1962a). Distribution of patterned ground is governed principally by topography and texture of the substrata. The flat, monotonous relief and fine-textured materials of the Coastal Plain result in the predominance of nonsorted polygons, frost scars, and various sorted nets, circles, and polygons (Fig. 3). The more sloping topography of the Foothills, with scattered exposures of bedrock and bentonite deposits, results in a variety of sorted and nonsorted features. Nonsorted patterns include large areas of frost scars, steps, and stripes. Where frost-shattered bedrock is exposed, sorted nets and stripes tend to occur. The complex topography and materials in the Brooks Range result in a juxtaposition of both Coastal Plain and Foothills patterns. Valley floors contain sorted and nonsorted circles, nets, stripes, and polygons. Ice-wedge polygons are common in organic deposits, and sorted nets and polygons in gravels on glacial and alluvial deposits. At higher elevations sorted nets are the dominant feature on flat bench-like surfaces, with nonsorted steps and stripes present elsewhere on slopes.

Presumably all these forms of patterned ground are presently active in northern Alaska. Polygonized ground repeatedly cracks during the winter, with subsequent growth of foliated ice masses.

Melting of ground ice along drainage divides results in the formation of high-center polygons. Mineral soil is actively heaved during seasonal freeze-back and results in the formation of frost scars in close-order packing or singly; this process perpetuates the characteristic spotty tundra surface in all physiographic provinces. The sorting process, although active today, may have been more intense under other climatic regimes.

The Coastal Plain, an unglaciated area of both marine and nonmarine sediments, is dominated by oriented lakes. These lakes migrate across the frozen land surface and continually erode old surfaces and create new ones as lake basins drain (Britton, 1957). Polygonal ground and the associated Tundra and Bog soils are constantly being destroyed and regenerated.

The Northern Foothills are largely unglaciated and presumably were active periglacial areas. Present mass wasting in the form of solifluction prevails in the area. During the time of maximum glaciation the soil surfaces were probably more denuded and frost-churning more intense than is now the case. The present climate along the central part of the Colville River Valley is warmer in summer than other areas of northern Alaska. This is reflected in the presence of alder vegetation and is associated with a July mean temperature of about 54°F. Thermokarst features, such as lakes, are locally present in the Foothill Province.

Remnants of glacial deposits are present throughout the eastern and central Brooks Range. Land surfaces at lower altitudes are consequently younger as one progresses from the Foothills southward into the mountains. The higher, unglaciated elevations have encountered repeated degrees of intense periglacial environment throughout the Pleistocene and up to the present. Surficial expression of patterned ground in both the glaciated and unglaciated areas does not differ substantially.

Acknowledgment

These studies were aided by a contract between the Office of Naval Research and the Arctic Institute of North America.

REFERENCES

Black, R. F., 1951, Eolian deposits of Alaska: Arctic, v. 4, pp. 89-111.
Britton, M. E., 1957, Vegetation of the Arctic Tundra. Arctic Biology: Corvallis, Ore., Biol. Colloq. Oregon State Chapter Phi Kappa Phi, pp. 26-61.
Brown, J., 1962a, Soils of the Northern Brooks Range, Alaska: New Brunswick, N.J., Rutgers Univ. Ph.D. thesis, 234 p.

_____ 1962b, An organic terrain from a glaciated valley, northern Alaska: Proc. 13th Alaskan Sci. Conf., Am. Assoc. Advan. Sci., pp. 159-160 (abstract).
_____ 1964, Soils of the northern Brooks Range, Alaska. 4. Well-drained soils of the glaciated valleys: Soil Sci., v. 97, pp. 187-195.
_____, and J. C. F. Tedrow, 1958, Characteristics of two tundra soils from the Arctic Slope of Alaska: Proc. 9th Alaskan Sci. Conf., Am. Assoc. Advan. Sci., p. 2 (abstracts).
Detterman, R. L., A. L. Bowsher, and J. T. Dutro, Jr., 1958, Glaciation on the Arctic Slope of the Brooks Range, northern Alaska: Arctic, v. 11, pp. 43-61.
Douglas, L. A., 1961, A pedologic study of tundra soils from northern Alaska: New Brunswick, N.J., Rutgers Univ. Ph.D. thesis, 147 pp.
_____, and J. C. F. Tedrow, 1960, Tundra soils of Arctic Alaska: Proc. 7th Intern Soil Sci. Congr., Madison, Wisc., Comm. 5, v. 4, pp. 291-304.
Drew, J. V., 1957, A pedologic study of Arctic Coastal Plain soils near Point Barrow, Alaska: New Brunswick, N.J., Rutgers Univ. Ph.D. thesis, 117 pp.
_____, and J. C. F. Tedrow, 1957, Pedology of an arctic brown profile near Point Barrow, Alaska: Soil Sci. Soc. Am. Proc., v. 21, pp. 336-339.
_____, and J. C. F. Tedrow, 1962, Arctic soil classification and patterned ground: Arctic, v. 15, pp. 109-116.
_____, J. C. F. Tedrow, R. E. Shanks, and J. J. Koranda, 1958, Rate and depth of thaw in arctic soils: Trans. Am. Geophys. Union, v. 39, pp. 697-701.
Gorodkov, B. N., 1939, Peculiarities of the arctic topsoil: Izv. Gos. Geogr. Obshch., v. 71, pp. 1516-1532.
Hill, D. E., 1957, The influence of the arctic environment on weathering and soil formation in the Arctic Slope of Alaska: New Brunswick, N.J., Rutgers Univ. Ph.D. thesis, 113 pp.
_____, and J. C. F. Tedrow, 1961, Weathering and soil formation in the arctic environment: Am. J. Sci., v. 259, pp. 84-101.
Kellogg, C. E., and I. J. Nygard, 1951, Exploratory study of the principal soil groups of Alaska: U.S. Dept. Agr. Monograph, No. 7, 138 pp.
Kubiena, W. L., 1953, The soils of Europe: London, T. Murby.
Leffingwell, E. deK., 1919, The Canning River region, northern Alaska: U.S. Geol. Surv. Prof. Paper 109, 251 pp.
MacCarthy, G. R., 1952, Geothermal investigations on the Arctic Slope of Alaska: Trans. Am. Geophys. Union, v. 33, pp. 589-593.
MacNamara, E. E., and J. C. F. Tedrow, 1966, An arctic equivalent to the Grumusol: Arctic, v. 19, pp. 145-152.
Porter, S. C., 1964, Late Pleistocene glacial chronology of North-Central Brooks Range, Alaska: Am. J. Sci., v. 262, pp. 446-460.

Rieger, S., 1963, A new soil map of Alaska: Proc. 14th Alaskan Sci. Conf., Am. Assoc. Advan. Sci., p. 18.

Tedrow, J. C. F., 1962, Morphological evidence of frost action in Arctic soils: Biul. Peryglacjalny, v. 11, pp. 343-352.

_____, and D. E. Hill, 1955, Arctic brown soil: Soil Sci., v. 80, pp. 265-275.

_____, and J. E. Cantlon, 1958, Concepts of soil formation and classification in arctic regions: Arctic, v. 11, pp. 166-179.

_____, and H. Harries, 1960, Tundra soil in relation to vegetation, permafrost, and glaciation: Acta Oecol. Scand., v. 11, pp. 237-249.

_____, and J. Brown, 1962, Soils of the Northern Brooks Range, Alaska. Weakening of the soil-forming potential at high arctic altitudes: Soil Sci., v. 93, pp. 254-261.

_____, and L. A. Douglas, 1964, Soil investigation on Banks Island: Soil Sci., v. 98, pp. 53-65.

_____, J. V. Drew, D. E. Hill, and L. A. Douglas, 1958, Major genetic soils of the Arctic Slope of Alaska: J. Soil Sci., v. 9, pp. 33-45.

Ugolini, F. C., and J. C. F. Tedrow, 1963, Soils of the Brooks Range, Alaska. 3. Rendzina of the arctic: Soil Sci., v. 96, pp. 121-127.

_____, J. C. F. Tedrow, and C. L. Grant, 1963, Soils of the Northern Brooks Range, Alaska: 2. Soils derived from black shale: Soil Sci., v. 95, pp. 115-123.

ARCTIC AND ALPINE ENVIRONMENTS (H. E. Wright, Jr., and
W. H. Osburn, eds.), 295-306, © 1967 Indiana University Press

21

Remote Sensing from Spacecraft as a Tool for Investigating Arctic Environments

DAVID S. SIMONETT AND STANLEY A. MORAIN
Department of Geography and Meteorology
The University of Kansas
Lawrence, Kansas

Abstract

Remote-sensor imaging systems on orbiting spacecraft may be used to obtain geomorphic and biogeographic data for theoretical and practical investigations of arctic environments. Previously inaccessible and remote areas of high latitudes may be "viewed" in the foreseeable future by all-weather day-or-night imaging systems from which both reconnaissance and large-scale maps and statistical data can be produced or updated. Multispectral photography and multifrequency infrared and radar imaging systems are currently under study that are potentially of great value for both long- and short-term environmental studies, including those involving the dynamics of the environment on a Holarctic scale. Research possibilities might include (1) extending inferences derived from sites studied in detail on the ground to other much more inaccessible regions, (2) mapping boundaries of continuous and discontinuous permafrost and relating them to vegetational patterns, (3) recording progress of break-up and freeze-up along major arctic drainage systems and lakes, (4) differentiating and mapping forests on the basis of physiognomy, especially in the forest-tundra ecotone, (5) preparing or revising maps of certain tree species, (6) mapping the economic limits of forests, polar tree line, and altitudinal timber line, (7) differentiating and mapping tundra landscapes characterized by particular associations of lichens and mosses, and (8) detecting forest fires, and measuring their extent and frequency.

The recent development of remote sensing from aircraft will aid mapping in the Arctic and sub-Arctic, where remoteness, climate, and poor trafficability have hindered field studies. However, an even more exciting potential exists in the coupling of these remote sensors with manned orbiting spacecraft. In polar orbit these can monitor changes at critical times of the year when both ground and flying conditions are abominable. It is the purpose of this paper to describe some of the research possibilities of this pairing of sensors and spacecraft.

NATURE OF REMOTE SENSORS

"Passive" remote sensors such as aerial photography and thermal infrared and microwave scanning and spectrometer systems depend respectively upon reflected solar energy and upon radiation emitted from terrestrial objects, while "active" sensors such as radar depend upon transmitted and received signals as their source of information. Each sensor records within a relatively narrow energy band of the electromagnetic spectrum; consequently each obtains different information about objects or phenomena that reflect or emit energy in that band.

Photography employs the "visible" region and part of the adjacent near ultraviolet and near infrared. This wavelength range (0.3 to 0.9 micron) may be recorded on film with appropriate film and filter combinations.

In the infrared region, thermal scanning methods may be used in a number of atmospheric windows between 2 and 14 microns. Techniques are being developed for internal reference calibration of imaging infrared systems such that semiquantitative spectral data may be obtained to improve identifications of different materials.

Imaging microwave systems on spacecraft are likely to lie in the wavelength range 2 to 4 cm for technical reasons. At 2 cm the spatial resolution from spacecraft would be about 1.3 km and the temperature sensitivity 1°C. The emitted radiation recorded is derived from the upper few centimeters of the ground.

Multifrequency polypolarized coherent radar systems have also been proposed for spacecraft. These radars will penetrate soils and other materials, depending on the wavelength used. They will also be sensitive to the natural orientations in trees, rocks, crystals, bedding planes, and so on.

Radar and passive microwave systems are also all-weather instruments, and they share with infrared the ability to obtain images at night or in the long Arctic winter.

An introduction to principles and applications of remote sensing is given by Parker and Wolf (1965), and the electromagnetic spectrum in relation to remote sensing by Colwell et al. (1963). The use of radars on spacecraft is discussed by Pierson et al. (1965), and some additional applications by Simonett and Brown (1967). Numerous papers on infrared and passive microwave systems may be found in the "Proceedings of the Symposia on Remote Sensing of Environment at the University of Michigan," published in 1962, 1963, and 1965.

REMOTE SENSORS ON SPACECRAFT

When a number of these sensors is used in concert, they give data of which no part is diagnostic but which together may be unmistakable. This concept, for which Colwell (1961) uses the phrase "multiband spectral reconnaissance," is the key to using spacecraft as an observation platform in studies of earth resources. For efficient diagnosis of the earth's landscapes a variety of remote sensors will be required.

With combinations of remote sensors on orbiting spacecraft it should be possible to (1) image continuous strips tens to hundreds of miles wide, (2) obtain physical data about objects or phenomena at any time of day or season, and (3) monitor conditions that change with time. These capabilities will enable continuous imagery to record transitions that take place over such long distances that similar coverage by conventional aerial photography would require weeks or months (Morrison and Bird, 1965). The remarkable color photographs of Arabia and elsewhere obtained by McDivitt and White on the Gemini-4 spacecraft mission with a hand-held Hasselblatt 70-mm camera give an indication of the possibilities with longer focal lengths and motion-compensation equipment.

MAPPING OF RESOURCES FROM SPACECRAFT

Reconnaissance maps of vegetation, soils, and permafrost in the Arctic are incomplete. Vegetation maps of Alaska by Spetzman (1963) and of Labrador by Hare (1959) are indicative of the small-scale coverage now available. Detailed studies of soil, vegetation, and permafrost are few and widely scattered. Multiband sensing can greatly assist the preparation of maps of all scales, especially those of intermediate scales (1:500,000 to 1:100,000) with Holarctic coverage.

The scale and reliability of spacecraft maps will depend on the resolution of each system at suitable orbital altitudes. Recently proposed experiments for the Manned Space Science Program of the National Aeronautics and Space Administration reveal the capabilities for ground resolution anticipated in earth orbit (Table 1).

TABLE 1

Anticipated Resolutions in Earth Orbit
by Imaging Remote Sensors at 370 km

Spectral region	Resolution
Visible, near UV and IR (0.3-0.9 μ)	1 m (high resolution) to 60 m (mapping, 550 x 550 km)
Infrared (2-14 μ, 3 or more bands)	100-300 m
Radar (3.8, 15, and 60 cm)	15 m
Microwave (2 cm)	About 1.3 km (3-m antenna)

Modified from Advanced Missions Division, 1965.

VEGETATION MAPPING

Multiband spectral reconnaissance promises to be of special value in mapping the natural vegetation of the Arctic and sub-Arctic. The use of multispectral photography and thermal infrared imagery for forest mapping has been documented by Colwell (1961), Colwell and Olson (1965), and others. Six bands in the 0.35 to 14 micron range have been used by the Infrared Laboratory, University of Michigan, to differentiate communities of mixed-deciduous forest (Colwell and Olson, 1965). The same technique could be used to map monospecific stands as well as diseased areas and communities under stress of deficient moisture and nutrition. The well-documented difference in day-and-night spectral reflectance (Wittgenstein, 1961) and apparent temperatures between coniferous and deciduous species will facilitate mapping by means of temporal variations in leafout, leaf fall, and changes in pigmentation that lead to changes in spectral reflectance (Gates et al., 1965).

By providing nearly synchronous Holarctic information regarding distribution of plant communities or even species, spacecraft sensing can give a datum against which future long-range changes could be followed and may thus reveal patterns of advance or retreat of forest and tundra still in active recovery from the latest stages of glaciation. This pattern of recovery will focus attention on microclimatic variations, and the fate of forest islands (Tikhomirov, 1962; Griggs, 1937).

Tundra landscapes present unique problems in vegetational analysis because of the complex mixture of cryptogams and small flowering plants. Many communities have characteristic color combinations during the flowering season and may be separable by color, infrared false color, and multispectral and other films on the basis of small changes in pigmentation (Gates et al., 1965). However, color studies will be aided by multifrequency thermal, infrared, and radar imagery to help differentiate these communities by extending the spectral region over which they are imaged.

REMOTE SENSING FROM SPACECRAFT 299

The unstable environment arising from freezing and thawing gives a complex mosaic of plant communities in a constant state of flux (Griggs, 1934). Thus detailed repeated ground study will need to be allied with spacecraft observations for effective study of the tundra, especially for remote areas in the Canadian Archipelago, where the flora and ecology are little known (Porsild, 1951, 1958).

Our experience with radar imagery in studies of cropped areas leads us to the view that multifrequency polypolarization radars on spacecraft will usefully supplement the data obtained from the other sensors discussed above. Even with a single radar frequency, very marked changes in crop image intensity occur throughout the growing season with changes in their heading and moisture content, and these changes are directly applicable to the study of phenologic variations among species in high latitudes irrespective of cloud conditions in this frequently overcast environment.

As an example of the potential use of radar systems in studying vegetation, we have prepared a gross vegetation map (Fig. 2) of a portion of the Yukon Flats – Christian River area, Alaska. This imagery was obtained October 22, 1957, through virtually continuous cloud overcast. The radar employed was the AN/APQ-56, a K_a band (8.6 mm) system with a resolution of about 30 m and an image ground scale of 1:350,000. One polarization only was transmitted and received. However, although this capability falls well short of that of the multifrequency polypolarized radars proposed for spacecraft, much information may be derived from this single system.

Yukon Flats is a complex of alluvial fans and floodplain locally mantled by about 20 ft of silt and underlain by large discontinuous areas of permafrost. The "active" layer ranges between 6 inches and 6 ft, being thickest near and along major streams. The flat to gently rolling or locally hummocky slopes are poorly drained and are greatly subject to frost heaving. Stands of black spruce *(Picea mariana)* 10 to 30 ft high occur on low, cold, wet flats, and stands of white spruce *(Picea glauca)* occur on well-drained alluvium. Other forest species include paper birth *(Betula papyrifera)*, quaking aspen *(Populus tremuloides)*, and balsam poplar *(Populus tacamahaca)*, normally on better-drained sites. Forest undergrowth consists of low shrubs of willow, dwarf birth, and heath plants with a thick cover of grass, moss, and lichens. Large areas have been burned since 1900 and are covered by willow brush or locally by very dense spruce saplings (Spetzman, 1963).

In the reproduction of radar imagery (Fig. 1), areas of high return show as dark grey on the negative imagery. These are delineated on the map of tentative vegetation types (Fig. 2) as possibly white spruce. Our experience with evergreens planted in close array in midwestern shelter belts is that they give a very high radar return, a feature we anticipate in dense spruce forests also. Some of the white spruce (?) cling to small streams with narrow floodplains,

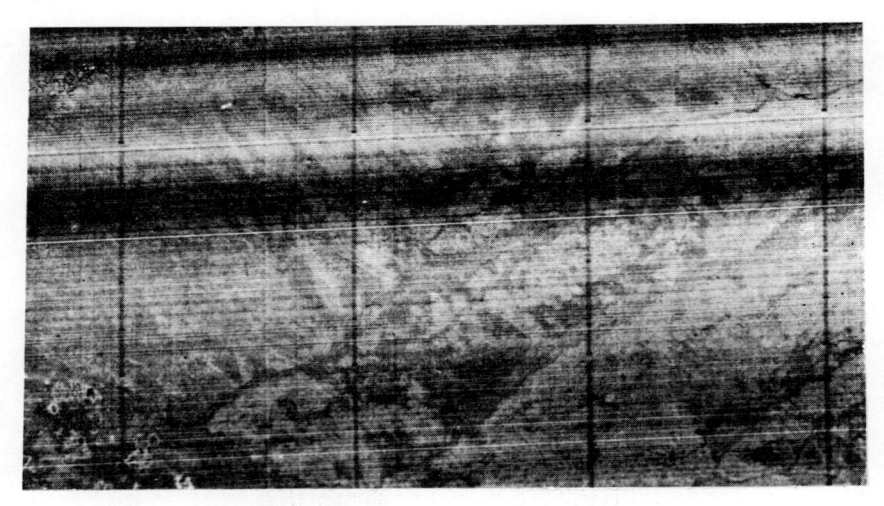

Fig. 1. AN/APQ - 56 radar imagery east of the Christian River, Yukon Flats, Alaska.

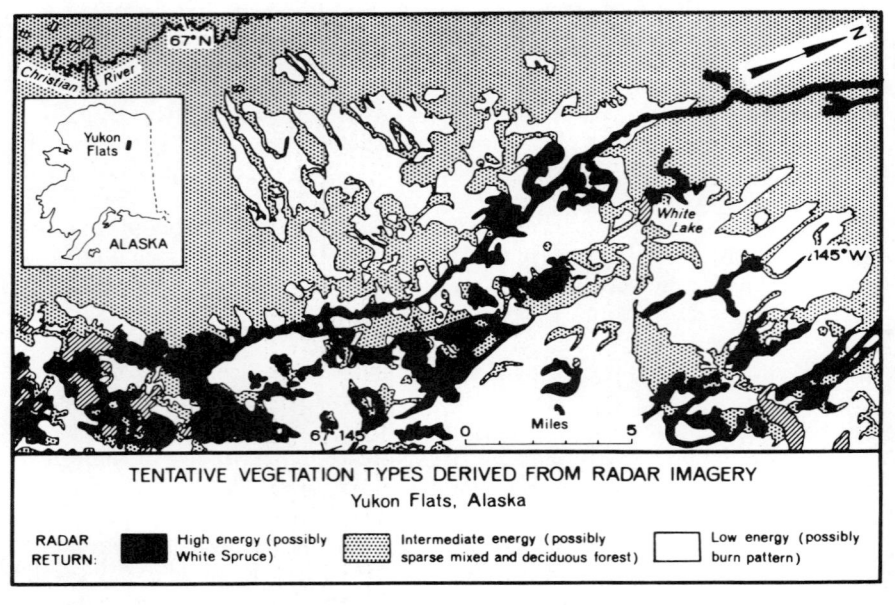

Fig. 2. Tentative vegetation types derived from radar imagery in Fig. 1.

others lie along the margins of lakes, others may be islands in fire burn, and some could even be spruce invaders in areas lightly damaged by fire. All these environments are reasonable for this area. Dr. Philip Johnson of the U.S. Army Cold Regions Research and Engineering Laboratory, on the basis of his field studies in Yukon Flats, suggested to us that white spruce is appropriate for these areas of high return.

Areas of low energy (pale on the imagery) appear in part at least to reflect a previous fire pattern. The east-west lenticular patterns and sawtooth edges of these areas are both suggestive of burns. In addition, there appears to be north-south belts of vegetation paralleling the major drainage lines; these could reflect a fire pattern influenced by soil-drainage conditions. The fire involved might be the Box Car Burn of 1940, which started in this general area on the Porcupine River, burned westward to the Christian River, and consumed about 192,000 acres (Lutz, 1960). Dr. Johnson (personal communication) notes from his field studies that "in particular the burn patterns north of White Lake can be substantiated." In this area active regrowth or invasion following a burn includes willows, aspen, and some white birch.

Areas of moderate energy (medium grey on the imagery) probably "correspond to woody plant communities of a more open type such as scattered black spruce or white birch in a matrix of ericaceous shrubs and mosses" (Johnson, personal communication).

FOREST-FIRE DETECTION

Fire and its persistence in certain locations has always been a very important factor in determining the extent and composition of the boreal forests (Lutz, 1960). Published estimates of the annual burn of timbered lands in Alaska are now reasonably accurate, but burn statistics are most inadequate for many other Arctic and sub-Arctic regions. Spatial and temperature resolution in orbiting infrared sensors are such that, whereas they could not detect very small fires of less than 1 acre of interest to fire-detection crews (Hirsch, 1963), they could record medium and large fires of obvious practical and scientific importance. The location and extent of major fires could also be obtained with radar imagery after the event.

POLAR TREE LINES

The northern limit of trees is a biotic and economic boundary of major significance similar in many ways to the transition from forest to prairie in the middle latitudes (Raup, 1941). Whereas the problem of locating the polar fringe of trees has stimulated considerable interest in the past, acquisition of remote sensor imagery from space may provide necessary information on a Holarctic scale for locating and mapping the economic and biotic limits of forests, as well as the tree line and polar limits of species as defined by Hustich (1953). Furthermore, these limits will represent actual vegetation boundaries rather than correlative climatic, edaphic, or topographic boundaries as have been necessary in the past because of data limitations in unstudied areas.

Tikhomirov (1962) argues that most theories advanced to account for forest-tundra boundaries share the common defect of inadequate analysis of ecologic interactions common in Arctic environments. Whereas throughout this paper we have stressed the value of multisensor methods as a means of *identification* of communities or species, the collection of data suitable for evaluating a number of other parameters either directly or by inference will focus attention on ecological interactions.

The ability of tree species to advance into tundra depends upon the nature of the specific habitat and their tolerance once they are established. Snow depth, through its insulating properties, and thaw depth, through its influence on rooting zones and wind throw, are two important conditions that may be studied from space by combinations of infrared, radar, and passive microwave systems. Johnson's (1964) valuable discussion of multiband aerial sensing, with examples drawn inter alia from the Yukon Flats, considers this problem of Arctic tree lines.

PERMAFROST

The significance of permafrost as a control of geomorphic, pedologic, and vegetational patterns in high latitudes has long been recognized (Hopkins, 1959; Tedrow and Harries, 1960; Hussey, 1962). It is interdependent with plant communities because rooting depth, soil depth, temperature, and moisture are closely tied. Permafrost plays a major role in the formation of patterned ground and pingos, and it accounts for the instability of soil in Arctic regions.

Permafrost stretches from high altitudes in temperate regions to sea level along the Arctic coast (Retzer, 1965), but it is neither continuous nor everywhere mantled by a uniform "active" layer. Somewhere in the high latitudes, changes in the environment occur that create a transition between continuous and discontinuous zones of permafrost. In North America this "permafrost line" is known only in broad terms, and in many Arctic areas its location is little more than conjecture (Tedrow and Harries, 1960).

With the aid of microwave, infrared, and radar imaging, it may be possible to delimit the "permafrost line" across the Arctic on the basis of trends in temperature anomalies, emittance variations, and the dielectric between frozen and unfrozen ground at selected times of the year. Improved vegetational mapping will allow improved mapping of the depth of the active layer and of the rooting zone. Spatial variations in the rate and depth of spring thaw could also be studied, as well as the dynamics of autumnal freezing of the active layer.

Aircraft measurements with VHF pulsed radar reflectivity developed by Barringer (Barringer and Geleynse, 1965) may be used in support of spacecraft imaging as a means of profiling subsurface undulations in permafrost. Undulations in the interface of permafrost and active layer may be measured and related to vegetational patterns. Subsurface permafrost topography may also reveal areas of continuous and discontinuous distribution.

BREAK-UP AND FREEZE-UP

Important features of Arctic and sub-Arctic environments are the annual break-up and freeze-up. These phenomena may be followed with multisensing techniques, so that substantial progress may be made in determining the frost regime of Arctic lakes, the flow characteristics of drainage systems, and the extent of flooding. Structure and thickness of Arctic lake ice as well as the dynamics of lake-ice formation and disintegration could be studied. Infrared and radar imagery will aid in qualitative and perhaps semiquantitative studies of ice types, thickness, and ice and water temperatures (McLerran, 1965). Continuous thermal monitoring of lakes might aid investigators to determine the beginning of circulation in cold monomictic lakes (Hutchinson, 1957) and to establish the boundary between these lakes of high latitudes and the dimictic lakes of temperate regions. From a number of known lakes good estimates of mean lake depth could be inferred from dates of freeze and break-up (McFadden, 1965).

Freeze-up and break-up data for major north-south oriented drainage systems such as the Mackenzie, Lena, and Yenesie would provide long-needed information on seasonal advances and insolation inputs (Mackay, 1963). Relationships between observed freeze and thaw and changes in vegetation would provide a basis for tracing the onset of spring and autumn. Seasonal transitions are short in high latitudes, and the rapid passage of spacecraft would be desirable to document these critical changes in the energy cycle and vegetational growth.

We anticipate a substantial role for radar imagery in studying break-up, freeze-up, and flooding phenomena on the Arctic Slope. The known very high frequency of overcast during the late spring will severely hamper both photography and infrared scanning systems. To obtain some contemporaneity in data an all-weather system must be used.

Acknowledgments

This study was supported under contract NSR 17-004-003 of the National Aeronautics and Space Administration. We are pleased to acknowledge the help of Mr. Bernard Scheps, who released recently declassified AN/APQ-56 radar imagery to us for this study. We are grateful for the careful criticism of the paper by Dr. Philip Johnson. Helpful suggestions were received from Mr. Lloyd Spetzman, Professor Harold J. Lutz, Mr. Robert N. Robertson, Dr. Michael Holter, and Dr. Frank Barath.

The writing of this paper owes much to Dr. Peter C. Badgley, whose grasp of the combined potential of remote sensors and spacecraft has stimulated our work.

We have drawn heavily on the reports of several panels of the Conference on the Use of Orbiting Spacecraft in Geographic Research held in Houston, January 1965. The panels most relevant were those on Energy and Water Balance, Soils and Vegetation, and Geomorphology.

REFERENCES

Advanced Missions Division, 1965, Manned earth orbital missions: Nat. Aeron. Space Admin., Manned Space Science Program Advanced Missions Division (2nd ed.), v. 1.

Barringer, A. R., and M. Geleynse, 1965, Recent progress in remote sensing with audio and radio frequency pulses: Univ. Mich. Inst. Sci. Tech., Proc. 3rd Symp. Remote Sensing Environ., pp. 494-496.

Colwell, R. N., 1961, Some practical examples of multiband spectral reconnaissance: Am. Scientist, v. 49, pp. 9-36.

_____, and D. L. Olson, 1965, Thermal infrared imagery and its use in vegetation analysis by remote aerial reconnaissance: Univ. Mich. Inst. Sci. Tech., Proc. 3rd Symp. Remote Sensing Environ., pp. 607-621.

_____, et al., 1963, Basic matter and energy relationships involved in remote reconnaissance: Photogrammetr. Eng., v. 29, pp. 761-799.

Gates, E. M., H. J. Keegan, J. C. Schleter, and V. R. Weidner, 1965, Spectral properties of plants: Appl. Opt., v. 4, pp. 27-44.

Griggs, R. F., 1934, The problem of Arctic vegetation: J. Wash. Acad. Sci., v. 24, pp. 153-175.

_____, 1937, Timberlines as indicators of climatic trends: Science, v. 85, pp. 251-255.

Hare, F. K., 1959, A photo-reconnaissance survey of Labrador-Ungava: Can. Dept. Mines Tech. Surv. Geograph. Branch, Mem. No. 6, 64 pp.

Hirsch, S. N., 1963, Applications of remote sensing to forest fire detection and suppression: Ann Arbor, Univ. Mich. Inst. Sci. Tech., Proc. 2nd Symp. Remote Sensing Environ., pp. 295-308.

Hopkins, D. M., 1959, Some Characteristics of the climate in forest and tundra regions in Alaska: Arctic, v. 12, pp. 215-220.

Hussey, K. M., 1962, Ground patterns as keys to photo interpretation of Arctic terrain: Iowa Acad. Sci., v. 69, pp. 332-341.

Hustich, I., 1953, The boreal limits of conifers: Arctic, v. 6, pp. 149-162.

Hutchinson, G. E., 1957, A Treatise on Limnology: New York, Wiley, v. 1, 1015 pp.

Johnson, P. L., 1964, The application of multiband aerial sensing to problems in plant ecology: 10th Intern. Botan. Congr. Edinburgh, 1964, pp. 1-16.

Lutz, H. J., 1960, Fire as an ecological factor in the boreal forests of Alaska: J. Forestry, v. 58, pp. 435-477.

McFadden, J. D., 1965, The inter-relationship of lake ice and climate in central Canada: Office Naval Res., Geograph. Branch, NR 387-002, Contract No. 1202(07).

Mackay, J. R., 1963, Progress of break-up and freeze-up along the Mackenzie River: Geograph. Bull., v. 19, pp. 103-116.

McLerran, J. H., 1965, Infrared sea ice reconnaissance: Univ. Mich. Inst. Sci. Tech., Proc. 3rd Symp. Remote Sensing Environ., pp. 789-800.

Morrison, A. and J. B. Bird, 1965, Photography of the earth from space and its non-meteorological applications: Ann Arbor, Univ. Mich. Inst. Sci. Tech., Proc. 3rd Symp. Remote Sensing Environ., pp. 357-376.

Parker, D. C. and M. F. Wolff, 1965, Remote sensing: Intern. Sci. Tech., No. 43, pp. 20-31 and 73.

Pierson, W. J., B. B. Scheps, and D. S. Simonett, 1965, Some applications of radar return data to the study of terrestrial and oceanic phenomena: Am. Astronaut. Soc., 3rd Goddard Memorial Symp., pp. 87-137.

Porsild, A. E., 1951, Plant life in the Arctic: Can. Geograph. J., v. 43, pp. 120-145.

_____ 1958, Geographical distribution of some elements in the flora of Canada: Geograph. Bull., v. 11, pp. 57-76.

Raup, H. M., 1941, Botanical problems in boreal America: Botan. Rev., v. 7, pp. 147-248.

Retzer, J. L., 1965, Present soil-forming factors and processes in arctic and alpine regions: Soil Sci., v. 99, pp. 38-44.

Simonett, D. S., and D. A. Brown, 1967, Possible uses of radar on spacecraft in contributing to Antarctic mapping, crevasse, sea ice, and mass budget studies: Proc. 7th Congr. Intern. Assoc. Quaternary Res., v. 16 (in press).

Spetzman, L. A., 1963, Terrain study of Alaska, Part V. Vegetation: U.S. Geol. Surv. Military Geol. Branch, map scale 1:2,500,000.

Tedrow, J. C. F., and H. Harries, 1960, Tundra soil in relation to vegetation, permafrost, and glaciation: Oikos, v. 11, pp. 237-249.

Tikhomirov, B. A., 1962, The treelessness of the tundra: Polar Record, v. 11, pp. 24-30.

Wittgenstein, L. S., 1961, Recognition of tree species on air photographs by crown characteristics: Photogrammetr. Eng., v. 25, pp. 792-807.

Index

Aeolian environment, 30, 37, 40, 91
    altitudinal limits, 41
    animals, 45
    climate, 47-49
    lichens, 51
    microorganisms, 48, 50
    nutrient sources, 41-43
Algae
    in snow fields, 43
    in glacial pools, 45
Antarctica and Subantarctica, 51-52, 72-73

Climatic change
    development of disjuncts, 175, 180-181, 184-185
    differentiation of faunas, 152, 162, 165
    evolution of tundra, 145, 159-162, 268-269
    formation of ground ice, 274
    glacial fluctuations, 197, 202, 257

Dispersal of plants, 173-175, 191
Disjunct plants, 148, 162
    Japan, 129, 132
    Rocky Mountains, 162
    Sierra Nevada, 95, 171-173, 183-185

Edemic plants, 160
    Australasia, 77
    Caucasus, 97
    Japan, 126, 131
    Sierra Nevada, 96

Fauna
    aeolian, 40-46
    alpine, 77, 94, 138, 146-149, 156-159, 162-164
    arctic, 147
Fire, 62, 64, 78, 92, 310

Flora, alpine
    Alps, 96
    Altai, 100
    Australia, 64
    Borneo, 58
    Caucasus, 96
    Central Asia, 176-177
    Japan, 122-135
    New Guinea, 60
    New Zealand, 67
    Pamir, 99
    Rocky Mountains, 183
    Scandinavia, 99
    Sierra Nevada, 96, 171, 184
    Subantarctica, 72
    Urals, 101
Frost action, 75, 93, 218, 231, 268, 289-292

Glaciers
    animals on, 46
    erosion by, 242-247, 251-254
    growth of, 260
    organic detritus on, 46
    recession of, 189, 192-198

Hydrology, 79, 101, 181-182

Ice crystals, 230
    force of crystallization, 231
Insects
    aeolian regions, 42-44
Insolation
    daily changes, 6, 9, 15
    different altitudes, 3
    different cloud cover, 5, 7-10
    different snow cover, 7
    seasonal changes, 6-7, 9

Krummholz, 91

Lichens
    aeolian regions, 51
    for dating, 191-192

INDEX

Microorganisms in aeolian regions, 48, 50
Migrations of plants, 161, 165, 175
Mountains
  Africa, 31
  Alaska, 192
  Alps, 96, 205, 251
  Andes, 31, 35
  Australasia, 31-32, 43, 55-79, 217
  Caucasus, 95, 97, 98, 138
  Central Asia, 100, 139, 267-269
  Himalaya, 32, 35-42, 46-50
  Japan, 120
  Mexico, 31, 36, 43, 46-48
  North America, 31-32, 35, 43-44
  Norway, 252
  Pyrenees, 255-265
  Sierra Nevada, 96

Needle ice, 218-219, 224-226

Permafrost
  Alaska, 283-284
  bogs, 176, 179-182
  ice wedges, 234
  mapping, 302
  multiple veins in Siberia, 272-273, 279
  types, 237
  Yukon Flats, 299

Radiation, terrestrial, 15
Refugia for tundra plants, 159, 160, 165
Remote sensing, 295-303
River floodplains, 272-274

Sea-level changes, 275-276, 278
Snow and meltwater
  chemical content, 205-213
  pH, 205-213
Soils
  alpine, 60, 93-94, 133
  arctic, 284-292

  erosion, 221-226
  hydration, 229
Succession in plants, 93-94

Tectonic movements, 251, 268, 273, 275-278
Temperature, atmospheric, with inverted profile, 15
  cloudiness, 18, 23
  humidity, 20, 22
  pressure patterns, 21, 25
  topography, 13, 16-17, 62, 265
  winds, 19, 25
Timberline, 29-30, 301
  absence in arid regions, 90
  distinguished from tree line, 30
  in Australia, 64
  in Borneo, 62
  movement with climatic change, 161
  in New Zealand, 68-69
  related to climate, 31-33, 74-76, 140
  related to July temperature, 33
  related to latitude, 31-32, 74-75
Tree-ring analysis, 190-192
Trim line by glacial advance, 190, 195-196
Tundra
  fauna in, 147, 152, 163
  origin of, 145, 148, 152, 156, 164

Vegetation, alpine
  altitudinal limits, 40
  climatic factors, 35-36, 76, 101-113, 178
  flowering season, 38-39
  geologic age, 77
  human factors, 62, 64, 78, 93
  in Australia, 66
  in Borneo, 60
  in New Zealand, 69-70
  mapping by remote sensors, 298
  topography, 36, 93, 218
Volcanic activity, 275

**WITHDRAWN
OWENS LIBRARY
N.W.M.S.U.**